GLOBAL POSITIONING SYSTEM

Papers

published in

NAVIGATION

VOLUME I

reprinted by

THE INSTITUTE OF NAVIGATION

Washington, D.C.

Copyright © 1980 by The Institute of Navigation

International Standard Book Number: 0-936406-00-3

Published in the United States of America
The Institute of Navigation
815 Fifteenth Street, Suite 832
Washington, D.C. 20005

PREFACE

The latest printing of this volume has been made necessary by a continued demand for its contents as primary references for the Global Positioning System. Since the first printing in 1980 there have been some modifications to GPS. However, development and deployment have reached a state such that no change could render obsolete the expositions of fundamental principles or structure without altering the basic character of the system itself. Much of the material found here, therefore, remains essential to an adequate understanding of GPS. Extended applications, evolving hardware architecture, alternative solution algorithms and other advances should be found in a second collection and in *Navigation*, journal of The Institute of Navigation.

P. M. Janiczek
Editor, *Navigation*

CONTENTS

Overview

B. W. PARKINSON

NAVSTAR heralds a new era in worldwide positioning and navigation capabilities. Indeed, 10 meter or better positioning errors in three dimensions has so many applications that a total recital of them would require more than a mere introductory comment.

Why has this potential worldwide revolution come into being at this point in time? Principally because of two things: first, an understanding of the powerful advantages of a satellite system in providing positioning information. TRANSIT, developed by APL and the Navy, is our first system of this type. It has shown the way. NAVSTAR promises order of magnitude improvements with seven dimensional information: three dimensions of position, three dimensions of velocity, as well as precise time. This capability is a consequence of satellite geometry, improved spaceborne clocks (begun under NRL's Timation program), and improved position-prediction techniques.

The second reason for NAVSTAR's momentum is that the using community has now started to focus on the limitations of the current methods of doing business. These limitations include the expense of maintaining proliferated navigation and positioning aids as well as the restricted performance they offer. As a result, the advantages of a "universal" system are becoming accepted.

The current development process for GPS has already provided initial test results that prove the first generation equipment is ready. These test results show that the user equipment is capable of accuracies better than three meters

Dr. Parkinson is a Professor at Colorado State University and a private consultant. He was formerly a colonel in the Air Force and for five years the Director of the NAVSTAR program.

in three dimensions and that the satellite signal of the NDS-I spacecraft is stable and capable of supporting user equipment operations. Yet to be verified is the full four satellite navigation capability. However, all indications are that the tests to be conducted next year will complete the verification of NAVSTAR.

The using community for NAVSTAR is extremely broad and includes civilian as well as military applications. I would like to discuss just a few of these as a means of tickling our imaginations and perhaps encouraging further exploitation of the NAVSTAR capability.

At sea, merchant vessels equipped with NAVSTAR will be able to carry out port-to-port operations with a single navigation aid. By differencing NAVSTAR earth–referenced velocity with pitometer–log velocity, they will be able to directly calculate ocean currents at sea and insure that they stay in the most favorable regions of ocean currents by avoiding the maritime analogy of aircraft headwind. In addition, they can use NAVSTAR position and velocity information to continuously steer great circle routes very accurately which will save time and fuel. A study performed for the Maritime Administration estimated that NAVSTAR could potentially save $17,000 per Trans-Atlantic passage for a large tanker. Collision avoidance and safety have also become a very important international concern for large tankers, particularly because of ecological damage due to oil spills. The day may come when there is sea-traffic control, analogous to present air traffic control. This will minimize the potential of collisions between merchant vessels, particularly in time of reduced visibility due to fog or darkness. NAVSTAR should make this sea control possible.

NAVSTAR will aid the commercial airlines. NAVSTAR's accurate positioning data will allow a reduction in flight path separation. They will be able to concentrate North Atlantic air traffic along the most favorable (i.e., minimum fuel) routes. In addition, NAVSTAR will allow airlines to directly calculate speed over the ground and thereby permit direct indication of altitudes and routes that insure most favorable wind conditions. NAVSTAR will provide a digital display of three dimensions of position and velocity in the cockpit of an airliner. This information can be interrogated from the ground by an air traffic control system. The three-dimensional vectors of position and velocity will make automated or semi-automated air traffic control systems much more feasible. The broad NAVSTAR coverage is available for the approach to airports as well as the letdown, and potentially allows a greater traffic density at the terminal area (now a bottleneck for many cities). In addition, precise time from NAVSTAR can be used in the collision avoidance mode for the airlines. The technique would have all aircraft transmit a radio pulse of tone at the same precise time. During pauses between tones, all aircraft listen for signals from other aircraft. By timing the difference between their transmission and any received signal, they can infer range (time multiplied by the speed of light) to all aircraft within line-of-sight. In addition, by counting the doppler shift on the incoming signal, closing rates can be directly estimated.

Both at sea and in the air, search and rescue operations can be greatly enhanced by NAV-STAR. This is because very precise position information prior to ditching an aircraft or abandoning a ship will allow the searchers to pinpoint the initial location and thereby speed up the rescue operations, saving both money and lives.

As we expand our search for fossil fuels, oil rigs are being put to sea in deeper and deeper waters. One of their major concerns is self-location. NAVSTAR can provide this to them continuously, and with time-averaging, potentially provide positioning accuracy of one to two meters. In the scientific area, NAVSTAR will act as a time distribution system. Precise timing is critical to radio astronomy and many other scientific applications. Also, NAVSTAR's two-frequency transmission allows direct measurement of ionospheric group delay, and hence measurement of the number of free electrons in the ionosphere in a wide range of geometrical relationships. The very precise position information provided by NAVSTAR can be time averaged for even greater accuracy and used as a very precise geodetic positioning technique. In designing NAVSTAR satellites, the needs of the radio astronomy service are borne in mind and given all practicable protection. These are but a few of the potential applications for NAVSTAR.

There are still key challenges in the NAV-STAR development. I would like to name three. First, the Air Force through the Joint Program Office must insure the timely development of a reliable and accurate system. This must precede any shifting from our current set of navigation aids. Second, the commercial developers must strive to make the user equipment affordable. Modern microcircuit technology gives us the potential for inexpensive receivers. Some of the commercial developers have suggested they can make equipment for as little as $2,000. Certainly this should be pursued and represents a challenge to the electronic designer as well as to the management of the company who must insure a disciplined design-to-cost effort. The third key challenge, I believe, is to the using community. They must understand NAVSTAR and strive to exploit its capabilities as quickly as possible. In the past, it has usually taken 10 to 15 years or more to field a new navigation system; perhaps NAVSTAR will not be an exception. However, if the potential applications are going to be fully realized, the using community must join with the developers in insuring that all potential applications are explored and, if feasible, pursued. With the quiet revolution of NAVSTAR, it can be seen that these potential uses are limited only by our imaginations.

Principle of Operation of NAVSTAR and System Characteristics

R. J. MILLIKEN AND C. J. ZOLLER*

SUMMARY

THE NAVSTAR/GLOBAL POSITIONING SYSTEM (GPS) will provide extremely accurate three-dimensional position and velocity information to users anywhere in the world. The position determinations are based on the measurement of the transit time of RF signals from four satellites of a total constellation of 24. Accuracies on the order of 10 meters may be anticipated. This paper discusses the basic technique by which the system operates, the navigation signal, the measurement of the transit time, error sources, accuracies, and other characteristics of the system.

INTRODUCTION

The baseline constellation of 24 satellites operates in 12-hour orbits at an altitude of 20,183 km (10, 898 nmi). It will provide visibility of 6 to 11 satellites at 5 degrees or more above the horizon to users located anywhere in the world at any time. Signals are transmitted at two L–band frequencies (1227 and 1575 MHz) to permit corrections to be made for ionospheric delays in signal propagation time. The signals are modulated with two codes: P, which provides for precision measurement of time, and C/A, which provides for easy lock–on to the desired signal. The satellites employ a shaped–beam antenna that radiates near–uniform power to

Messrs. Milliken and Zoller are with Rockwell International Corp., Space Division, 12214 Lakewood Blvd, Downey, CA 90241

* Appreciation is expressed to Mr. Edward M. Lassiter, of Aerospace Corporation, who provided source material for this paper, and to Mr. Paul S. Jorgensen, also of Aerospace Corporation, from whose work some of the material has been drawn.

system users of at least -163 dBW for the L_1 P–code and -160 dBW for the L_1 C/A code. The corresponding L_2 power level carrying only the P–code is at least -166 dBW. Navigation fixes can be made in a time interval of from tens of seconds to several minutes, depending on the sophistication of the receiving system.

NAVIGATION TECHNIQUE

Four satellites are normally required for navigation purposes, and the four offering the best geometry can be selected manually or automatically by receivers using ephemeris information transmitted by the satellites. Ranges to the four satellites are determined by scaling the signal transit time by the speed of light. The transmitted message contains ephemeris parameters that enable the user to calculate the position of each satellite at the time of transmission of the signal.

Operation of the system requires precise synchronization of space vehicle (SV) clocks with "GPS system time," which is accomplished by the use of an atomic frequency standard in each space vehicle and use of clock correction parameters that are provided by the Control Segment. The requirement for users to be equipped with precision clocks is eliminated by the use of range measurements from four satellites. If users maintained precision clocks synchronized with GPS system time, navigation could be accomplished with only three satellites. In that case, the user could be thought of as being at the intersection of three spheres, with centers located at the satellites. The fourth satellite permits an estimate of the user's clock error. In this case, the user position equations contain four unknowns consisting of position in three dimensions and the error, or fixed bias, in the user's imprecise clock, which can be solved by simultaneous solution of the four equations. A discussion of the solution follows. A mathematical derivation is included in the last section of the paper.

The measurement of range to the satellites, made by the user with an imprecise clock, is called "Pseudo-range" because it contains a bias of fixed magnitude in each range estimate due to the clock error.

The pseudo-range is defined as

$$\bar{R}_i = R_i + C\Delta t_{Ai} + C\ (\Delta t_u - \Delta t_{Si})$$

where

$\bar{R}_i$ = pseudo-range to the satellite

R_i = true range

C = the speed of light

Δt_{Si} = satellite i clock offset from GPS system time

Δt_u = user clock offset from GPS system time

Δt_{Ai} = propagation delays and other errors

Pseudo-range is illustrated in Fig. 1.

The GPS user measures the apparent (pseudo-range) transit time by measuring the phase shift of identical pseudo-range noise (PRN) codes that are generated in both the space vehicle and the user receiver, each synchronized with its own clock. The receiver code is shifted until maximum correlation is achieved between the two codes; the time magnitude of the shift is the receiver's measure of pseudo-range time.

The concept of finding a user position based on the removal of the fixed range bias from each range estimate is illustrated in a two-di-

mensional situation with three satellites in Fig. 2. The figure illustrates that the pseudo-range radii from the three satellites do not meet at a point but enclose the shaded triangular area. However, a range value of fixed magnitude ($\Delta t_u C$) can always be found that when removed from the pseudo-ranges (or added, as the case may be) will cause the radii to meet at a point, which is the user position. The value of $\Delta t_u C$ represents the range equivalent of the user clock error. If other errors (of unequal magnitude) exist in the pseudo ranges, which we will call independent errors, a value of fixed magnitude can still always be found that when removed from the pseudo-ranges will cause the radii to meet at a point. In this case, the point is an estimate of the user position that differs from the true user position by an error that is a function of the independent range errors. Similarly, the fixed magnitude that is removed then provides an estimate of the equivalent user clock error, which differs from the true user clock error by an amount that is also a function of the independent errors. The illustration in Fig. 2 represents only a two-dimensional situation in which the three satellites and user all lie in the same plane. However, the same statements and logic apply in a three-dimensional situation when ranges to four satellites are used.

GPS TIME STANDARD

In terms of navigation accuracy, one nano-

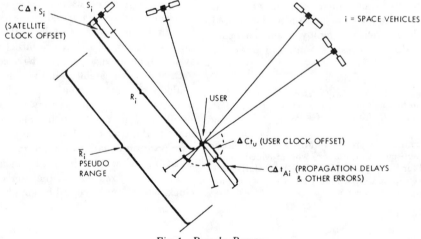

Fig. 1—Pseudo-Range.

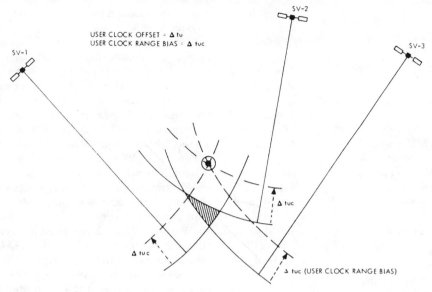

Fig. 2—Determination of User Position and Time Offset (Two Dimensional Case).

second of time error is equivalent to approximately 0.3 meters (0.984 ft) of range error so that precision timing and frequency control are essential to the GPS system. All system timing requirements are synchronized with GPS system time, which is maintained by the Master Control Station (MCS) through the use of a set of highly accurate cesium clocks. Precision timing is maintained in the space vehicles by the use of a highly stable atomic clock in each vehicle with a known or predictable offset from GPS system time. The MCS monitors the SV time standards daily with reference to GPS system time and generates clock correction parameters for transmission to the space vehicles where they are retransmitted to users with the navigation signals and used to determine the precise magnitude of the clock offsets.

GPS system time necessarily differs from UTC (Universal Coordinated Time), which must be adjusted for leap seconds at periodic end-of-year intervals. Such adjustments in GPS time would disrupt the continuous availability of the space vehicles for navigation purposes. Knowledge of the difference between GPS system time and UTC is maintained within 100 microseconds and the difference will be published regularly for the benefit of users interested in the use of GPS as a time standard. Time

users with known positions and highly stable frequency standards can determine GPS time by the use of signals from only one space vehicle. Accuracies can be on the order of 15 to 20 nanoseconds.

The space vehicle clock frequency is nominally 10.23 MHz, which is offset slightly to a center frequency of 10.22999999545 MHz to allow for relativity effects. Its maximum allowable uncertainty is one part in 10^{12} per day. The MCS has the capability of adjusting both the clock time phase and frequency, if required. The phase can be adjusted to a resolution of one chip ($\approx$98 nanoseconds). The frequency can be set in steps no smaller than 4×10^{-12} delta f/f over a range of ± 2 parts in 10^9 around the center frequency. Upload of clock correction parameters into the space vehicles and adjustment of the clocks is accomplished by uplink commands. The pseudo-random noise codes, which are synchronized with space vehicle time, are maintained within 976 microseconds of GPS system time in order to preclude secondary control problems such as almanac word-length limitation that would otherwise arise.

All frequencies in the space vehicle are derived from, and synchronized with, integrals of the basic 10.23 MHz SV frequency standard. These include:

	Repeat Interval or Frequency
P-code:	
Reset	7 days
Frequency	10.23 MHz
C/A code:	
Epoch	1 millisecond
Frequency	1.023 MHz
X1 Epoch (Z-count change)	1.5 seconds
HOW (handover-word) change	6 seconds
Data bit stream frequency	50 bps
L_1 RF frequency	154×10.23 $= 1575.42$ MHz
L_2 RF frequency	120×10.23 $= 1227.6$ MHz

SIGNAL STRUCTURE AND THE MEASUREMENT OF TIME

The navigation signal transmitted from the space vehicles consists of two RF frequencies, L_1 at 1575.42 MHz and L_2 at 1227.6 MHz. The L_1 signal is modulated with both the P and the C/A pseudo-random noise codes in phase quadrature. The L_2 signal is modulated with the P-code. Both the L_1 and L_2 signals are also continuously modulated with the navigation data-bit stream at 50 bps. The functions of the codes are twofold: (1) identification of space vehicles, as the code patterns are unique to each space vehicle and are matched with like codes generated in the user receiver, and (2) the measurement of the navigation signal transit time by measuring the phase shift required to match the codes. The P-code is a long precision code operating at 10.23 Mbps but difficult to acquire. The C/A (clear access) code is a short code, readily acquired, but operating at 1.023 Mbps, which provides a grosser measurement of time. The C/A code is normally acquired first and a transfer is made to the P-code by the use of the handover word (HOW) contained in the navigation data stream (see the Navigation Message). It is possible, however, for users with precision clocks precisely synchronized with GPS time and the approximate knowledge of their position (10,000 ft-20,000 ft) to bypass the C/A code and acquire the P-code directly.

The P-code generated in each space vehicle is a pseudo-random noise chip sequence of seven days in length.[1] That is, the pattern repeats only once every seven days. The code is initiated at midnight each Saturday. GPS system time is counted from the initialization of the P-code each week. Counting is accomplished by a count of the epochs (recurrences of the initial state) of a subsidiary code generator designated X1, used in the generation of the P-code, that occur every 1.5 seconds. The count of the X1 epochs, termed Z, rises to 403,199 at the end of each week, when it is reinitialized at zero. The system time of the week is transmitted to users every six seconds in the form of the handover word, HOW.

In order for the ground receiver to lock onto the P-code, it must know approximately what time-slice in the seven-day code to search. At typical receiver search rates, on the order of 50 bits per second, the time required to search as much as one second of the seven-day P-code would require many hours. It is therefore necessary to resort to the C/A code for initial code match and lock-on.

The C/A code is a pseudo-random noise chip stream unique in pattern to each space vehicle that repeats every millisecond. It is relatively easy for the receiver to match and lock onto the C/A code because the search is limited to the time interval of one millisecond and the chip rate is only one-tenth that of the P-code. After lock-on to the C/A code, the transfer to the P-code is facilitated by the HOW word. Its change, which is synchronized with the P-code,

---

[1] The P-code generated in each space vehicle is actually a seven-day-long phase segment of the P-code, which has a complete cycle of 267 days. The P-code is the modulo-2- sum of the output of two PRN code generators designated X_1 and X_2, each of which employs an input from the sum of the output of two subsidiary generators. All the space vehicles employ the same P-code generator, with each one assigned and generating a unique and mutually exclusive seven-day-long code-phase segment of the 267-day code. The P-code epoch (initial state) is made to occur in each space vehicle every seven days by resetting the X_1 and X_2 code generators to their initial states at the end of each week. The P signal generator in the jth space vehicle is made to generate its unique phase segment of the P-code by offsetting (delaying) its X_2 generator j bits from its initial state at the time of reset. This technique places each X_2 register in the configuration existing at the beginning of its assigned seven-day phase segment of the P-code.

indicates the point in the incoming P–code that will occur at the next change, i.e., within the next six seconds. The receiver–generated P–code is shifted in phase to synchronize with the designated point in the incoming P–code when triggered by the change in the HOW. The total phase–shift required for lock–on is the measured pseudo–range time, including the offset in the user clock as well as the propagation delays and system errors. The P–code frequency affords the degree of accuracy required for the measurement of signal transit time that the C/A code frequency could not. Use of the P–code also avoids ambiguity in the C/A code epoch, which repeats every millisecond, if the user clock offset exceeds this amount.

THE NAVIGATION MESSAGE

The navigation message contains the data that the user's receiver requires to perform the operations and computations for successful navigation with the GPS. The data include information on the status of the space vehicle; the time synchronization information for the transfer from the C/A to the P–code; and the parameters for computing the clock correction, the ephemeris of the space vehicle and the corrections for delays in the propagation of the signal through the atmosphere. In addition, it contains almanac information that defines the approximate ephemerides and status of all the other space vehicles, which is required for use in signal acquisitions. The data format also includes provisions for special messages.

The navigation message is formatted in five subframes of six seconds in length, which make up a data frame of 30 seconds, 1500 bits long. The data are nonreturn–to–zero (NRZ) at 50 bps and are common to the P– and C/A signals on both the L_1 and L_2 channels. The format of the data is shown in Fig. 3.

Each data subframe starts with a telemetry word (TLM) and the C/A to P–code handover word (HOW). The latter permits the C/A to P transfer to be made at the termination of any six–second subframe. The initial 8 bits of the TLM contain a preamble that facilitates acquiring the data message. The balance of the TLM contains information designed primarily for the use of the Control Segment in determining the accuracy with which the daily update of the

space vehicles has been received and utilized and is ordinarily not decoded by the user receivers. A space vehicle health–status word is provided in the fifth subframe (Data Block III) which indicates the status of the SV and permits the user the option of selecting another SV. The HOW is the second word of each subframe and occupies 30 bits, including parity. It starts with the uppermost significant 17 bits of the 19–bit Z–count word, which is the running indicator of time in the space vehicle. The Z–count changes every 1.5 seconds; the HOW every 6 seconds. Bit number 18 is used to indicate when a roll–momentum dump has occurred since the last upload. Momentum dumps have some affect on the ephemeris accuracy and this information provides the option for a sophisticated user to select a new SV. Bit 19 of the HOW is significant in that it indicates whether or not the leading edge of the TLM word is in synchronization with the X1 epoch that is required for a successful transfer from the C/A to P–code lock–on. Bits 20 through 22 contain subframe identification.

The remaining information in the navigation message is provided by the Control Segment and includes three blocks of data plus a block reserved for special messages. Block I data, which is contained in subframe 1, includes the clock correction parameters a_0, a_1, and a_2 and the presently unused parameters α_0, α_1, α_2, α_3, β_0, β_1, β_2, and β_3 used in the model for correction of atmospheric delays in propagation of the signal. Both the clock correction parameters and the ephemeris parameters that are contained in Data Block II are updated every hour. The Control Segment provides values for each hour in the 24 hours following update of the SV and the SV updates the navigation message each hour. Block I data also include 8 bits for the parameter T_{GD}, which permits an approximation of the atmospheric delay for receivers using only the L_1 signal and requiring less precision in their navigation. An 8–bit word, age of data (AODC), indicates the time since the last navigation upload for the use of more sophisticated receivers who may wish to select a satellite with a more recent update. The data block includes two spare words with 24 bits available in each.

Data Block II, which contains the ephemeris prediction parameters, covers Subframes 2 and 3. This block also includes an age–of–data word

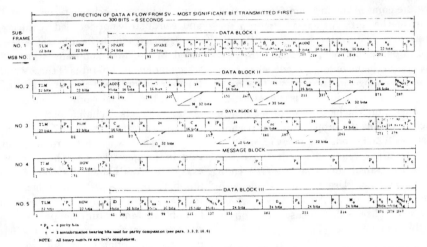

Fig. 3—Signal Data Frame Content.

(AODE) that indicates the time of the last measurement that was used to estimate the parameters and a spare 14 bits.

Subframe 4 is reserved for special messages which may be included in the data.

Block III data, which is located in Subframe 5, contains the "Almanac data." These data include information on the ephemerides, clock correction parameters, and atmospheric delay parameters for the normal complement of 24 satellites, plus one spare. The data are a subset of Block I and Block II parameters with reduced precision plus health and identification words for the space vehicles. The data are required to facilitate the rapid selection of four space vehicles for use in the navigation solution. The receiver uses the information first to identify which satellites are in view and to solve the algorithm that indicates the four that will provide the best navigation solution. The codes of these four are then generated by the receiver for matching with the corresponding codes among all the incoming signals. The almanac data also permit computation of the approximate range to each space vehicle and thereby facilitate the selection of the correct time slice in searching the codes for match.

The total Almanac data exceeds the capacity of the single Subframe 5 so that it is transmitted on a rotating page basis. The complete Almanac is contained in 25 frames. Sophisticated receivers will maintain almanacs in their data storage that preclude the need to wait for the transmis-

sion of the complete Almanac. The current information in their data storage is updated at the time of a GPS navigation fix. External almanacs, maintained from published data, may be used by operators with unsophisticated receivers.

The user algorithms for computing ephemeris position with almanac data are essentially the same as the user algorithms for computing the precise ephemeris from Block II parameters. The Block III data include the health word for each spacecraft to permit user rejection of space vehicles with unsatisfactory operation.

ERROR SOURCES

Errors contained in the pseudo–range measurements can be divided into the categories listed in Table 1. Various corrective techniques are employed in the system to reduce the magnitude of these errors in range that impact the estimates of user position. These are discussed below with the magnitude of the residual uncorrected errors summarized in Table 1. As discussed earlier, the range error resulting from the user clock bias is determined by the solution of the range equations so that it does not appear as an error in the ultimate range estimate.

Space Vehicle Clock Errors

Individual space vehicle clocks, although highly stable, may deviate as much as 976 microseconds from GPS system time. The offset is corrected by the model used by the receiver that employs the clock correction coefficients which

Table 1—Range Error Budget

Uncorrected Error Source	User Equivalent Range Error, 1σ	
	Meters	Feet
SV clock errors } Ephemeris errors	1.5	5.0*
Atmospheric delays	2.4–5.2	8.0–17.0
Group delay (SV equipment)	1.0	3.3
Multipath	1.2–2.7	4.0–9.0
Receiver noise and resolution } Vehicle dynamics	1.5	5.0
RSS	3.6–6.3	11.8–20.7

* Two hours after update.

are transmitted as data in the navigation message. The uncorrected errors due to clock deviation alone are very small (on the order of one foot of equivalent range); however, they are indistinguishable from certain components of ephemeris errors so that they are combined with the ephemeris errors in the error budget.

Atmospheric Delays

The time delay of RF signals passing through the ionosphere is due to a reduction in speed and the bending of the ray, both effects being due to refraction. The overall delay in the signal is nearly inversely proportional to the square of the frequency. The transmission of the navigation signal at the two frequencies (L_1 and L_2) is provided so that the magnitude of the delay can be calculated by a comparison of the two frequencies and removed with a satisfactory degree of accuracy. Forms of models are currently being evaluated during the Phase I program for users of both L_1 and L_2 and users of L_1 alone. These models employ the correction parameters ($\alpha_{0,1,2,3}$ and $\beta_{0,1,2,3}$) that are generated by the MCS and are uploaded periodically in the space vehicles for transmission to GPS users. Tropospheric errors are independent of frequency. They are relatively small but can be modeled fairly simply by receivers, using the elevation angle of the spacecraft. The combined effect of unmodeled ionospheric and tropospheric errors are estimated to result in a SV-to-user range error of from 2.44 to 5.18 meters (8 to 17 feet).

Group Delay

Group delay is defined as the delay resulting from uncertainties caused by the processing and passage of the signal through the SV equipment. The magnitude of these delays are calibrated during ground tests of the equipment. Corrections for the overall effect of these delays are included in the SV time offset correction parameters a_0, a_1, and a_2, discussed above. The estimated allowance for uncertainties in the group delay is 1 meter (3.28 feet).

Ephemeris Errors

Satellite ephemerides are determined by the MCS based on monitoring of individual space vehicle navigation signals by four monitoring stations. This operation results in a sort of inverted range process which enables the MCS to calculate the position of a space vehicle as if it were the user and the four monitoring stations were the space vehicles. The ephemeris determination is aided by precision clocks at the monitoring stations and by daily tracking over long periods of time with optimal filter processing. The determination process derives progressively refined information defining the gravitational field influencing the spacecraft motion; solar pressure parameters; and the locations, clock drifts, and signal delay characteristics of the monitoring stations. Based on this process, the MCS generates the ephemeris parameters that are uploaded in the SV periodically and included in the navigation data message where they are employed in the ephemeris model to calculate spacecraft position at the time of transmission of the received signals.

The satellite position errors resulting from this process are still on the order of several meters. However, it is the ranging errors that are of primary significance, and the effect of these is relatively small. Errors that are common to the four range measurements, for example, will cause an apparent error in the user's clock, which tends to be compensated for in calculation of the user clock bias. The combined effects of residual uncertainties in SV clock offsets and ephemeris determinations are estimated to result in range errors of about 1.5 meters (5 feet).

Multipath

Multipath errors result from the combination of data from more than one propagation path that distorts the signal characteristics from which the range measurements are made. These errors are dependent on the nature and location of reflective surfaces peculiar to each user location. Aircraft simulations have indicated these errors to be relatively small and have resulted in an error estimate of from 1.2 to 2.7 meters (4.0 to 9.0 feet).

Receiver Noise and Resolution

Noise and resolution errors resulting from the processing of signals by the receiver hardware and software will contribute to errors in the determination of range. With high–performance four–channel receivers, it is expected that these errors will be about 1.52 meters (5 feet).

Receiver Vehicle Dynamics

User vehicle dynamics will contribute to the total ranging errors. These can be compensated for by special receiver designs and by Kalman optimal processing of received signals, which would be required, for example, by high–speed, very low altitude aircraft. The estimated error due to receiver noise and resolution, above, is based on nominal receiver vehicle dynamics. No allowance is made in the overall error budget for high vehicle dynamics.

The overall SV–to–user range uncertainties due to the combined error sources identified in Table 1 are estimated to be from 3.6 to 6.3 meters (12 to 21 feet). The uncertainties in range to the space vehicles combine with the geometry of the SV positions in their effect on the accuracy of user position estimates.

SYSTEM ACCURACY

Geometric Dilution of Precision (GDOP)

The magnitude of the ranging errors, combined with the geometry of the four selected satellites, will determine the magnitude of the user position errors in the GPS navigation fix. The effect of geometry is expressed by the geometric dilution of precision (GDOP) parameters. The use of GDOP was originally developed in connection with LORAN navigation systems. Extended to the GPS system, with fixes in three dimensions plus time, the parameters include PDOP, which reflects the dilution of precision in position in three dimensions; HDOP, dilution of precision in the two horizontal dimensions; VDOP, dilution of precision in the vertical di-

mension; and TDOP, dilution of precision in time, i.e., in the estimate of the range equivalent of the user clock bias.

PDOP × User to Satellite Range Error, 1σ
  = Radial error in user position 1σ, in 3 dimensions
HDOP × User to Satellite Range Error, 1σ
  = Radial error in user position, 1σ, in the horizontal plane
VDOP × User to Satellite Range Error, 1σ
  = Vertical error in user position, 1σ
TDOP × User to Satellite Range Error, 1σ
  = Error, 1σ, in the range equivalent of the user clock offset

Hence, small values of the GDOP parameters indicate good arrangements in the geometry of the selected satellites and correspondingly small errors in position and time fixes. Fig. 4 gives the values of PDOP for cumulative proportions of users evenly distributed over the globe and around the clock who select the best four satellites from those that are visible 5 degrees or more above the horizon. The *rms* value of PDOP is in the neighborhood of 2.60 which, when combined with the range errors taken from Table 1 of from 3.6 to 6.3 meters (11.8 to 20.7 feet), gives user three–dimensional position errors of from 9.4 to 16.4 meters (31 to 54 feet) 1σ. The horizontal component of the position error reflected by HDOP is usually less. The corresponding *rms* value of HDOP is about 1.45, which yields horizontal position errors of from 5.2 to 9.1 meters (17 to 30 feet) 1σ. The corresponding *rms* value of TDOP is about 1.2 which, when range is converted to time, yields a 1σ time error of from 14 to 25 nanoseconds.

The value of GDOP itself is a composite measure that reflects the influence of satellite geometry on the combined accuracy of the estimate of user time (user clock offset) and user position.

$$GDOP = \sqrt{(PDOP)^2 + (TDOP)^2}$$

The four "best" satellites selected by the user receivers are those with the lowest GDOP. A high correlation between GDOP and the volume of the tetrahedron formed by the points of unit vectors from the user to the satellites has provided a relatively simple algorithm that can be

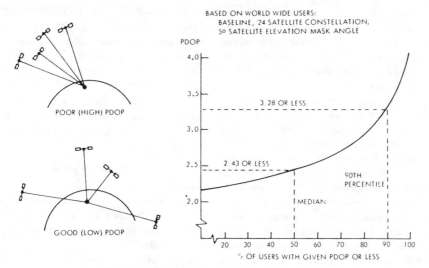

Fig. 4—PDOP (Position, Dilution of Precision).

used by receivers for the selection. A derivation of GDOP is given below in the section with that heading.

User Error Distribution

The GDOP parameters are generally given in terms of percentiles, such as the fiftieth and ninetieth percentiles, because the values of the GDOP parameters are statistically distributed in a non–Gaussian fashion that tends to distort average or mean square values. The lack of a mathematical expression for the distribution of the GDOP parameters, however, has prevented the establishment of a mathematical relationship between percentiles of GDOP and percentiles of user navigation errors; i.e., there is not a correspondence between the fiftieth or ninetieth percentile of GDOP parameter and the fiftieth or ninetieth percentile of user navigation error.

Paul Jorgensen of Aerospace Corporation has addressed the problem of determining the distribution of user navigation errors by conducting a Monte Carlo simulation that has provided a good approximation.[2] The simulation was based on a trial for several thousand user observations evenly distributed over the globe and in time, using the NAVSTAR twenty–four satellite baseline constellation. Calculated GDOP parameters for the best four satellites in each case were

combined with random selections from a Gaussian distribution representing pseudo–range errors to calculate the user navigation and time errors. The range errors were normalized with zero expected means and 1σ values equal to unity. Their distribution can justifiably be assumed to be Gaussian because they are a composite of a large number of generally independent error sources. The results have been provided in the form of normalized user error distribution parameters. When mean, *rms*, or percentile values of these parameters are multiplied by 1σ range errors, they yield corresponding values of the user navigation error and range equivalent time error distributions. Values of the parameters are given in Table 2, along with corresponding values of the user errors based on the 1σ range error estimation of from 3.6 to 6.3 meters (11.8 to 20.7 feet) given in Table 1. Also shown are the corresponding values of GDOP parameters which indicate the smaller spread of their distributions.

Velocity Measurement with NAVSTAR

Although the NAVSTAR system is designed primarily for precision position estimates, it will also provide precision velocity measurements, which will be of interest to military and other classes of users. The velocity estimates are made by measuring the doppler shift in the carrier frequency of the navigation signal from the satellites. Precision measurements are possible because of the precise knowledge of the satellite ephemerides and because of the short wave-

[2] P.S. Jorgensen, "Normalized Accuracy of the NAVSTAR/Global Positioning System," The Aerospace Corporation, Report No. TOR-0078(3475-10)-2 (28 February 1978).

length of the carrier frequency, which is approximately 19 cm. In addition, the error offset in the frequency of the receiver oscillator can be solved by the use of four satellites and four range rate equations in a manner analogous to the solution for the user clock offset.

The effect of satellite geometry on the relationship between range rate error and user velocity errors is completely analogous to that between range errors and user position errors so that the GDOP parameters, satellite selection algorithm, and the user navigation error parameters described above are equally applicable to the velocity measurements.

Receiver dynamics will have a major impact on the accuracy of velocity measurement which can be attained. It is anticipated that other error sources will be small. Receiver dynamics can impact the measurements both by introducing noise in the phase-lock tracking loop and by affecting the oscillator frequency.

High quality receivers in a benign environment with averaging intervals on the order of a second will be able to make user-to-satellite range rate measurements with accuracies of a few hundredths of a foot per second, 1σ. Accuracies of 0.061 to 0.15 mps (0.2 to 0.5 fps) are anticipated, with high quality receivers, in a severe dynamic environment with loadings up to the order of 5 g's. Table 3 gives the estimated magnitude of user velocity errors based on range rate errors of 0.015 and 0.061 mps (0.05 and 0.2 fps) using the navigation measurement error parameters described in the foregoing section.

THE GPS NAVIGATION SOLUTION

The GPS navigation solution can be implemented by the use of vectors and matrix algebra, with the initial range equations set up as follows. (See Fig. 5.)

$$\bar{R}_u = \bar{R}_i - \bar{D}_i \qquad (1)$$

where

$\bar{R}_u$ = the vector from the center of the earth to the user

$\bar{D}_i$ = the vector from the user to the *ith* satellite

$\bar{R}_i$ = the vector from the center of the earth to the *ith* satellite

i = 1 to n satellites ≥ 4

A solution for the vector $\bar{R}_u$ will yield the desired three unknowns of user position, identified as R_{uj} in a three-axes reference coordinate system. The components of $\bar{R}_i$ are known based on the satellite ephemerides. $\bar{D}_i$ must be dealt with in terms of its magnitude, which is determined by the measured value of pseudo-range with allowances for user and satellite clock corrections.

By defining $\bar{e}_i$ as the unit vector from user to

Table 2—Anticipated Worldwide User Position Error Distribution

	Horizontal				Vertical				Time		
	HDOP	User Error Parameter	User Error (Meters)	User Error (Feet)	VDOP	User Error Parameter	User Error (Meters)	User Error (Feet)	TDOP	User Error Parameter	User Error (Nanoseconds)
50th percentile	1.39	1.15	4.1–7.2	14–24	1.99	1.39	5.0–8.8	16–29	1.05	0.73	8–15
rms	1.44	1.45	5.2–9.1	17–30	2.16	2.21	8.0–13.9	26–46	1.21	1.22	14–25
90th percentile	1.71	2.19	7.9–13.8	26–45	2.80	3.57	12.9–22.5	42–74	1.76	1.96	23–40

Based on Range Error Budget 11.8–20.7 feet; 24-Satellite Baseline Constellation; 5-degree Satellite Elevation Mask Angle.

Table 3—World-Wide User Velocity Measurement Errors

	Based on 0.015 mps (0.05 fps) Range Rate Errors				Based on 0.061 mps (0.2 fps) Range Rate Errors			
	Horizontal Velocity Error		Vertical Velocity Error		Horizontal Velocity Error		Vertical Velocity Error	
Distribution Measure	mps	fps	mps	fps	mps	fps	mps	fps
50th percentile	.02	.06	.02	.07	.07	.2	.08	.3
rms	.02	.07	.03	.11	.09	.3	.13	.4
90th percentile	.03	.11	.05	.18	.13	.4	.21	.7

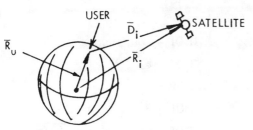

USER

$\bar{D}_i$

SATELLITE

$\bar{R}_u$

$\bar{R}_i$

Fig. 5—Navigation Solution Geometry.

satellite and noting that $\bar{e}_i \cdot \bar{D}_i = D_i$ (the magntiude of $\bar{D}_i$). (1) becomes

$$\bar{e}_i \cdot \bar{R}_u = \bar{e}_i \cdot \bar{R}_i - D_i \qquad (2)$$

The range, D_i, to the satellite can be expressed as

$$D_i = \rho_i - B_u - B_i, \qquad (3)$$

where ρ_i is the measured pseudo–range. B_u and B_i, respectively, are the range equivalents of the user and satellite clock offsets.

Then (3) combined with (2) gives

$$\bar{e}_i \cdot \bar{R}_u - B_u = \bar{e}_i \cdot \bar{R}_i - \rho_i + B_i \qquad (4)$$

The set of equations (4) are the basic range equations which contain four unknowns, consisting of the three axis components of user position in $\bar{R}_u$ and the range equivalent of the user clock offset, B_u, and therefore require four equations for solution. A solution can be provided employing the following matrix definitions:

$$X_{u(4\times1)} \triangleq |R_{u1}, R_{u2}, R_{u3}, -B_u|^T,$$

which contain the unknowns of user position and clock correction.

$$G_{u\,(nx4)} \triangleq \begin{vmatrix} r_1 \\ r_2 \\ r_3 \\ \vdots \\ r_n \end{vmatrix} \qquad A_{u(nx4n)} \triangleq \begin{vmatrix} r_1 & O & O & \cdots & O \\ O & r_2 & O & & O \\ O & O & r_3 & & O \\ \vdots & \vdots & & \ddots & \vdots \\ O & O & O & \cdots & r_n \end{vmatrix}$$

WHERE,

$$r_i \triangleq (e_{i1}, e_{i2}, e_{i3}, 1)$$
$$O \triangleq (0, 0, 0, 0)$$

Note that e_{ij} are the components of the unit vectors, $\bar{e}_i$, in each of the three axes and are the direction cosines from the user to the satellites.

$$\bar{S}(4n\times1) \triangleq |R_{11}, R_{12}, R_{13}, B_1, R_{21}, R_{22}, R_{23}, B_2 \ldots$$
$$\ldots R_{n1}, R_{n2}, R_{n3}, B_n|^T$$

$$\bar{\rho}_{(nx1)} \triangleq |\rho_1, \rho_2, \rho_3, \ldots \rho_n|^T$$

The following arrangement of the defined matrices represents the set of equations (4) and will facilitate the desired solution for $\bar{X}_u$:

$$G_u \bar{X}_u = A_u \bar{S} - \bar{\rho} \qquad (5)$$

A general least squares solution usable with any number of satellites ≥ 4 may be had by factoring G^T into both sides of (5) giving

$$G_u{}^T G_u \bar{X}_u = G_u{}^T [A_u \bar{S} - \bar{\rho}]$$

Then,

$$\hat{X}_u = [G_u{}^T G_u]^{-1} G_u{}^T [A_u \bar{S} - \bar{\rho}], \qquad (6)$$

which provides the desired solution for $\bar{X}_u$. Note that the G_u and A_u matrices are made up primarily of e_{ij}, which are the direction cosines from the user to the satellites. The solution of (6) requires an iterative solution based on initial estimates of the direction cosines e_{ij} made from an independent estimate of user position.

Derivation of GDOP

The covariance matrix of the error, $\delta \bar{X}_u$, in the estimate of $\bar{X}_u$ is given by

$$\text{Cov}\delta \bar{X}_u = (G_u{}^T G_u)^{-1} G_u{}^T \text{ Cov}\delta [A_u \bar{S} - \bar{\rho}] \qquad (7)$$
$$[(G_u{}^T G_u)^{-1} G_u{}^T]^T$$

This gives the covariance of the errors in user position and user time ($\delta \bar{X}_u$) if the measurement error statistics represented by Cov $\delta(A_u \bar{S} - \bar{\rho})$ are accurately known. GDOP is calculated by setting Cov $\delta(A_u \bar{S} - \bar{\rho})$ equal to the identity matrix. The remaining portions of (7) can then be reduced to the following:

$$\text{Cov}\delta \bar{X}_u = (G_u{}^T G_u)^{-1} \qquad (8)$$

$Cov\delta(A_u \bar{S} - \bar{\rho})$ primarily reflects range measurement error statistics (e.g., satellite ephemeris, ionospheric model, and instrumentation errors), whereas, G_u reflects only the geometry of the systems. A good approximation to the effect of geometry is therefore measured when it is assumed that $(\text{Cov}\delta(A_u \bar{S} - \bar{\rho})$ equals the identity matrix. This assumption normalizes the relationship by setting the range errors equal to one, with zero mean, and implies that the range errors are both equal and independent.

Cov$\delta\tilde{X}_u$ appears as,

$$(G_u{}^T G_u)^{-1} = \begin{array}{c} \\ X \\ Y \\ Z \\ \text{Time} \end{array} \begin{array}{cccc} X & Y & Z & \text{Time} \\ \begin{bmatrix} \sigma_{xx}^2 & \sigma_{xy}^2 & \sigma_{xz}^2 & \sigma_{xt}^2 \\ \sigma_{yx}^2 & \sigma_{yy}^2 & \sigma_{yz}^2 & \sigma_{yt}^2 \\ \sigma_{zx}^2 & \sigma_{zy}^2 & \sigma_{zz}^2 & \sigma_{zt}^2 \\ \sigma_{tx}^2 & \sigma_{ty}^2 & \sigma_{tz}^2 & \sigma_{tt}^2 \end{bmatrix} \end{array}$$

where the diagonal values are the variance of the estimated user position in each axis and in the user time offset. The GDOP factors are defined as

$$HDOP = \sqrt{\sigma_{xx}^2 + \sigma_{yy}^2}$$

$$VDOP = \sigma_{zz}$$

$$PDOP = \sqrt{\sigma_{xx}^2 + \sigma_{yy}^2 + \sigma_{zz}^2}$$

$$TDOP = \sigma_{tt}$$

$$GDOP = \sqrt{\sigma_{xx}^2 + \sigma_{yy}^2 + \sigma_{zz}^2 + \sigma_{tt}^2}$$

The product of the GDOP factors and estimates of the errors in the range measurements then give an estimate of the corresponding errors in user position or in user time.

The Navigation Technology Program

R. L. EASTON

The Navigation Technology Program at the Naval Research Laboratory formally came into being with the merger, directed by the Secretary of Defense in 1973, of the Navy's TIMATION Program and the Air Force 621B Project. Both these programs had been established in the mid-1960s to investigate the possibility of developing a satellite passive ranging system to meet contemporary military navigation requirements. The Air Force program used an ingenious "inverted range" whereby satellite-type signals were generated by ground stations to provide ranging signals for aircraft positioning, while the Navy actually launched satellites. Both projects made major contributions which were later used in the NAVSTAR Global Positioning System joint program that grew out of the merger.

The technology base for the TIMATION system was developed at the Naval Research Laboratory during the 1950's in the search for a practical method of tracking early satellites. The Minitrack system used RF interferometry to track frequencies transmitted from the satellites. Minitrack was followed by the Naval Space Surveillance System, an interferometer system which detected satellites by means of coplanar transmitters and interferometer receivers. An advanced model measured distance to the reflector by means of a synchronized transmitter and receiver. The synchronization was obtained from the use of cesium standards at receiver and transmitter with a third unit travelling between the two.

From this experiment it was a small step to propose a passive ranging scheme using satellites for navigation. Thus the anagram TIMe navigATION was born and the concept took

Mr. Easton is with Naval Research Laboratory, Code 7960, Washington DC 20375.

shape, as the atomic clock technology necessary to support such a navigation system developed during the 1960s and early 70s. The navigation satellite clock development program is described in this issue of *Navigation* by C. A. Bartholomew in his article entitled "Satellite Frequency Standards." The NRL TIMATION project began with a task from the Bureau of Naval Weapons in September 1964. This work is currently sponsored by the Naval Electronics Systems Command (PME-106).

The basic method of position fixing by means of man-made satellites is as old as the science of celestial navigation except for one minor particular. In the case of star navigation, the distances are not known but the angles may be calculated in accordance with the laws of Newton and Kepler so that they can be predicted in advance and reduced to tabular form for use in calculating lines-of-position. In the case of satellite navigation, distances are known and are used as the basis for solving the navigation equation. On Fig. 1 we see the basic navigation triangle. The height of the satellite above the earth's center is determined within a few meters. The earth's radius is also known and the range from the observer to the satellite is measured electronically. Since the other sides of the triangle are known, the range line serves to describe a line-of-position on the surface of the earth upon which the observer must be located. Two such lines-of-position determine a two dimensional fix. Three are needed to determine a position plus an altitude in the case of an aircraft. Additional lines of position, if more than three satellites are available, can be used to provide more accuracy or to measure time.

The next two figures show the method of determining a fix based on lines-of-position from satellites. With modern computer technology, this can all be done automatically so that the aircraft pilot or ship's captain can read his

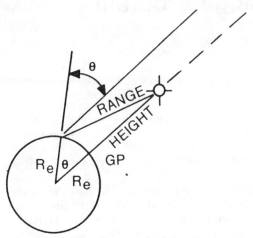

Fig. 1—Transform to celestial navigation.

27, 1967. It weighed 85 lbs, produced 6 watts of electrical power, and contained a quartz clock capable of maintaining its stability within 3 parts in 10^{11} ($\Delta f/f$) per day. The satellite, ready for launch, is shown in Fig. 5.

During June 1967, this TIMATION I satellite demonstrated that lines of position could be determined from ranging satellites and fixes from a single satellite could be obtained using range and doppler measurements. Fig. 6 shows a Timation I fix for a ship taken on May 15, 1968. The fix and the charted position disagreed by 0.2 NM. Fig. 7 shows a Timation I position of an aircraft which differed by 0.3 NM from the actual track. Timation I was also used to transfer time between the Laboratory and Ft. Collins,

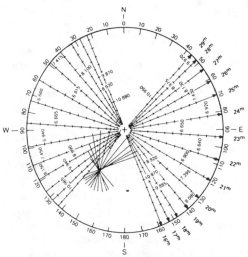

Fig. 2—Fix determined on intercept chart.

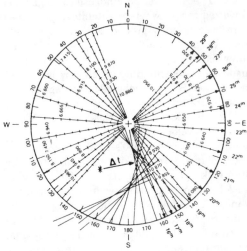

Fig. 3—Intercept chart showing effect of synchronization error on plot.

position continuously from a dial. The second graph shows the effect of a timing error which results in the equivalent of a "large triangle" in conventional navigation terminology.

Fig. 4 shows the basic Timation geometry as seen from a ship. Precise ranges are measured from two or more satellites to determine a fix. To make use of this form of navigation, accurate orbits must be known for the satellite, precise clocks must be available and the clocks in the satellites must be synchronized with the clock of the observer.

The first satellite experiment to demonstrate the validity of this passive ranging technique was launched into a 500 mile high orbit on May

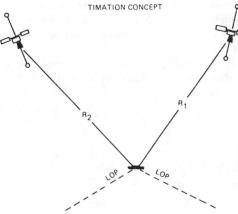

Fig. 4—The TIMATION navigation concept.

Fig. 5—TIMATION I, the rectangular black box in this photo hitched a ride aboard a Thor Agena carrying a higher priority military satellite on 27 May 1967.

mile orbit on September 30, 1969. It also contained a quartz oscillator, however the stability was better, about 1 part in 10^{11}. It weighed 125 lbs. and produced three times the power of Timation I.

A large frequency shift in the Timation II clocks was observed during the early part of August 1972 and this coincided with a solar proton storm. From this happy accident it was determined that protons instead of electrons were the major cause of quartz clock frequency shifts. This phenomenon is shown in Fig. 8.

Ionospheric effects were investigated with Timation II by using dual frequency coherent transmissions from the satellite. This allowed

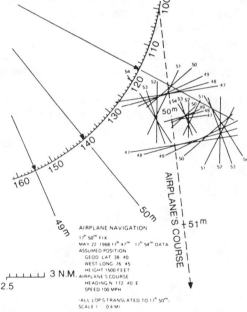

Fig. 7—Aircraft navigation fixes using TIMATION I.

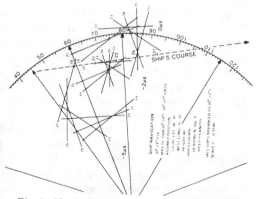

Fig. 6—Navigation of a ship using TIMATION I.

Colorado; Crane, Indiana; and Sanford, Florida. The accuracy of these time transfers was consistantly below 1 microsecond.

Timation I results displayed significant errors from two sources; solar radiation and ionospheric refraction. Initially it was suspected that electrons produced most of the errors produced by the ambient radiation environment. For this reason, Timation II's crystal oscillators were surrounded by $\frac{1}{8}''$ lead shield.

The second Timation was launched into a 500

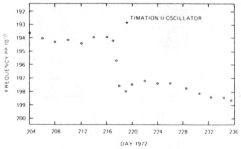

Fig. 8—Quartz oscillator frequency shift caused by August, 1972 proton storm.

measurement of the ionospheric delay and, of considerable scientific interest, displayed its fine structure as the satellite passed over the observer.

Fig. 9 shows a block diagram of the equipment used to determine the ionospheric scintillations with TIMATION II and Fig. 10 shows a comparison of delays derived from measurements of the electron content and those achieved from TIMATION II range measurements. From these and other data it was determined that the ionosphere can have appreciable irregularities and can vary tremendously in total ionospheric content over a few days time.

Several techniques were used in making navigation fixes. One can obtain several range lines of position, advance them to the same time and thereby obtain a fix. One can do the same with doppler or use a combination of a range and doppler to obtain nearly instantaneous fixes from a single satellite. The major problem with doppler arises from the fact that it is sensitive to the user's velocity. Only for a user who knows his velocity accurately (or keeps it constant for several measurements) is the doppler measurement method a practical one.

Other parameters that were measured with

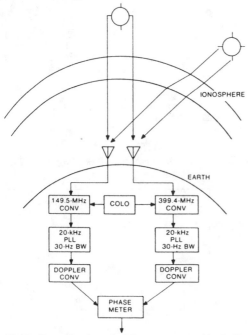

Fig. 9—Ionospheric path delay e⌐ ·ment block diagram.

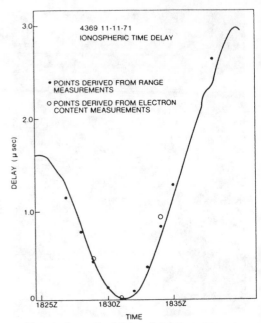

Fig. 10—Ionospheric time delay measurements.

Timation II were position accuracy as a function of maximum modulation frequency and ionospheric correction.

Fig. 11 shows the accuracy of fixes determined by Timation II as a function of maximum modulation frequency read out at two stations. It shows that there is but a slight difference in the results from a quiet station (Ft. Valley) and a noisy station (Chesapeake Bay or CBD). This figure also demonstrated that the resolution level was still limiting the system accuracy.

Another comparison was also made—that of a single (400 MHz) frequency versus a dual frequency observation. Fig. 12 shows this comparison for three cases. The best accuracy was obtained with the dual frequency in which the effect of the ionosphere was measured and removed. Second best was the modeled ionosphere and poorest was the single frequency which shows an error of approximately 1 microsecond. For the single frequency case it was apparent that there is no accuracy improvement as one goes from the 300 KHz to the 1 MHz modulation. The reason is that for this case the accuracy was limited by the ionosphere—not by the resolution.

In addition to measuring range lines of position it was possible to measure range rate or doppler lines of position with Timation II. Fig.

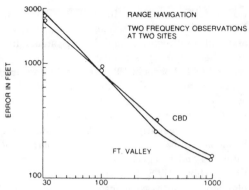

Fig. 11—A comparison of range measurements at Fort Valley and NRL Chesapeake Bay station.

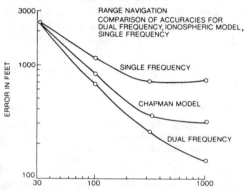

Fig. 12—A comparison of the accuracies of three methods of correcting for ionospheric path delay.

13 shows both range and range–range rate fixes. The range–range rate fix is made from a single range LOP and a single range rate LOP while the range only fix uses a complete satellite pass during which 10 LOPS were obtained. As one might suspect, the range only fixes demonstrated better accuracy than the range–range rate fixes.

The final satellite in the Timation series was launched on the 14th of July 1974, after the program had been merged with the Air Force 621B project to form the NAVSTAR Global Positioning System (GPS). This spacecraft was renamed Navigation Technology Satellite ONE (NTS–1) and became the first of a new series of satellites launched by NRL to provide technical support for the GPS Joint Service Project Office. Fig. 14 shows the configuration of NTS–1. The executive service for the GPS program is the Air Force.

Numerous changes were introduced in Timation III/NTS–1 as a result of lessons learned from the earlier Timations. An altitude of 7,500

NM was selected to reduce errors due to atmospheric drag and more nearly reflect the environment of operational satellites which would be at even higher altitudes. The weight was increased to 650 lbs. and the power to 125 watts. In addition to the UHF frequencies of the earlier satellites, an L–band Pseudo Random Noise (PRN) signal at the same frequency as that of the operational GPS satellites was added. Perhaps the most significant change was the addition of two rubidium clocks. These had become available about eight months prior to the launch date and were readied for operation in space by an intensive effort. The rubidiums performed well in NTS–1, demonstrating a stability of

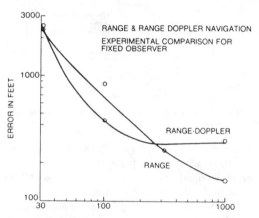

Fig. 13—The accuracy of range only vs range/range doppler.

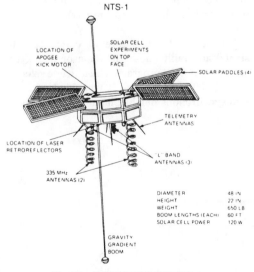

Fig. 14—TIMATION III/NTS-1.

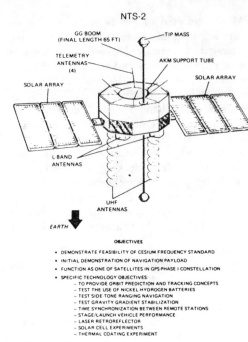

NTS-2

GG BOOM
(FINAL LENGTH 65 FT)   TIP MASS

TELEMETRY
ANTENNAS   AKM SUPPORT TUBE
(4)
                              SOLAR ARRAY
SOLAR ARRAY

L BAND
ANTENNAS

UHF
ANTENNAS

EARTH

OBJECTIVES

• DEMONSTRATE FEASIBILITY OF CESIUM FREQUENCY STANDARD
• INITIAL DEMONSTRATION OF NAVIGATION PAYLOAD
• FUNCTION AS ONE OF SATELLITES IN GPS PHASE I CONSTELLATION
• SPECIFIC TECHNOLOGY OBJECTIVES
    – TO PROVIDE ORBIT PREDICTION AND TRACKING CONCEPTS
    – TEST THE USE OF NICKEL HYDROGEN BATTERIES
    – TEST SIDE TONE RANGING NAVIGATION
    – TEST GRAVITY GRADIENT STABILIZATION
    – TIME SYNCHRONIZATION BETWEEN REMOTE STATIONS
    – STAGE/LAUNCH VEHICLE PERFORMANCE
    – LASER RETROREFLECTOR
    – SOLAR CELL EXPERIMENTS
    – THERMAL COATING EXPERIMENT

Fig. 15—Navigation Technology Satellite Two.

about one part in 10^{12} per day. As a result, they are to be used as the primary standards in the early Navigation Development Satellites (NDS) built by Rockwell International.

In addition to its clocks NTS-1 contained a number of other experiments, all tailored to meet requirements of the GPS. It space qualified improved solar cells which should increase the power and reliability of future navigation satellites.

NTS-2 was the first satellite completely designed and built under the sponsorship of the NAVSTAR GPS program. The altitude selected was 10,980 NM because it coincided with the semisynchronous height planned for the opera-

tional GPS satellites. Instead of rubidium, NTS-2 contained two cesium clocks, designed and built by Frequency and Time Systems, Inc. and the frequency stability consequently increased to 1–2 parts in 10^{13} per day. In addition, NTS-2 contains a duplicate of the navigation system planned for use in the NDS satellites. Both the navigation system and the clocks have performed excellently in NTS-2, and data is now being accumulated for use in the operational satellites and to checkout the ground stations. Fig. 15 shows NTS-2 and the major objectives planned for this experiment.

Looking into the future, an NTS-3 is planned for launch in 1981. This satellite will contain hydrogen maser clocks as well as an advanced cesium. The clock stability is expected to be an order of magnitude better than that of NTS-2. NTS-3 will also fly other advanced technology experiments to qualify new components for later operational use.

REFERENCES

1. An Advanced Space Surveillance System, NRL Memo Report 8 Feb 1961.
2. Determination of the U. S. Naval Space Surveillance System Range Capability, NRL Memo Report 5786, 18 June 1962.
3. Navy's Space Surveillance Systems Two–Point Orbits, NRL Memo Report 6072 13 March 1964.
4. Satellite Celestial Navigation, NRL Memo Report, 27 Feb 1967.
5. "The Timation I Satellite," NRL Report 6781, 18 Nov 1968.
6. "Timation Annual Report for Fiscal Year 1970"— NRL serial 5160–69, 21 July 1970.
7. Radiation Effects on Satellite Crystal Oscillators, NRL Report 7368, 15 Feb 1972.
8. "The Role of Time/Frequency in Navy Navigation Satellites," Proceedings IEEE, Vol. 60, No. 5, May 1972.
9. "Navy Navigation Satellite Experiments," National Telecommunications Conference, 27 November 1973.

Satellite Frequency Standards

C. A. BARTHOLOMEW

INTRODUCTION

Satellite Frequency standards have progressed from quartz oscillators used in Navy Navigation Satellite System (NNSS) satellites and early TIMATION launches to rubidium units used in the NTS–1 of NAVSTAR GPS, cesium units in NTS–2, and hydrogen maser units projected for NTS–3.

The reasons that a large NRL effort has been made is that the character of satellite navigation systems has changed.

The NNSS operates on a navigation technique suitable for objects having well known velocities. The parameter used is frequency; the satellites operate at low altitudes so the passes last only for 15 minutes or so. The frequency stability of the satellite clock must be such that the change in frequency does not introduce appreciable error in position fix.

The NAVSTAR GPS is designed to give positions continuously in three dimensions. To do so it uses satellites in much higher altitudes than NNSS. At these altitudes continuous fixes by means of frequency measurement is impractical so ranging is used instead. Since a further requirement is that the user be passive the ranging measurement is obtained by having all satellites have clocks that are synchronized so the user can make measurements on enough satellites that he can determine the clock synchronization parameters. The problem of clock synchronization without near continuous updating of the satellite clocks has determined the search for better satellite clocks, programming through quartz, rubidium, cesium and now hydrogen maser standards.

Mr. Bartholomew is with Naval Research Laboratory, Code 7960, Washington, DC 20375.

QUARTZ STANDARDS

The NNSS used a quartz crystal oscillator designed by APL/JHU as the satellite clock. The principal stability requirements were an overall accuracy of parts in 10^9 with a "short term" stability of a part in 10^{11} for several minutes. Quartz crystal oscillators for laboratory or ground station use were available with stabilities on the order of from a part per 10^{10} to a few parts per 10^{12} per day after an extensive burn in period. The development of this class of oscillator into a flight qualified, low power, highly reliable device with a fractional frequency stability of one part per 10^{12} for averaging times on the order of 10^4 seconds was the first design goal. Such a clock stability would contribute a 10 foot error to the navigator's error budget assuming satellite clock update at 10^4 second intervals.

The only commercial firm expressing an interest in developing a space quality improved quartz crystal oscillator at that time was Frequency Electronics, Inc. (FEI) currently of New Hyde Park, N.Y. Under this program[1] a series of improved oscillators were designed and fabricated using most of the contemporary techniques available to the industry. The principal design considerations were in the preparation of the quartz crystal to minimize aging and the thermal control design necessary to take advantage of the longer term stability available with reduced aging.

It should be noted at this time that the current multihundred watt power supplies for spacecraft were not then generally available and the low power and weight and the high reliability of the quartz oscillator made this type a natural choice for the early satellites. The weight, power, and reliability of 1965 era rubidium vapor and

[1] Quartz Crystal Oscillator Development for Timation, C. A. Bartholomew, NRL Report 7478

cesium beam frequency standards limited their use to ground station functions.

Table one has been prepared to show the sequence of flight experiments to trace the modest experiment that was Timation I launched in 1967 to the multi-hundred watt satellites that are Navigation Technology Satellites one, two and three of the GPS program.

TIMATION I

TIMATION I was launched into an orbit of opportunity

$$(h = 500 \text{ n.mi}; \ i = 70°, \ e = .001)$$

and provided the first demonstration of Navigation based on range measurements from a time synchronized satellite. Fig. 1 is a view of the disassembled TIMATION I frequency stan-

dard. Fig. 2 shows the aging rate for this class of oscillator.

Fig. 3 is a frequency history of the TIMATION I oscillator compared with temperature for the first eight months of orbital life. The temperature coefficient determined from the data was approximately 2 parts per 10^{11} per degree Celsius. This coefficient was higher than expected and was the primary limiting feature in the oscillator's performance. If the frequency is considered at various points of equal temperature, the apparent aging rate is on the order of +2 parts per 10^{12} per day. This value is lower than that measured before launch. Radiation is the most probable cause of this favorable compensation. Fig. 4 shows segments of frequency versus time and temperature at later periods. It is seen that the apparent aging rate changed

Table 1—Technology Satellites

	T-1	T-II	NTS-1	NTS-2	NTS-3
Launch Date	5/31/67	9/30/69	7/14/74	6/23/77	10/81
Alt. (N.Mi.)	500	500	7,400	10,980	10,980
Inc.°	70	70	125	63	63
Ecc	.001	.002	.007	.0004	.0004
Wt(Kg)	39	57	295	440	490
Power (W)	6	18	125	400	450
Freq.'s	UHF	VHF/UHF	UHF/L	UHF/L_1/L_2	UHF/L_1/L_2
Clock	Qtz	Qtz	Qtz/Rb	Qtz/C_s	C_s/H-M
$\frac{\Delta f}{f} \left(\frac{PP10^{13}}{day} \right)$	300	100	5–10	1–2	0.1

Fig. 1—View of disassembled TIMATION I satellite frequency standard.

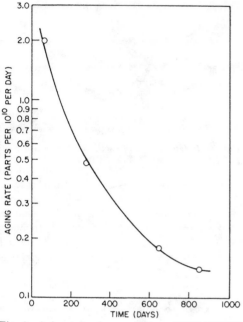

Fig. 2—Aging rate of an oscillator of TIMATION I class.

THE INFLUENCE OF SUNLIGHT ON TEMPERATURE AND FREQUENCY

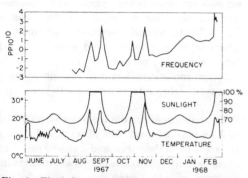

Fig. 3—The influence of sunlight/temperature on the frequency of the TIMATION I oscillator.

from a small positive rate to a negative one of approximately −1 part per 10^{11} per day.

By this time the backup oscillator in the laboratory, kept running for comparison, had reached an aging rate of approximately +1 part per 10^{11} per day. If it is assumed that the flight oscillator had reached a similar aging rate, then the effect due to radiation was −2 parts in 10^{11} per day. Fig. 5 shows the aging-rate performance of the backup oscillator and the performance of the flight oscillator. The values for the flight

oscillator after launch were obtained by compensating the apparent aging rate by removing the inferred radiation effect.

TIMATION II

TIMATION II was launched into an orbit nearly identical to that of its predecessor. This satellite was designed with a two frequency ranging system to allow for the compensation for ionospheric refraction.

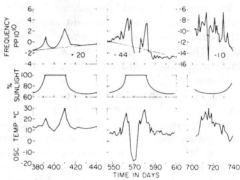

Fig. 4—Apparent aging extracted from frequency/sunlight, temperature data for TIMATION I oscillator.

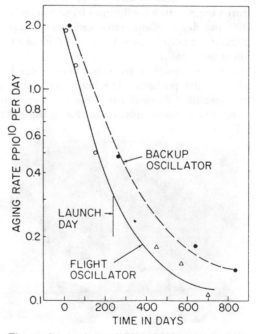

Fig. 5—Comparison of TIMATION I oscillator to identical model on the ground.

The TIMATION II oscillator included two major improvements. The first, a quartz crystal using thermal–compression–bonded leads, a cold–welded enclosure seal, and a high–temperature bake-out under high vacuum. The second improvement, a triple proportional oven system designed to improve the temperature coefficient by a factor of ten.

A thermal electric temperature–control system was developed for TIMATION II as an experiment to determine whether a critical satellite component could be successfully maintained at a relatively constant temperature above the expected ambient temperature variations. This device was installed with the oscillator to provide improved thermal control and is shown in Fig. 6.

Fig. 7 is a graph of the satellite percent of time in sunlight, and satellite temperature and oscillator temperature versus time. The thermal electric system maintained the oscillator temperature at 24° ± 0.1°C, while satellite temperature varied from about −2°C to + 24°C. The vertical lines for satellite temperature for each day show the range of temperatures measured during from three to five passes a day from a telemetering station. These data, and the oscillator's measured temperature coefficient of 1 to 2 parts per 10^{12} per degree Centigrade, indicate that the oscillator's performance is independent of ambient temperature.

Fig. 8 is a graph of frequency versus time for the satellite oscillator. The lower curve shows the measured frequency and the times and increments of tuning operations. During the early

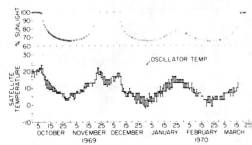

Fig. 7—Independence of oscillator temperature due to TED.

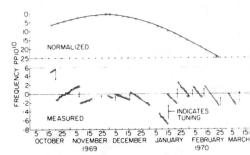

Fig. 8—TIMATION II frequency drift.

phase, the aging rate was positive and gradually approaching zero. It was optimistically assumed that the oscillator was recovering from the effects of launch vibration and zero g environment. The low aging rate observed prior to launch (approximately 1 part per 10^{11} per day) and the expected radiation effect could possibly yield a long-term aging rate of a few parts in 10^{12} per day.

The balance of the data shows that this optimism was short lived. The effect of radiation is apparent from the curve, and it can be seen that aging became approximately constant following a period of adjustment due to perturbation caused by orbital injection. It appears that the oscillator has reached a relatively low constant aging rate, but the effect of radiation was not that expected. The upper curve is the normalized frequency–versus–time curve and provides a more graphic view of the results.

Subsequent studies provided the probable answer. Different pieces of quartz exhibit different frequency variations with radiation dosage. For example, Fig. 9 is a graph of frequency shift versus radiation dosage for a crystal carried approximately to saturation (graph A). The slope of the curve (extrapolated in graph B) for low

Fig. 6—TIMATION II oscillator with thermal electric device (TED) temperature compensation.

dosage is highest. This crystal showed a maximum value of 4 parts per 10^{11} per rad initially, and decreased from that point. The Q of this unit changed from 1.4×10^6 before radiation to $.7 \times 10^6$ after near saturation.

A set of improved quartz crystal oscillators were specified for Timation III. Fig. 10 is a $\sigma -$ plot showing the design goal for these oscillators along with data from three units showing typical performance.

NTS-1

In 1973 the Navy's Timation effort was merged with the Air Force 621B program, with the Air Force named as executive service, to form the NAVSTAR Global Positioning System (GPS) program. NRL's Timation III satellite was redesignated Navigation Technology Satellite One (NTS-1) and launched 14 July 1974 as part of the NAVSTAR effort.

The launch system selected by the Air Force

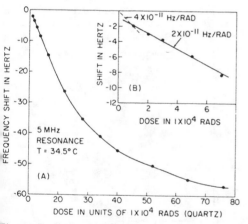

Fig. 9—*Radiation influence on crystal oscillator frequency.*

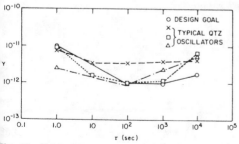

Fig. 10—*Typical quartz crystal oscillators for spacecraft.*

Space Test Program (STP) for NTS-1 provided sufficient weight margin for the flight of rubidium vapor frequency standards as a first experiment in the newly formed GPS program.

A small, lightweight rubidium vapor standard with low power requirements had just become available commercially from EFRATOM of Munich, Germany (now EFRATOM of California). Fig. 11 is a photo of the 10 x 10 x 11 centimeter commercial unit which weighed 1.3 kilograms and required a nominal 13 watts of power. Based on the short time schedule and a low budget (100K) it was decided that a simple program consisting of only those modifications necessary to make the commercial units flight–worthy would be possible[2]. Feasibility and vibration post mortem tests were performed on several units to determine the necessary modifications in structure and components. Suitable electrical interfaces were designed to provide tuning of the VCXO and telemetry monitoring.

Six production units were purchased for modification and flight qualification. Of these six modified units, two were selected for flight on the basis of their overall performance under environmental conditions. Fig. 12 is a $\sigma - \tau$ plot showing the performance of some of these units prior to modification. Fig. 13 is a $\sigma - \tau$ plot showing typical pre and post modification performance of the flight candidates. The probable cause of the deterioration is the modification to electronic components particularly in the VCXO area. Fig. 14 is a plot of frequency versus temperature in vacuum and in air. The change of temperature coefficient of 7 parts per 10^{13} per °C to -2 parts per 10^{11} per °C from air to vacuum is an indication of lack of optimization of commercial units designed to operate in air. On–orbit performance has been reported[3] on these units. However, the lack of attitude stabilization system on NTS-1 resulted in large temperature variations which ultimately masked any quantitive evaluation of rubidium standard performance. Fig. 15 is a coarse plot of frequency versus time which shows variations of frequency

[2] Design and Ground Test of the NTS-1 Frequency Standard, S. A. Nichols, et all, NRL Report 7904, 5 Sept 75

[3] NTS-1 Quartz and Rubidium Oscillator Frequency Stability Results Buisson & McCaskill, NRL Report #7932

Fig. 11—Commerical Rubidium unit by EFRA-
TROM.

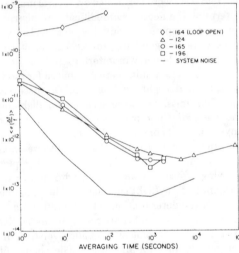

Fig. 12—Preflight Rubidium stability data.

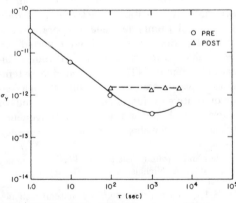

Fig. 13—Pre and post modification stability comparisons.

caused by temperature variations of the space
craft. Fig. 16 is a long term plot of the frequency
of the quartz crystal oscillator which was the
principal frequency standard on NTS-1. The
general negative trend in frequency is probably
due to radiation. Two tuning operations are seen
in two years of data.

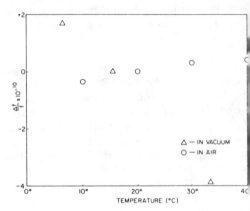

Fig. 14—Comparison of temperature performance
Rb units in vacuum and in air.

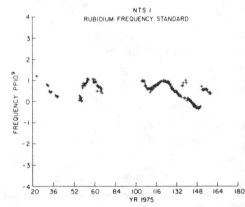

Fig. 15—Long term frequency performance of NTS-
Rb standard.

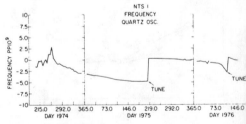

Fig. 16—Long term frequency performance of NTS-
quartz crystal standard.

NTS-2

While NTS-1 rubidiums standards operated in space and showed sufficient capability to be used in other GPS satellites, cesium standards offered even greater promise. The promises involved somewhat better long term stability, smaller temperature coefficients and longer life.

Just as the EFRATOM unit became available in time for NTS-1 so also did a cesium unit become available for modification for NTS-2. This unit is based on a cesium tube developed by Frequency & Time Systems, Inc. of Danvers, Mass.

This new tube was particularly attractive in that its dimensions were 7.6 x 7.6 x 30.5 cm with a weight of 4 Kg. A development contract was let to modify the tube to operate through the launch vibration environment and was followed by the development of a prototype frequency standard to be flight qualified and evaluated on the NTS-2 spacecraft. (HP subsequently modified the design of their option 004 tube to meet a tough vibration specification and thereby provided a backup to the FTS prime effort). Fig. 17 is a photograph of one of the prototype standards flown on NTS-2. Fig. 18 is a $\sigma - \tau$ plot showing the FTS specification along with preflight data taken from the two flight units and the backup. During the first four months of operation of the NTS-2 cesium standard the following milestones have occurred:

Initial frequency measurements precise to one to two parts per 10^{12} have confirmed the calculated offset due to relativity of 4.45 parts per 10^{10}. This offset has been compensated with a digital synthesizer in the clock system. Current frequency measurements are yielding daily un-

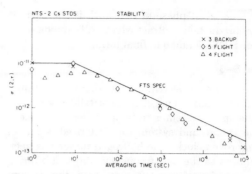

Fig. 18—*NTS-2 cesium beam frequency standard performance.*

Fig. 19—*Engineering Development Model cesium beam frequency standard.*

certainties of a few parts in 10^{13}. These uncertainties are principally caused by anomallies in the orbit making process.

Once the FTS program had completed the critical brassboard demonstration phase a follow-on program for the design of Engineering Development Models (EDM) was initiated. One of these to be included in each of the Navigation Development Satellites (NDS) beginning with NDS 4 as a supplementary frequency standard to the rubidium vapor units. The EDM design included a repackage as shown in Fig. 19 to provide a unit with dimensions 12.8 x 19.5 x 38.1 cm weighing 11.3 Kg compared to 25.4 x 30.5 x 40.6 cm weighing 13.6 Kg for the prototype units. A radiation hardening program supported and funded by the Defense Nuclear Agency made a significant contribution to the successful development of a hardened frequency standard meeting GPS requirements. Analysis for this program was by Itelcom Rad Tech (IRT) and by FTS. Coordination and much of the test work was by and at NRL.

Fig. 17—*NTS-2 cesium beam frequency standard.*

The latest phase of this work is the current preproduction contract which will provide units for NDS's 7 and 8 in final form.

NTS–3

Cesium clocks require updating to maintain a specified error budget in the satellite system. If the space system is to be made less dependent on the ground system the first need is for an improved clock. The hydrogen maser has been chosen as the best frequency standard offering a significant improvement over the cesium beam. A dual program (Hughes Research Labs and RCA) has been underway for the past year and a half to develop a capability in industry to provide these highly specialized devices in a spacecraft configuration.

A third technology satellite (NTS–3) has been designated to carry advanced development model (ADM) hydrogen maser frequency standards to determine the feasibility of operating the GPS Space Segment independent of ground support for extended periods such as might be encountered in a "short war".

ACKNOWLEDGMENT

This work is sponsored by the Naval Electronics Systems Command PME–106.

GPS Signal Structure and Performance Characteristics

J. J. SPILKER, Jr.

ABSTRACT

DETAILS OF THE GPS signal structure are discussed as relates to the signal generation and the performance of the navigation system. GPS performance objectives, orbit geometry, and propagation effects are summarized in order to gain better understanding of the signal and what characteristics it must provide. With these performance objectives as a preface, the details of the signal are described, showing the details of the dual frequency transmission and both the precision P and clear/acquisition C/A codes and their characteristics. Finally, the basic performance of simplified receivers operating on this received signal is discussed. It is shown that an rms position error of less than 10 meters is well within the achievable performance bounds of the system.

SECTION 1—INTRODUCTION AND PERFORMANCE OBJECTIVES

1.1 Introduction

In this paper we describe the detailed signal structure used in the Global Positioning System satellite navigation system. In order for one to understand the performance characteristics in a meaningful sense, we begin by discussing, in an idealized sense, the concepts for high accuracy, real-time navigation using satellites. The various perturbation effects on the navigation signal and overall system are then described. These perturbations include relativistic effects, multiple ac-

Dr. Spilker, Jr., is with Stanford Telecommunications, Inc., 1195 Bordeaux Drive, Sunnyvale, CA 94086.

cess interference between satellites, tropospheric and ionospheric propagation delays, multipath, thermal noise, and other interference effects. We conclude the first section with a summary of the performance objectives for the signal.

The paper then continues with a detailed discussion of the signal structure, the code properties, and the performance of the signal relative to the various objectives and constraints in the first section.

In the concluding section the performance capability of a typical receiver for this signal is described and briefly analyzed. The search, acquisition, and tracking accuracy for the GPS codes are included. Effects of user dynamics are considered. Multipath and other interference error effects are summarized.

1.2 Performance Objectives

There are several key performance objectives for the GPS system which distinguish it from previous satellite and landbased navigation systems. Some of the more important are summarized below:

- High Accuracy 10–30 meter rms position error
- Real-Time navigation from users with high dynamics
- World–Wide Operation
- Tolerant to Nonintentional or Intentional Interference

In addition to these constraints, the user cannot be required to carry a precision atomic clock, and an initial navigation fix should be obtained within a reasonable period (minutes rather than hours) after initial turn-on of the receiver.

Obtaining high accuracy in real–time without ambiguity requires a relatively large bandwidth (≥ 10 MHz) and a signal with a long period. The high dynamics of the user particularly in an aircraft requires the use of a omni–directional or hemispherical pattern antenna. Coupling these two requirements together leads to an RF frequency selection which is large compared to the bandwidth but not so large as to give too great a space loss. Space loss is computed with a combination of an earth coverage satellite antenna and a 0 dBI gain receive antenna. The RF frequency must also be consistent with available frequency allocations. L–band is selected.

The demand for world–wide operation primarily places a constraint on the satellite orbits. One must employ at least some satellites in inclined orbits in order to provide coverage to the polar regions. Secondly, the signals received from the satellite are of relatively low power. Hence the signal should be tolerant to low level interference which might, for example, be nothing more than a spurious harmonic of some lower frequency narrow-band signal.

1.3 Satellite Navigation Concepts

As an elementary example of the use of satellites for navigation, examine the single satellite in Fig. 1–1. The satellite carries a display of the satellite on–board clock and position $\bar{x}_1 \triangleq (x_1, y_1, z_1)$ in earth–center–earth–fixed coordinates. If this hypothetical display could be viewed by an observer on earth through a telescope then simultaneous photographs can be taken of the satellite clock through the telescope and a local clock. Both satellite and local clocks are assumed to be precisely at GPS system time. The time difference between the two clocks as observed by the user is exactly the propagation delay (neglecting relativistic effects).

From this measurement and the knowledge of the satellite position one can of course determine that the user position is on the surface of a sphere centered at the satellite. Clearly if one takes a sequence of measurements and forms a sequence of spheres one can determine position from only one satellite. However, two of our performance objectives then have been violated: the solution is not in real–time, and an accurate clock has been assumed at the user.

The system configuration of Fig. 1–2 eliminates the requirement for a local precision clock and provides a real–time position measurement through the use of 4 measurements, 4 equations

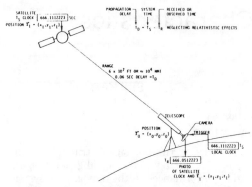

Fig. 1-1—Satellite & User Clock Timing Concepts—Simultaneous Photographs of Clocks.

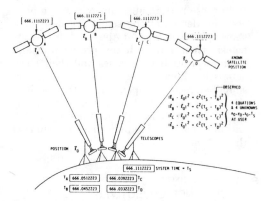

Fig. 1-2—Multi-Satellite Clock Timing and Position Measurement.

to solve for the 4 unknowns, x_o, y_o, z_o, and T_S. One simultaneously photographs the 4 satellite displays to obtain T_A, T_B, T_C, T_D, and $\bar{X}_A$, $\bar{X}_B$, $\bar{X}_C$, $\bar{X}_D$. In addition one can measure the derivatives of these quantities and solve for user velocity.

In order to be useful, these simplified models of a navigation system must first be transformed into a realizable form. The clock display must be transformed into an equivalent RF signal which carries with it the time–of–day with sufficient precision and lack of ambiguity; the position of the satellite and any errors in the satellite clock must be carried to the user in a down–link data stream. Even a satellite atomic standard has some inaccuracy relative to system time (a set of atomic clocks). See Fig. 1–3 for a typical plot of satellite clock count vs "true" system time showing the clock time error.*

It is also easily shown that if the user has a good crystal clock that solutions of the above equations for user time, together with doppler measurements can correct the user clock rate. This correction will be valid over a reasonable period thereafter, depending on the crystal clock stability. For that time period one needs only to solve for three unknowns, and hence only needs 3 satellites in view.

1.4 GPS Orbit Configuration and Multiple Access

Fig. 1-4 shows the GPS satellite configuration of 24 satellites. There are 3 orbit planes, each inclined by 63° with respect to the equatorial plane and offset from one another by 120° in longitude. Eight satellites are in circular pro-grade 12 hour** orbits in each orbit plane. The satellite altitude is approximately 19,652 Km or 10,611 nm. Fig. 1-5 shows the orbit traces (not ground tracks) and the relative positions of each satellite in the 6 satellite Phase I configuration— 2 orbit planes. The earth rotates under these orbit traces.

Each satellite crosses the equator in a northerly direction *twice* a day at 2 points separated by exactly 180° with a *fixed* "sinusoidal" ground track. Satellites with different phases but in the same orbit plane have different ground tracks which are displaced by the amount of earth rotation between crossings. Thus if a satellite crosses (northerly) the equator at 0° and 180° longitude, another satellite in the same plane but 6 hr sidereal behind crosses (northerly) the equator at 90°E and 90°W longitude and crosses southerly at 0° and 180° longitude.

In the fully implemented 24 satellite system there are always at least 6 satellites in view and as many as 11 (depending on user location and orbit inclination). One required characteristic of the GPS signals then is that one must be able to observe these multiple satellite signals simulta-

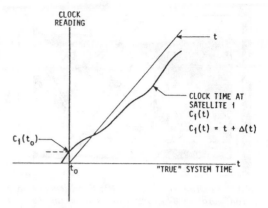

CLOCK READING

$c_1(t_0)$

t_0

"TRUE" SYSTEM TIME t

CLOCK TIME AT SATELLITE 1
$c_1(t)$

$c_1(t) = t + \Delta(t)$

Fig. 1-3—Satellite Clock Time Characteristics. "True" system time is defined as the time at the GPS Master Control Center—an average of a set of atomic clocks.

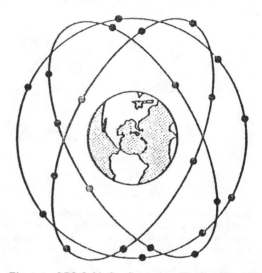

Fig. 1-4—GPS Orbit Configuration. The Satellite Altitude is Approximately 19,652 km or 10,611 nm.

neously without mutual interference. This property is analogous to multiple access in satellite communications.

Path Delays and Doppler Shifts

Closer examination of the signals received by a given user from multiple satellites illustrates the fact that these signals have different path delays and different doppler shifts (see Fig. 1-6). In Fig. 1-7 the maximum doppler shift (nsec/sec) is shown as a function of user position for stationary users. The maximum doppler shift is

---

* J. J. Spilker, Jr., *Digital Communications By Satellite*, Prentice-Hall, Engelwood Cliffs, N.J., Chapter 17, description of precise measures of time.
** The 12 hour period is in sidereal time, not solar time. Thus the subsatellite point at noon slowly shifts each day on its fixed ground track since a sidereal day is roughly 4 minutes shorter than a solar day.

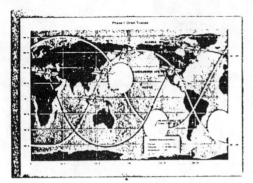

Fig. 1-5—Orbit traces of the GPS Satellites in Phase 1 configuration. The earth rotates under these 2 orbit traces. The third curve without the arrows defines the visibility region from Yuma, Arizona, and is fixed with respect to the earth. Ground tracks on a fixed earth would show a sinusoidal pattern at twice this frequency with 2 northerly-going equatorial crossings separated by 180° in longitude.

on the order of 2700 nsec/sec or a v/c = 2.7 × 10^{-6} where v is the radial velocity to the user and c is the speed of light.

If a stationary user is at the North Pole (zero earth rotation effect), the receiver can observe a +2600 nsec/sec velocity from one satellite and a −2600 nsec/sec velocity from another satellite nearly simultaneously. Thus the differential radial velocity can exceed 5000 nsec/sec. For a 1.56 GHz signal, this differential corresponds to 7500 Hz.

Geometric Dilution of Precision (GDOP)

The accuracy with which one can measure position and time is related to the accuracy in radial range measurement by factors known as the GDOP or Geometric Dilution of Precision. The rms position error

$$\sigma_p \triangleq \sqrt{\sigma_x^2 + \sigma_y^2 + \sigma_z^2} \qquad (1\text{-}1)$$

is related to the rms radial range error σ_r by

$$\frac{\sigma_p}{\sigma_r} \triangleq \text{PDOP} \qquad (1\text{-}2)$$

PDOP is the Position Dilution of Precision, and we similarly define $\sigma_h \triangleq \sqrt{\sigma_x^2 + \sigma_y^2}$, the Horizontal Dilution of Precision which is given by

$$\frac{\sigma_h}{\sigma_r} \triangleq \text{HDOP} \qquad (1\text{-}3)$$

The value of PDOP can be determined geometrically by relating it to the volume of a special tetrahedron as shown in Fig. 1-8. The user position is at point $\bar{P}$, and the satellites are located at points $\bar{R}_n$ which generate a unit sphere centered at the user $\bar{P}$. Vectors intersecting the sphere to each satellite are shown in Fig. 1-8(b)

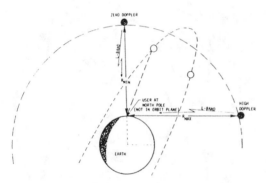

Fig. 1-6—GPS Range and Doppler for a User at the Pole. Range Variations, ≤ 6378 Km − Max Range Variation if User is on satellite ground track. Doppler Variation, ±2654 nsec/sec at poles. (1 nm = 1.852 km).

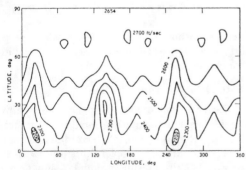

Fig. 1-7—GPS Phase III − 3 × 8 Baseline, Maximum Range Rate (Doppler) for a stationary user.

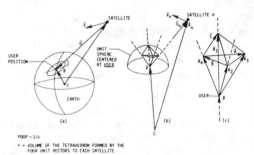

Fig. 1-8—Relationship between user satellite geometry and PDOP.

where one of the satellites is shown at the user's zenith. The tetrahedron formed by connecting these points together and the user point $\bar{P}$ has a volume V. It can be shown that

$$PDOP \sim 1/V \qquad (1\text{-}4)$$

Thus as the volume of the tetrahedron becomes larger, the PDOP becomes smaller, and hence the position accuracy improves. The volume is maximized when the one satellite is at the user's zenith and the other three are separated by 120° and are as low on the horizon as permitted by the user's antenna elevation angle (maximize the horizontal cross-sectional area).

Fig. 1-9 shows the various GDOP factors vs the cumulative probability of achieving a given GDOP or lower. The values shown are for a 5° elevation mask, i.e. only satellites in the 24 satellite constellation above 5° elevation angle are assumed to be in view. Clearly one has a high probability of a PDOP of 3 or less. Thus if one is to have a 10 meter accuracy goal the desired accuracy in range measurement should be on the order of (1/3) 10 meters or roughly $\sigma_r < 10$ nsec.

If one assumes that a modulation component or code chip modulating the signal can be resolved to 1-10% of its width with reasonable ease then the 10 nsec value for σ_r leads to a code chip width of 1 μsec to 100 nsec or a 1-10 Mbps code clock rate.

1.5 Satellite Clock Errors and Relativistic Frequency Shifts

Although the satellites carry atomic standards on board, even these clocks are subject to drifts and clock errors as time passes. For this reason the clock's timing errors are continually checked by receivers at ground monitor stations, and at least once per day, a clock correction signal is uploaded to each satellite for relay down to each user as part of the satellite data stream along with the satellite position information (ephemeris).

In addition to these slowly varying oscillator generated clock errors there are also general and special relativistic clock shifts. The received clock frequency f_r differs from the transmitted clock frequency by the expression given in Table 1-1. These are two types of effects. The first is caused by the difference in gravitational poten-

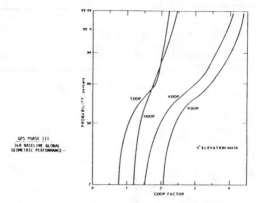

Fig. 1-9—GDOP vs. the Cumulative Probability of a GDOP Less Than the Value Shown, (From Bogen, 1974).

tial between the satellite and the user. The second effect is caused by the difference in velocities of the users. Velocities are defined relative to a fixed geocentric inertial frame. Both of these effects depend somewhat on where the user is on the earth. The average effect is a net fractional increase in frequency of 447.9×10^{-12}. The effect of the earth oblateness and sun causes a minor perturbation in this value, and the moon a still smaller effect (Kleppner, et al, 1970).

Much of this relativistic effect can be corrected by purposely setting the satellite clock frequency slightly low by the factor 4.45×10^{-10}. The satellite signal speeds up as it approaches earth causing the observed frequency to increase. The remaining correction is carried in the downlink data steam.

1.6 Ionospheric and Tropospheric Range Errors

Both the ionosphere and the troposphere generate range errors. The ionospheric error is caused by the integrated electron count over the ray path after one has accounted for the ray bending effects of the ionosphere. Thus the effect is dependent on both the character of the ionosphere at zenith and the elevation angle to the satellite.

Fig. 1-10 illustrates the typical effects of the elevation angle relative to the total ionospheric delay. The obliquity factor gives the factor with which the ionospheric delay is increased relative to the delay for a ray to a satellite at zenith. As

Table 1-1—Relativistic Clock Frequency Shifts

- Receiving station clock frequency f_r
- Transmitting satellite clock frequency f_t

$$\frac{f_r}{f_t} = 1 + \frac{1}{c^2}(\phi_t - \phi_r) + \frac{1}{2}\left(\frac{V_r^2}{c^2} - \frac{V_t^2}{c^2}\right) + \frac{\vec{k}}{c} \cdot (\vec{V}_t - \vec{V}_r) + \ldots = 1 + \delta$$

↑	↑	↑	↑
Gravitational Potential (General Relativity)	Special Relativistic Shifts	Normal Doppler	Higher Order Terms ($V/c)^3$ etc.

- Observed satellite increase in frequency (observed at receiver) $\delta \simeq 447.9 \times 10^{-12}$ or 448 μsec/sec of time offset. (38.7 μsec/day)
- Earth oblateness and solar perturbation: Varies from 445.8 to 450.2×10^{-12}
- Satellite clock is purposely set low to 10.22999999545 MHz or 4.45×10^{-10} low in frequency relative to a nominal 10.23 MHz.

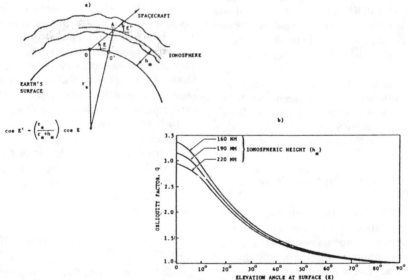

Fig. 1-10—Oblique Ionospheric Path Geometry and the Relationship to Surface Elevation Angle, (From Elrod, 1975).

shown, the obliquity factor is on the order of 3 for low elevation angles.

Fig. 1-11 shows typical measurements of ionospheric delay for an L-band signal received at vertical incidence (obliquity factor of 1). The mean ionospheric delay at nighttime is on the order of 10 nsec. During daytime the delay increases to as high as 50 nsec. In regions near the geomagnetic equator or near the poles the delays can be significantly larger, particularly during periods of magnetic storms.

At low elevation angles then the ionosphere delay can be 3 times the values given above and thus can be on the order of 30 nsec at nighttime or 150 nsec during daytime. Some of this delay can be eliminated by ionospheric modeling. However, more precise corrections can be made by making use of measurements at two L-band frequencies, 1575.42 MHz = L1 and 1227.6 MHz = L2, and making use of the approximate inverse

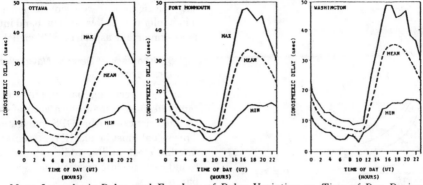

Fig. 1–11—Mean Ionospheric Delay and Envelope of Delay Variation vs. Time of Day During—March, 1958—Satellite at Zenith f = 1.6 GHz (From Elrod, 1975).

Table 1–2—Ionospheric Group Delay and Doppler Variation with Frequency

$$\tau_{GD} = \frac{R}{C} + \frac{A}{f^2} + \frac{B}{f^3} + \frac{C}{f^4} \cdots$$

$$\approx \frac{R}{C} + \frac{A}{f^2}$$

where

$R =$ true range
$C =$ speed of light
$f =$ carrier frequency
$B \propto$ (averaged earth magnetic field strength along the path)[3]

Term Neglected	Range Error at $f = 1.5$ GHz
B/f^3	≤ 1 inch
C/f^4	≤ 3 inches

$$\Delta f = \frac{d\phi}{dt} = \frac{1.34}{f} \times 10^{-7} \frac{d(TEC)}{dt}$$

where TEC is integrated total electron count
Δf is doppler error

$$\Delta f_{L2} - \Delta f_{L1} = 1.34 \times 10^{-7} \left[\frac{f_{L1} - f_{L2}}{f_{L1}f_{L2}} \right] \frac{d(TEC)}{dt}$$

$$= \Delta f_{L1} \left[\frac{f_{L1} - f_{L2}}{f_{L2}} \right]$$

square-law behavior of the ionospheric group delay as shown in Table 1–2.

The excess delay caused by the ionosphere is mainly contributed by the term A/f^2. The B/f^3 term caused by magnetic field effects on the ionosphere and C/f^4 term generated by the binominal expansion are both small in significance. Thus one measures the total delay at both L1, L2 and computes the difference $\Delta\tau$ between the total group delays at F_{L1} and F_{L2}. The only difference between these two total group delays is caused by the frequency dependent ionospheric group delays, τ_{GDL1}, τ_{GDL2}. Thus the difference $\Delta\tau$ in total propagation delays reduces to

$$\Delta\tau \triangleq \tau_{GDL2} - \tau_{GDL1} = A \left[\frac{1}{f_{L2}^2} - \frac{1}{f_{L1}^2} \right]$$

$$= \frac{A}{f_{L1}^2} \left[\frac{f_{L1}^2 - f_{L2}^2}{f_{L2}^2} \right]$$

or

$$\Delta\tau \triangleq \tau_{GDL2} - \tau_{GDL1} = \tau_{GDL1} \left[\left(\frac{f_{L1}}{f_{L2}} \right)^2 - 1 \right] \quad (1-5)$$

Thus a measurement of $\Delta\tau$ gives an estimate of τ_{GDL1}. One can make a similar correction for doppler as shown in Table 1–2.

The other significant contributor to delay error is the group delay effects of the troposphere caused by water vapor and other atmospheric constituents. Fig. 1–12 shows the frequency independent tropospheric effect and its sensitivity to the elevation angle and user altitude. This effect can also be significant at low elevation angles. However, the tropospheric effect is more easily predicted by making use of relatively simple atmospheric (temperature, pressure, water vapor) measurements at sea level and should not contribute a large residual error for elevation

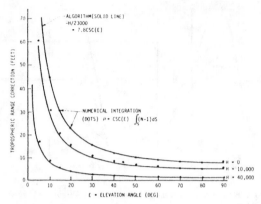

Fig. 1-12—Tropo Range Correction (Comparison of Algorithm with Numerical Integration) vs. User Altitude H in Feet.

angles above 5°. The more easily predicted dry air component is 80-90% of the total (Black, 1978).

1.7 Multipath and Interference Effects

Many of the navigation users are in aircraft and often are above water where a substantial multipath reflection exists. See Fig. 1-13. When the satellite is at zenith the differential path delay is equal to twice the aircraft altitude, perhaps 1000 to 80,000 ft, or 2 to 160 μsec. At lower elevation angles, the differential delay might be $\frac{1}{10}$ of this value. The magnitude of the reflected ray can sometimes be almost as large as the direct ray. The GPS signal should be tolerant to this multipath reflection.

Spurious interference from harmonics of narrow band CW transmitters is another possible interference source. The signal from the satellite received by an omni-directional antenna (0 dBIC) is at −130 dBm for the C/A signal. Many potential navigation signals cannot tolerate an interference level greater than $\frac{1}{10}$ the received signal power. Some signals, on the other hand, can tolerate much larger interference power.

The power received from an isotropic interference transmitter to our isotropic receiver antenna is

$$P_r = P_t/(4.56 \times 10^3 f^2 d^2) \qquad (1\text{-}6)$$

where f is in MHz and d is in miles. For $f = 1.57542 \times 10^3$ MHz, $d = 10^2$ miles, $P_t = 10$ dBm. We have $P_r = P_t/1.13 \times 10^{14} = -140.5$ dB $+ P_t = -130.5$ dBm. Hence even a 10 mw transmitter, 100 miles away, could interfere with the received

satellite signal if it were not designed properly. Thus tolerance to low level in-band interference is an important aspect in GPS signal selection.

1.8 Summary of Desired Navigation Signal Characteristics

In the preceding paragraphs we have attempted to examine in turn each of the desired characteristics of the GPS navigation signal. This signal must be an RF representation of the satellite clock and in addition must carry data to indicate satellite position and clock correction parameters.

We summarize these requirements below and in Table 1-3.

- Allow accurate pseudo-range measurements ($\sigma_r < 10$ nsec) without ambiguity.
- Allow accurate doppler shift measurements (<0.1 Hz).
- Provide dual frequency measurements to provide ionospheric group delay measurements ($>20\%$ frequency separation).
- Provide an efficient data channel for the transmission of satellite ephemeris, clock correction information, and other data (50 bps).
- Provide both a high accuracy "precision" signal along with a simpler signal which provides somewhat lower accuracy and is easily acquired in a short time ($\approx$1-2 minutes) by the receiver.

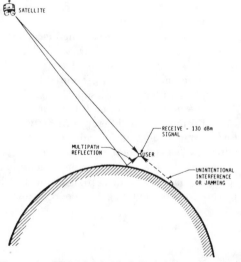

Fig. 1-13—GPS Multipath & Interference Considerations.

Table 1–3—Desired GPS Signal Properties

- Allow accurate real-time time-of-arrival measurement ($\sigma_\tau < 10$ nsec) without ambiguity.
- Allow accurate Doppler shift measurement.
- Provide an efficient data channel.
- Provide a rapid acquisition navigation capability with good accuracy along with a high accuracy capability for more demanding users.
- Provide ionospheric group delay correction.
- Good multiple access properties.
- Good interference rejection properties.
- Tolerance to multipath interference.
- Signal generation compatible with current space electronics technology.
- Avoid excessive bandwidth relative to the center frequency.

- Good multiple access properties. The user will typically receive simultaneous transmissions from 6–11 satellites.
- Ability to resist interference from low power narrow band interference as well as moderate power intentional interference.
- Ability to reject or to reduce greatly multipath interference problems where the differential multipath delay is 200 nsec or greater.

SECTION 2—GPS SIGNAL STRUCTURE

2.1 Introduction

In this section the structure of the GPS signal is described in detail. The general properties of the codes employed are discussed along with a consideration of many of the system requirements, e.g., multiple access discussed in Section 1. The remaining requirements are discussed later in Section 3.

2.2 GPS Signal Frequency Characteristics

The GPS signal consists of two components, Link 1, L1, at a center frequency of 1575.42 MHz and Link 2, L2, at a center frequency of 1227.6 MHz. The L-band center frequency selection has advantages over UHF in that the channel bandwidth allocation is more readily obtainable at L-band. In addition, the ionospheric delay effects (without correction) are substantially smaller. As compared to C-band, the space

losses to an isotropic receive antenna are substantially larger for C-band than L-band and give L-band the advantage. Thus the frequency separation is 347.82 MHz or 28.3% relative to L2. As discussed earlier, this dual frequency measurement permits measurement of the ionospheric group delay error. Each of these center frequencies is a coherently selected multiple of a 10.23 MHz clock. In particular the link frequencies are:

$$L1 = 1575.42\ MHz = 154 \times 10.23\ MHz$$
$$L2 = 1227.6\ MHz = 120 \times 10.23\ MHz \qquad (2\text{-}1)$$

Thus the ionospheric group delay correction equation (1–5) of Section 1 becomes

$$\Delta\tau \triangleq \tau_{GDL2} - \tau_{GDL1} = \frac{A}{f_{L1}^2}\frac{1}{1.5336} = \tau \frac{{}_{GDL1}}{1.5336} \qquad (2\text{-}2)$$

or

$$\tau_{GDL1} = 1.5336\ \Delta\tau$$

where τ_{GDL1} is the ionospheric group delay at L1 and $\Delta\tau$ is the measurable difference between total propagation delays at L1, and L2. Similarly the ionospheric doppler correction at L1 from Table 1–2 is

$$\Delta f_{L1} = 3.529\ [\Delta f_{L2} - \Delta f_{L1}]$$

where $\Delta f_{L1} - \Delta f_{L1}$ is the measurable doppler difference

As discussed earlier, the relativistic effects are partially compensated for in the satellite by offsetting the 10.23 MHz clock rate. Thus, as the signal approaches the earth from the satellite, the frequency increases by approximately the same factor and the signal appears to a stationary user on the earth to have a frequency very close to 10.23 MHz. Henceforth when reference is made to 10.23 MHz, the frequency will always be this offset frequency as far as satellite clocks are concerned.

Each of these two signals L1 and L2, is modulated by either or both a 10.23 MHz clock rate precision P signal and/or by a 1.023 MHz clear/acquisition (C/A) signal. Each of these two binary signals has been formed by a P-code or a C/A code which is modulo-2 added to 50 bps data D, to form P⊕D and C/A⊕D, respectively.

The L1 in-phase component of the carrier is modulated by the P signal P⊕D and the quadrature carrier component is modulated by C/A⊕D. A phasor diagram of the L1 signal is shown in Fig. 2–1.

The L2 signal is biphase modulated by either the P code or the C/A code. Normal operation would provide P code modulation on the L2 signal. The transmitted signal spectrum showing both L1 and L2 is shown in Fig. 2–2.

2.3 Detailed Signal Structure

The Link 1 signal L1 contains both in-phase and quadrature signals. The signal transmitted (see Fig. 2–1) by the satellite is then

$$S_{L1i}(t) = A_P X P_i(t) D_i(t) \cos(\omega_1 t + \phi) \qquad (2\text{--}3)$$
$$+ A_c X G_i(t) D_i(t) \sin(\omega_1 t + \phi)$$

where ω_1 is the L1 frequency as defined above, ϕ represents a small phase noise and oscillator drift component. Oscillator stability is obtained using redundant cesium or rubidium frequency standards. (The first satellite in the GPS series NTS-2, has a clock stability better than 2×10^{-13}). The P-code, $XP_i(t)$, is a ±1 pseudo-random sequence with a clock rate of 10.23 Mbps and a period of exactly 1 week. Each satellite, i, transmits a unique P-code. The data, $D_i(t)$, also has amplitude ±1 at 50 bps and has a 6 sec subframe and a 30 sec frame period. The C/A code XG_i is a unique Gold code of period 1023 bits and has a clock rate of 1.023 Mbps. Thus the C/A code has a period of 1 msec. The

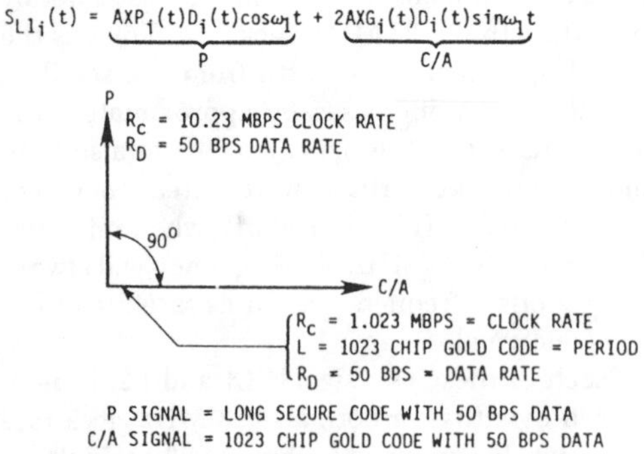

relative amplitudes of the P and C/A codes are controlled by the constants A_P and A_C. In GPS Phase 1 the C/A code strength is between 3 and 6 dB stronger than the P-code. As already mentioned above, the code clocks and transmitted RF frequencies are all coherently derived from the same on-board satellite frequency standard. The rms clock transition time difference between the C/A and P-code clocks is less than nsec.

P–Code

The P-code for each satellite i is the product of 2 PN codes, $X1(t)$ and $X2(t + n_i t)$, where X has a period of 1.5 sec or 15,345,000 chips and $X2$ has a period of 15,345,037 or 37 chips longer both sequences are reset to begin the week at the same epoch time. Both $X1$ and $X2$ are clocked in phase at a chip rate $1/T = 10.23$ MHz Thus, the P-code is a product code of the form

$$XP_i(t) = X1(t)X2(t + n_iT), \; 0 \leq n_i \leq 36 \qquad (2\text{--}4)$$

Reset at beginning of week.

where the delay between $X1(t)$ and $X2(t)$ is n_i code clock intervals of T sec each. Each satellite has a unique code offset n_iT which makes the P-code unique as well. The increase in code period for $X2$ by 37 relative to $X1$ allows the values of n_i to range over 0 to 36 without having any significant segment of a P-code of one satellite match that of another. Thus we have 37 different P-codes.

The period of a product of P-codes each of relatively prime period is the product of the periods. Thus if the P-code were allowed to continue without being reset it would continue without repetition for slightly more than 38 weeks. This overall period has been in effect subdivided so that each satellite gets a one week period which is non-overlapping with every other satellite.

The Z-count is defined as the number of 1.5 sec $X1$ epochs since the beginning of the week. Thus there are 4 X1 epochs per data subframe of 6 sec. In order to acquire the P-code, the 50 bps data stream contains a new Hand-Over-Word (HOW) each 6 sec subframe. The HOW word, when multiplied by 4, gives the Z-count at the beginning of the *next* 6 sec subframe. Thus if one knows the subframe epoch times and the HOW word, one can acquire the P-code at the next subframe epoch.

GPS SIGNAL

$$S_{L1i}(t) = \underbrace{AXP_i(t)D_i(t)\cos\omega_1 t}_{P} + \underbrace{2AXG_i(t)D_i(t)\sin\omega_1 t}_{C/A}$$

P

R_C = 10.23 MBPS CLOCK RATE
R_D = 50 BPS DATA RATE

90°

C/A

R_C = 1.023 MBPS = CLOCK RATE
L = 1023 CHIP GOLD CODE = PERIOD
R_D = 50 BPS = DATA RATE

P SIGNAL = LONG SECURE CODE WITH 50 BPS DATA
C/A SIGNAL = 1023 CHIP GOLD CODE WITH 50 BPS DATA

Fig. 2–1—GPS Signal Structure for L1 Signal.

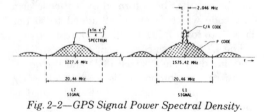

Fig. 2–2—GPS Signal Power Spectral Density.

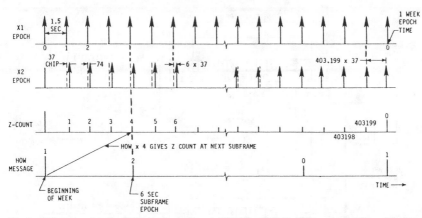

Fig. 2-3—Timing Diagram for the P Code Components X1, X2, and the Z-Count and How Message Relationship. The How Message is Carried in the 50 bps Data Stream.

Fig. 2-3 summarizes the timing relationships between $X1$, $X2$ epochs and the Z-count and HOW words.

C/A Code

The clear/acquisition (C/A) code is a relatively short code of 1023 bits or 1 msec duration at a 1.023 Mbps bit rate. This code is selected to provide good multiple access properties for its period. The C/A codes for the various satellites are Gold codes formed as the product of two 1023 bit *PN* codes $G1(t)$ and $G2(t)$. Thus this product code is also of 1023 bit period and is represented as

$$XG(t) = G1(t)\ G2[t + N_i(10T)] \qquad (2\text{-}5)$$

where N_i determines the phase offset in chips between $G1$ and $G2$. Note that C/A code chip has duration $10T$ sec. There are 1023 different offsets N_i and hence 1023 different codes of this form.* Each code $G1$, $G2$ is generated by a maximal-length linear shift register of 10 stages. The $G1$ and $G2$ shift register, are set to the all ones state in synchronism with the $X1$ epoch. The tap positions are specified by the generator polynomial for the two codes

G1: $\quad G_1(X) = 1 + X^3 + X^{10}$

G2: $\quad G_2(X) = 1 + X^2 + X^3 + X^6 + X^8 \qquad (2\text{-}6)$
$$+ X^9 + X^{10}$$

Since the Gold code has a 1 msec period, there

* There actually are 1025 different Gold codes of this period and family. The codes, $G1(t)$ and $G2(t)$, by themselves, are the other two codes.

are 20 C/A code epochs for every data bit. The 50 bps data clock is synchronous with both the C/A epochs and the $X1$ epochs.

Fig. 2-4 shows a simplified block diagram of the C/A code generator. The unit is comprised of two 10 stage feedback shift registers clocked at 1.023 Mbps having feedback taps at stages 3 and 10 for $G1$ and at 2, 3, 6, 8, 9, 10 for $G2$. The various delay offsets are generated by tapping off at approximate points on the $G2$ register and modulo-2 adding the two sequences together to get the desired delayed version of the $G2$ sequence ("Cycle-and-add" property).

Epochs of the G code at 1 Kbps are divided down by 20 to get the 50 bps data clock. All clocks are in phase synchronism with the $X1$ clock as shown in Fig. 2-4.

L2 Signal

The $L2$ signal is biphase modulated by either the P-code or the C/A code as selected by ground command. The same 50 bps data stream modulates the $L2$ carrier as transmitted on $L1$. Thus the $L2$ signal is represented in the normal P format as

$$S_{L2}(t) = B_P XP_i(t) D_i(t)\ \cos(\omega_2 t + 4) \qquad (2\text{-}7)$$

where B_P represents the signal amplitude at the satellite, $XP_i(t)$ is the P-code for the ith satellite clocked in synchronism with the $L1$ codes. Both carrier and code are synchronous with one another. In the future the $L2$ signal also might be modulated with the codes without the data. This feature would permit the receiver tracking loops to be reduced further in IF bandwith

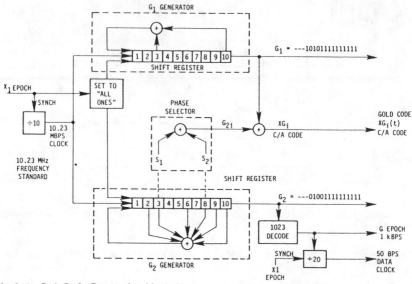

Fig. 2-4—C/A Code Generation block diagram showing G epoch and data clock generation.

Table 2-1—Summary of GPS Signal Parameters and Data Formats. The TLM word contains an 8-bit Barker sync word. The HOW contains a 17 bit Z-count for handover to the *P* code

Parameter	C/A Signal	*P* Signal
Code Clock (Chip) Rate	1.023 Mbps	10.23 Mbps
Code Period	1023	$\approx 6 \times 10^{12}$; 1 week
Data Rate	50 bps	50 bps
Tansmission Frequency	L1	L1, L2

Data Format—Frame and Subframe Structure

Subframe No.	Ten, 30-bit words, 6 sec Subframe	
1	TLM | HOW | Block 1—Clock Correction	
2	TLM | HOW | Block 2—Ephemeris	
3	TLM | HOW | Block 3—Ephemeris Continued	1-Frame 30 sec 1500 bits
4	TLM | HOW | Block 4—Message	
5	TLM | HOW | Block 5—Almanac—(25 frames for complete almanac)	

GPS Signal Summary

Table 2-1 summarizes the signal and data characteristics discussed above. One of the key points to be made in the signal structure discussion is that acquisition by a receiver of the relatively short period C/A code and recovery of a single full subframe of data permits one to acquire with minimal or zero search the *P*-code. Knowledge of the C/A epoch plus the data subframe epoch and the HOW word gives the exact phasing of the *P*-code. Navigation solutions require, as a minimum, reception of data subframes 1, 2, 3 containing clock-correction and ephemeris data and on the average require reception of a full 30 sec frame of data.

Table 2–2—Phase 1 GPS Received Signal Power Levels at Output of a 0 dBIC antenna with RH Circular Polarization. The satellite is at an elevation angle $\geq 5°$.

Link	GPS Signal Component (Minimum Strength)	
	P	C/A
L1	−163 dBw	−160 dBw
L2	−166 dBw	−166 dBw

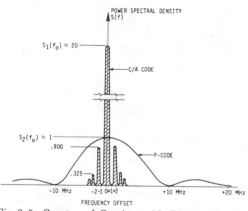

Fig. 2–5—*Spectra of Carriers with Bit Rates of 1 Megabit/Sec and 10 Megabits/Sec. The Ratio of C/A Power to P-Code Signal Power is 3 dB in this Figure.*

The received signal strength at a user receiver employing a 0 dBIC antenna is given below in Table 2–2 for the GPS Phase I.

The signal power spectral densities for the P and C/A signal components are shown in Fig. 2–5. Figure 2–6 shows the measured RF power spectral density of the L1 signal. Note the narrow band high power density C/A signal in the center of the signal spectrum.

2.4 Signal Characteristics

In the previous paragraph we defined the structure of the GPS signal but did no more than begin to examine its characteristics and performance. In this section we begin to examine the multiple access characteristics of the C/A and P-codes and to give some of the reasons for their selection. In particular, the cross-correlation properties are examined for the P and C/A signals both with and without doppler offset.

Cross-Correlation Properties

The key multiple access performance param-

eter of the GPS signals is the generalized cross–correlation performance. Any GPS receiver must in effect perform a cross–correlation operation if it is to extract the signal and recover the data.

Fig. 2–7 shows the typical received signal format and cross-correlation receiver where two satellites are in view; satellite h, the desired signal, and satellite j, the interfering satellite. Of course, one must realize that a parallel or time multiplexed correlator will next be reversing these roles and satellite j would be the desired signal and satellite h would be the interference. In general, of course, more than 2 satellites are in view and the receiver operates on at least 4 satellite signals. The interfering satellite signal in Fig. 2–7 is time off-set by $k_j T$ and doppler offset by f_d.

The received signals are asummed to be modulated by codes $X_h(t)$ and $X_j(t) = \pm 1$ respectively. These signals can represent either the

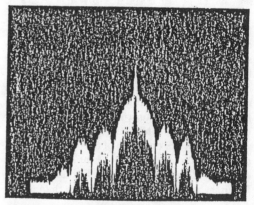

Fig. 2–6—*RF Spectrum photograph of Received L1 Carrier with C/A and P QPSK Modulation, Generated by STI Test Transmitter. Spectrum Scales: Horizontal: 10 MHz/Division; Vertical: 10 dB/Division.*

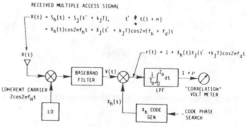

Fig. 2–7—*Multiple Access Interference in User Receiver—The Received Signal Consists of the Desired Signal Plus a Time Offset, Doppler Shifted Multiple Access Signal from Another Satellite.*

P-code or the C/A code or an arbitrary signal. For the moment the data modulation is ignored and the signals are of equal strength. Noise effects are additive and can be considered separately.

The block diagram of Fig. 2–7 shows a coherent correlation operation where the coherent carrier is multiplied with the received signal and the resultant baseband output is multiplied by a phase synchronized replica of the desired code $X_h(t)$. The output of the multiplier is then integrated for some time T_m sec to produce the "correlation" output. If T_m is equal to or a multiple of the period of the waveforms or approaches infinity, the output will be the true correlation, otherwise it will be a partial correlation function.*

The output of the "correlation" meter would be exactly unity if there is no cross–correlation between X_h and X_j codes. However, in general there will be some finite cross–correlation either positive or negative and $1 + \rho \neq 1$ in Fig. 2–8. This non-zero cross–correlation can cause interference in the receiver or possible false lock in a code search and acquisition operation if $|\rho|$ is sufficiently large, e.g., $|\rho| > 0.3$. The effect can be made more severe by the user receiver antenna pattern which might have more gain in the direction of the interfering satellite and perhaps less space loss for that satellite as well. For example, if the interfering satellite is at the zenith and in the direction of maximum antenna gain while the desired signal is at a 5° elevation angle, the difference in received signal levels can favor the interfering signal by more than 6 dB.

P–Code.

Fig. 2–8 shows the amplitude spectra and signal-to-interference ratio (multiple access gain) computed for the P-codes where we have assumed:

- The desired and multiple access interference signals are received at equal power and the same doppler offset
- Both are received with 50 bps data
- The two signals are clocked in synchronism

The output spectrum at the multiplier output, $W(t)$, then takes the form shown in Fig. 2–9(b). The desired component gives simply the data

---

* Spilker, op cit, pp. 597–600

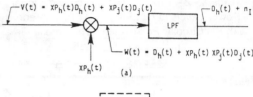
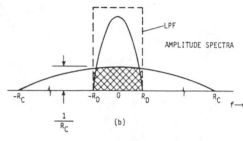

(a)

(b)

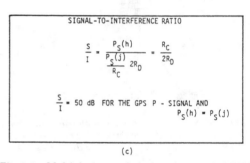

(c)

Fig. 2–8—Multiple Access Gain for a long period PN sequence.

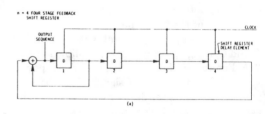

(a)

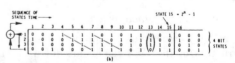

(b)

Fig. 2–9—Generation of a PN Sequence using a feedback shift register.

spectrum $D_h(t)$ here assumed to be a random data stream. The interfering multiple–access component has the spectrum of the product of the two PN codes which is for all purposes of interest here, a pseudo–random bit stream with a continuous spectrum. Thus both $(\sin x/x)^2$ spectra, one with bandwidth to the null of $R_d =$

50 Hz and the other at 10.23 MHz. Clearly one can place a low pass filter of bandwidth R_d and get most of the power (the added power by using a larger bandwidth would be less than 0.44 dB). The power passing to the output of the low–pass filter from the multiple access interference is reduced by a factor of $2R_d/R_c$ where the chip rate R_c = 10.23 MHz. Thus the output signal-to-interference power ratio for the *P*-code is S/I = 10^5 or 50 dB.

2.5 C/A Code Properties

The multiple access properties of the Gold codes are substantially different from the *P*-code signal in two respects:

- Cross-correlation sidelobes are not of equal height and are much larger than those of the *P*-code.
- The cross-correlation property is dependent in a significant way on both doppler offset as well as code offset. The C/A code spectrum consists of discrete line components. The *P*-code on the other hand has multiple access properties essentially independent of doppler and time offset.

Linear Feedback Shift Register Sequence

Before we discuss details of the Gold codes, we review briefly the properties of the *PN* codes. Fig. 2-9 shows a 4–stage linear maximal length shift register and the sequence it generates at

each clock pulse. The sequence of shift register states is shown in Fig. 2-10(b), the initial state is

$$S = \begin{pmatrix} 0 \\ 1 \\ 0 \\ 0 \end{pmatrix} \qquad (2\text{-}9)$$

where the state vector components are defined as the state of each of the binary shift register delay elements. As long as this shift register is not forced to the "all zero" state, it will cycle through all $2^4 - 1 = 15$ states in a periodic manner. In general, an *n* stage linear feedback shift register (LFSR) with proper taps produces a code of period $P = 2^n - 1$. Note that the LFSR generates all state factors except the all zero state, thus it cycles through each of the possible state vectors. Thus there are $2^n - 1$ states in the period.

Fig. 2-10 shows the *PN* sequence at the output of a selected stage. The autocorrelation of the *PN* sequence where $s(t) = +1$ is

$$R(i) = (1/15) \int_0^{15} s(t)s(t+i)dt \qquad (2\text{-}10)$$

For a unit time offset $i = 1$, the product $s(t)s(t + i)$ is shown in Fig. 2-10(b). This product is easily seen to form a shifted version of the same sequence. This property is variously known as the shift–and–add or cycle–and–add property in

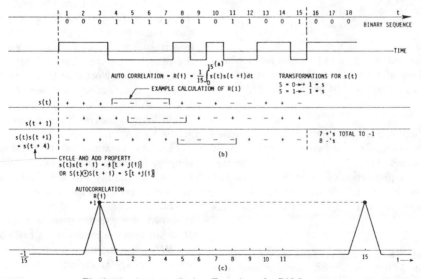

Fig. 2-10—Autocorrelation Function of a PN Sequence.

Table 2-3—Gold Code Properties

Product codes: Product of 2 PN codes of same period

$G_k(t) = x_i(t)x_j(t + k)$ where x_i have period P

P different values of k. Hence P different codes plus x_i, x_j

Family of codes generated for different values of k with low cross-correlation

Cross correlation for zero delay off-set

$$\overline{G_k(t)G_l(t)} = \overline{x_i(t)x_j(t + k)x_j(t + l)} = \overline{x_j(t + k)x_j(t + j)}$$

$$= \overline{x_j(t + m)} = \frac{-1}{P}$$

Use cycle and add property of PN sequence

For other values of code shift $G_k(t)G_l(t + n)$ the cross correlation is bounded

$$\overline{G_k(t)G_l(t + n)} = \overline{x_i(t)x_j(t + k)x_i(t + n)x_j(t + k + n)}$$

$$= \overline{x_i(t + r)x_j(t + r + s)} = \overline{G_s(t + r)} = \overline{G_s(t)}$$

reference to the fact that shifting the sequence $S(t) = (0, 1)$ by i clock pulses and modulo-2 addition with the original unshifted sequence forms a shifted version of the same sequence with a different offset.

Since the PN sequence has one more -1 than $+1$, the average value of $S(i)$ is simply $-1/(2^n - 1) = -1/15$ where $2^n - 1$ is the code period. Thus, it is easily seen that the autocorrelation function of a LFSR is a two level function as shown in Fig. 2-10(c) for integral values of i.

$$R(i) = \; 1 \qquad\qquad i = 0$$
$$= -1/(2^n - 1) \qquad i \neq 0$$
(2-11)

For the autocorrelation function for nonintegral values of time offset, simply connect the values of $R(i)$ by straight lines.

Gold Codes

The Gold codes* are a family of codes formed as the product of two different LFSR, both of the same period $P \triangleq 2^n - 1$. Table 2-3 illustrates some of the properties of a Gold code. The two PN sequences $X_i(t)$, $X_j(t)$ are specially selected from the set of LFSR sequences having the same period.

---

* R. Gold, "Optimal Binary Sequences for Spread Spectrum Multiplexing," IEEE Trans. on Info. Theory, Oct. 1967, pp. 619-621.

Using Table 2-3 it is easily seen that the cross-correlation between any two different Gold codes of the same family $G_k(t)$ and $G_e(t)$ with no time offset is simply $-1/P$ the same as for the PN code autocorrelation. More generally, however, the cross-correlation

$$\overline{G_k(t)G_e(t + n)} = \overline{G_s(t + r)} = \overline{G_s(t)} \qquad (2\text{-}12)$$

is simply the time average of another code in the same family. Table 2-4 summarizes the quantitative results for cross-correlation with zero doppler offset.

Table 2-5 summarizes the performances of three types of sequences; linear maximal length shift register sequences, nonlinear maximal length shift registers (contains one more state in the period since they have all zero states) and the Gold codes. Note that there are $2^n + 1$ Gold codes in a family of codes of period $2^n - 1$. There are all shift offsets k allowed as indicated in Table 2-3 plus the two PN components by themselves $X_i(t)$, $X_g(t)$.

Thus the advantage of the Gold codes is not simply a low cross-correlation between all members of the family but that there are a large number of codes all of similar good properties.

The amplitude spectral density of a PN code is shown in Fig. 2-11. If the PN code period is 1023 bits and the clock rate is 1.023 Mbps, then the PN code spectrum is a set of line components with a $(\sin kf)/kf$ variation in amplitude level. The line components are, of course, separated

Table 2-4—Cross Correlation Properties of Gold Codes

Code Period	Number of Shift Register Stages	Normalized Cross-Correlation Level	Probability of Level
$P = 2^n - 1$	n	$-\dfrac{\left(2^{\left(\frac{n+1}{2}\right)} + 1\right)}{P}$	0.25
	n-ODD	$-\dfrac{1}{P}$	0.50
		$\dfrac{\left(2^{\left(\frac{n+2}{2}\right)} - 1\right)}{P}$	0.25
$P = 2^n - 1$	n	$-\dfrac{\left(2^{\left(\frac{n+2}{2}\right)} + 1\right)}{P}$	0.125
	n-EVEN	$-\dfrac{1}{P}$	0.75
	$n \neq 4i$	$\dfrac{\left(2^{\left(\frac{2+n}{2}\right)} - 1\right)}{P}$	0.125

Table 2-5—Generalized Properties—Maximal Length Codes

	Linear Shift Registers	Nonlinear Shift Registers	Gold Codes
Period for n-Stages	$2^n - 1$	2^n	$2^{n'} - 1$ $n' = n/2$
Cycle and Add Property	Yes	No	Yes
Autocorrelation Function	Two-Level	Cannot be Two-Level	4-Level
Number of Codes of Period	$N = \dfrac{\phi(2^n - 1)}{n} \leq \dfrac{2^n - 2}{n}$	$\approx \dfrac{2^{2^n}}{2^n}$	$2^{n'} + 1$
$2^n - 1$ or 2^n	For $2^n - 1 = 8191$, $N = 630$		8193

Where $\phi(m)$ is the number of integers relatively prime to m.

by the inverse code period rate $R_c/P = 1$ kHz apart where R_c is the code clock rate and P is the period.

The Gold codes of the same period are composed of a similar set of line components. However, in this instance, the line components are not all of the same amplitude although the frequency spacing is the same. Fig. 2-12 shows an example spectrum for a code period $P = 1023$. Note that instead of a line component power 30 dB down from the total signal power, P_s, as would be if we had 1000 line components of equal power, the line component power level can vary significantly about this level.

The cross-correlation between two Gold codes with both time offset and doppler offset is

$$\overline{G_k(t)G_e(t + n)} \cos \omega_d t = \overline{G_s(t)} \cos \omega_d t$$

where bar denotes the time average. Thus if the doppler offset is an integral multiple of the line component spacing, the cross-correlation is simply the amplitude of that line component. Recall that even with a stationary user the doppler offset between satellites can vary by as much as 7500 Hz.

Table 2-6 summarizes the cross-correlation results for both zero doppler and the worst possible doppler. Note that the zero doppler cross-correlation changes by 6 dB at every 2 stage increase in the number of shift registers. Thus the zero doppler cross-correlation decreases by 6 dB by going from period $P = 511$ to

$P = 2047$ whereas an increase from 511 to 1023 causes no improvement.

It is easily seen, however, that the zero doppler condition is not the one of greatest importance. When worst case doppler shifts are considered, the peak cross–correlation changes by 3 dB with each increase in code period.

Fig. 2-13 shows the cumulative probability of various cross–correlation interference levels for the GPS C/A code for various doppler shifts from $f_d = 0$ to ± 5 kHz. Note that the 4 kHz doppler gives the worst cross–correlation side-lobe over this range; however, the other doppler shifts give similar results. These cumulative av-erages are formed by averaging results for all 1023 of the Gold codes of period 1023 in the GPS family. All possible code time offsets are consid-ered for each doppler offset and all possible pairs of codes in this family.

Note one additional point. If there is a doppler shift between two signals, then the delay differ-ence is changing between codes. For example, if there is a 1 kHz doppler shift at $L1$, then the code C/A clock rate differs by 1 kHz/1540 = 1/1.54. Thus the two codes will shift in relative

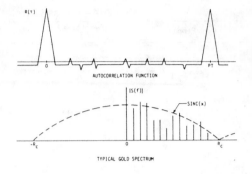

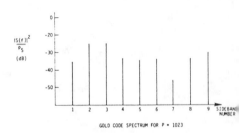

Fig. 2-12—Gold Code Spectrum.

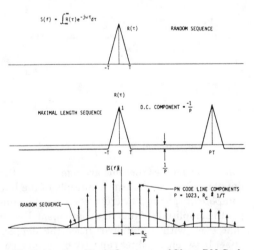

Fig. 2-11—Amplitude Spectrum of Short PN Code.

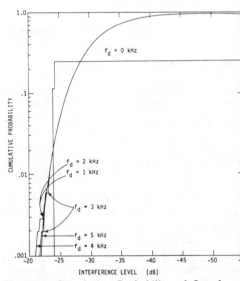

Fig. 2-13—Cumulative Probability of Interference Level for 1023 bit Gold Code at 1.023 Mbps (Courtes H. Chang, Stanford Telecommunications Inc.).

Table 2-6—Cross-Correlation Sidelobes for Gold Codes

Parameter	Code Period		
	511	1023	2047
Peak Cross-correlation (any doppler shift)	−18.6 dB	−21.6 dB	−24.6 dB
Peak Cross-correlation (zero doppler)	−23.8 dB	−23.8 dB	−29.8 dB
Probability of worst case or near worst case cross-correlation (zero doppler)	0.5	0.25	0.5

elay by one C/A code chip every 1.54 sec. Thus by their very nature these sidelobes with doppler shift are only temporary in nature.

ECTION 3—GPS SIGNAL TRACKING AND ACQUISITION

1 Introduction

Thus far, the GPS signal has been described and its tolerance to multiple access interference has been discussed. Described as well is its lack of time ambiguity and the dual frequency ionospheric correction capability.

Yet to be demonstrated, however, is the accuracy of the receiver tracking, the ease in acquiring the signal, the multipath interference and other interference rejection performance. In order to analyze this performance, it is first necessary to describe the basics of delay–lock loop receiver operation. There is no attempt here to analyze the performance of these receivers. These analyses are contained elsewhere already.* Rather, the attempt is to summarize the key performance results as applicable to the GPS signal.

3.2 Delay-Lock Receivers

The receiver must accurately track the received GPS signals even though they are received at low signal levels, usually well below the thermal noise level in the receiver. In addition, the receiver must be able to track the dynamics of motion of the user platform, perhaps a high performance aircraft. As shown later, these two contending requirements can still be satisfied while producing the desired performance accuracy.

The essential elements of the delay–lock loop (DLL) is the correlator shown in Fig. 3–1. A received code is multiplied by a reference code time offset by $\tau < T$ where T is a code chip interval. The multiplier output V_3 is averaged by a low-pass filter having an integration time $T_m = 1/B \gg T$, i.e., much greater than the chip interval. For the moment, the code period is assumed to be essentially infinite. Thus, the output $V_4(\tau) = R_P(\tau)$ is the autocorrelation function of the code. The correlator output itself is not sufficient for code tracking, however, it does not provide an indication of the sign of the delay

error of a tracking reference signal.

Fig. 3–2 shows a simplified design of a coherent delay-lock loop where the received signal has been converted to the baseband code and the data modulation is absent. For purposes of this discussion, assume that the initial delay error has somehow been decreased to the vicinity of zero.

In the delay-lock loop the outputs V_1 and V_2 of early and late correlation are subtracted to form a correction signal, $V_3(\tau)$, which is then used to drive a voltage–controlled-oscillator (VCO) or clock. This clock in turn drives the PN generator in such a manner that if the clock is lagging in phase, the correction signal, V_3, drives the clock faster and the reference code speeds up and runs in coincidence with the received signal. Thus the reference code is tracking the received code. The epoch time ticks are then a measure of the received signal time. The receiver also contains a coincident or punctual channel as is shown in the top portion of the block diagram in Fig. 3–2.

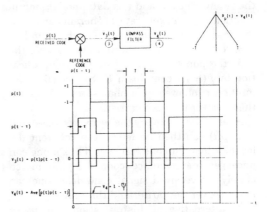

Fig. 3–1—Waveforms in a PN Code Correlator.

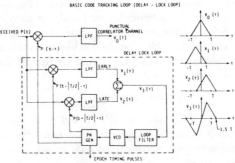

Fig. 3–2—Coherent Delay Lock Loop.

---

* Spilker, op cit, Chapter 18.

If the received signal delay increases suddenly because of user platform motion the delay error increases momentarily and the correction signal increases from zero. The reference code then slows down and increases its delay until it matches the received signal at which point the correction signal decreases to zero again. Thus it is clear that given an initial small error ($|\tau| <$ 1.5T, the locked-on state) and sufficiently slow dynamics of delay change relative to the filter bandwidths the delay–lock loop will track the incoming signal.

If additive noise is present at the input the form of the correction signal of Fig. 3–2 does not change, however there is additive noise on top of this correction component.

If data modulation is present at a low rate the outputs V_1 and V_2 are replaced by $V_1 D(t)$ and $V_2 D(t)$. Since the data is ±1 the data effect can be removed (not without a noise degradation) by taking the magnitude of V_1, V_2 prior to the subtractor.

The actual received signal of course arrives at the receiver at RF and has data modulation in addition. One can generate a coherent carrier for the down–conversion operation as shown in Fig. 3–3. Note that if one is accurately tracking the code the punctual channel output (multiplication by $p(t-\tau)$) contains a BPSK signal. A X2 multiplier followed by a phase–locked loop can then recover the pure carrier.

After carrier recovery the recovered baseband code $p(t)$ can then be fed to the coherent de-lay–lock loop for code tracking. Thus if one can once get the reference code delay to match closely the received signal code delay one can both recover the carrier and the code.

An alternative to this operation is to use a noncoherent delay–lock as shown in Fig. 3–4. In this instance the coherent correlators of Fig. 3–2 are replaced by noncoherent bandpass correla-tors followed by envelope detectors. The outputs of each of the multipliers in this instance contain a narrowband bandpass signal at the IF fre-quency of the form

$$D(t)V_1(\tau)\cos(\omega_1 t + \phi) \qquad (3\text{--}1)$$

The bandpass filter (BPF) is the bandpass equivalent of the integrator (finite memory) and has sufficient bandwidth to pass only the com-bination of

- Residual doppler frequency uncertainty o frequency drift
- Data modulation

The IF bandwidth should be made narro enough to reject as much of the noise as possibl The output of the BPF is then envelope detecte to remove the data modulation. Subtraction o the two components then gives an error signa as in Fig. 3–2 or something similar.

It is easily seen that the noise performance o these loops is improved by decreasing the loo bandwidth to as small a value as possible. Hov ever, beyond a certain limit improvement caus a serious degradation in the dynamic trackir performance of the loop.

τ Dither Delay-Lock Loop

The τ dither loop shown in Fig. 3–5 is a usef variation of the delay lock loop. In this variatio

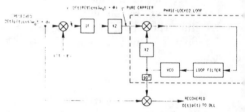

Fig. 3–3—*Carrier Recovery of the Received PN/PS. Signal.*

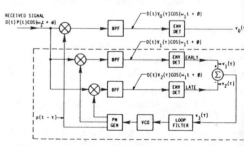

Fig. 3–4—*Noncoherent Delay Lock Loop (DLL).*

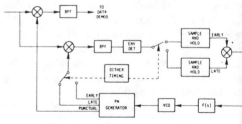

Fig. 3–5—τ-*Dither Code Tracking.*

he early and late channels are processed in time
equence rather than in parallel. The dither or
me multiplexing rate must be large compared
o the overall loop bandwidth but not so large as
o substantially widen the bandpass filter.

Although the τ dither loop in general does not
erform quite as well as the delay–lock loop it
as an implementation advantage in that it re-
uires only a single channel correlator and still
ften has good performance.

3.3 Receiver Tracking Performance

The tracking error of the receiver operating
n the GPS code has two major components,
ransient error caused by imperfectly tracking
he user dynamics, and noise error caused by
hermal noise.

ransient Errors

In order to model the dynamics, we assume
he receiver is on an airborne platform where
he radial range has a control stick jerk from 0g
o a 5g steady state acceleration. The accelera-
on transient is shown in Fig. 3–6.

The tracking error in the delay–lock for 3g
nd 5g transients is shown in Fig. 3–7. The
losed–loop bandwidth is $B_L = 9$ Hz and the
ode clock rate is 10 MHz. A second–order de-
y–lock loop is assumed. Fig. 3–8 shows the
teady state and peak transient tracking errors
lotted as a function of the loop bandwidth B_L.
ote that a $B_L = 3$ Hz yields a steady state delay

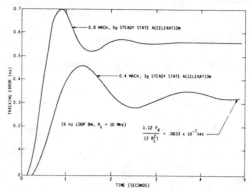

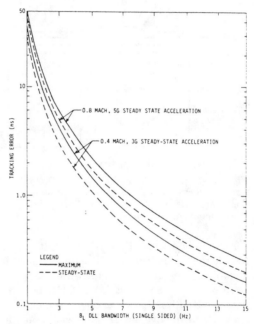

Fig. 3–7—DLL Tracking Error for Step of Stick Deflection of Fig. 3–6.

Fig. 3-8—Maximum and Steady-State Dynamic
Transient Error (2nd Order Loop, $R_c = 10^7$ Hz).

error of approximately 3 and 5 nsec for 3g and
5g steady state accelerations respectively. Thus
for many purposes a $B_L = 3$ Hz is a reasonable
value.

Thermal Noise Errors

With the 3 Hz closed–loop bandwidth the
tracking error caused by received thermal noise
is shown in Fig. 3–9 for various values of IF
bandwidths B_{IF} in the noncoherent delay-lock
loop.

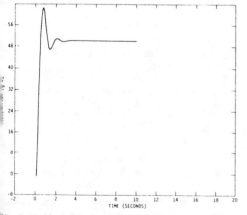

ig. 3–6—User Platform Driving Function—Step of
tick Deflection—5 g Steady State Acceleration with
ransfer Function Corresponding to 0.8 Mach Num-
er at Sea Level.

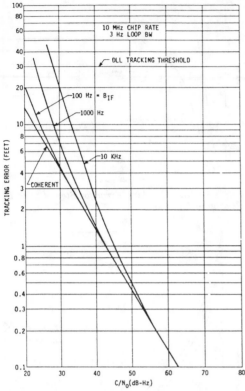

Fig. 3-9—*Noise Tracking Error in the Delay Lock Loop vs Received Carrier-to-Noise Density Ratio. Code chip rate = 10^7 bps. F. D. Natali, Stanford Telecommunications, Inc.*

As already discussed the IF bandwidth must be able to pass undistorted the data modulation and tolerate any residual doppler frequency offset. Since the data modulation is 50 Hz, the PSK data bandwidth is 100 Hz and adding a doppler residual might give an IF bandwidth on the order of 1 kHz. Note from Fig. 3-8 that with a carrier-to-noise density ratio $C/N_0 = 30$ dB-Hz the thermal noise rms tracking error is only 7 ft. This error compares with a 4.5 ft rms errors if the IF bandwidth had been reduced to 10 Hz or a coherent loop had been employed.

Combined Tracking Error

Finally Fig. 3-10 shows the sum of the maximum dynamic tracking error ϵ_D plus the rms thermal noise error σ_T vs B_L for various C/N_0. Note that for $B_L = 3$ Hz this error is $\epsilon = \epsilon_D + \sigma_T = 10$ nsec for a chip rate of $1/\tau = 10$ Mbps.

If one assumes a PDOP of 3.0 then the position

error for this condition is 10m and we hav satisfied our original position error objective.

Table 3-1 summarizes the performance equa tions for the second-order code tracking loop

3.4 Received Carrier/Noise Density Ratio (C/N_0)

The received C/N_0 is a key parameter in t system performance analysis. The received si nal level to a 0 dBIC antenna has already bee stated. The noise density, N_o, of the receive

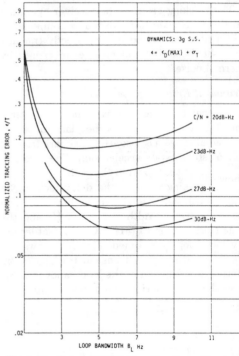

Fig. 3-10—*Coherent DLL Tracking Error Due to D namics and Noise.*

Table 3-1—Delay-Lock Loop Performance Summary

Dynamics	$\tau_{ss} = \dfrac{1.12\,\tau_d T_c}{4\,B_L{}^2}$

for constant doppler rate
τ_d = Doppler rate, (acceleration)
T_d = chip period.

Noise	$\sigma_\tau{}^2 = \dfrac{N_0 B_L}{2P_s}\left[1 + \dfrac{2}{\mathrm{SNR}_I}\right]$

Threshold	$\dfrac{\tau_{ss}}{T_c} + 3\sigma_\tau = .9$

ignal is kT_{eq} where k is Boltzmanns constant 198.6 dBm/°k-Hz and T_{eq} is the equivalent noise temperature of the receive system. To the received signal level we must add losses in the antenna to receiver link, correlation loss, etc.

A sample calculation of the received C/N_0 is given in Table 3-2.

The system noise temperature T_{eq} is related to the antenna temperature T_a, antenna system loss, ambient temperature T_0, and receiver noise figure F by the equation

$$T_{eq} = \frac{T_a}{L} + \frac{L-1}{L}T_0 + (F-1)T_0$$

This $C/N_0 = +38.6$ dB-Hz is then the effective C/N_0 for the C/A signal in this example. This result can be used in the previous calculations to determine performance and performance margin.

3.5 Data Demodulation

Once the code tracking has been accomplished by the delay–lock loop, the BPSK data at 50 bps can be recovered by the punctual channel as shown in Fig. 3-11. The received signal, either the P or C/A code signal is fed to a mixer where it is correlated with the punctual code $p(t - \tau)$ in ωt.

The output of this mixer/bandpass correlator is then the BPSK data signal plus additive thermal noise. This signal is then demodulated by a conventional BPSK demodulator as shown in Fig. 3-12. The filtered IF signal is first fed to either a $X\,2$ multiplier or a Costas loop as shown. The recovered coherent carrier then is mixed with the IF signal and the baseband output is the 50 bps data stream plus noise. Data detection

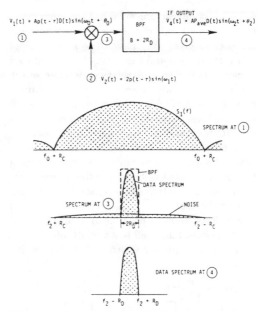

Fig. 3–11—Data Detection (Biphase Data Modulation).

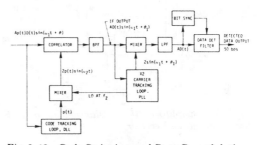

Fig. 3–12—Code Stripping and Data Demodulation.

is then performed by bit synchronization and data detection with an integrate–and–dump filter or comparable data detector.

Fig. 3-13 shows a simplified receiver block diagram for a GPS signal C/A code. The block diagram shows both the code tracking and carrier tracking/data demodulation functions. Not shown are the code acquisition, data demultiplexing and P-code handover functions. (For a detailed discussion of performance of BPSK data detection see Spilker, 1977, Chapters 11, 12.)

3.6 Search and Acquisition of GPS Codes

The tracking performance discussion of the GPS signals has assumed that somehow the

Table 3-2—Typical received C/N_0 calculation for the C/A signal

Received carrier power (C/A)	−160 dBw-Hz
Cable/Filter Losses	−1 dB
Correlation Loss	−1 dB
Net Effective C	−162 dBw
k Boltzmanns Constant	−228.6 dBw/°k-Hz
T_{eq} Equivalent Noise Temp. °K	+28 dB
N_0	−200.6 dBw/°k-Hz
C/N_0	38.6 dB-Hz

reference code tracking error has been decreased to less than +1 code chip error. Initially however the user receiver may have little knowledge of its exact position and there may be a significant uncertainty as to the relative doppler offset. With the C/A code however there are a limited number, 1023, of code chips in the period; hence even with no initial knowledge of position relative to the satellite, one need only search a maximum of 1023 code chips. The maximum residual doppler uncertainty is a combination of the satellite radial velocity and the user velocity minus any prediction of these parameters available to the user.

Fig. 3–14 shows the time–frequency uncertainty region. Each cell has a width of 1 chip in time and a frequency width of 1 IF bandwidth.

As an example the C/A chip width is approximately 1 μsec and the IF bandwidth may be of the order of 1 kHz. The overall time uncertainty ΔT is then 1023 μsec and the frequency uncertainty may be perhaps 10 kHz. Thus there are some 10^4 time–frequency cells to search. One must also account for the effect of doppler on the time cell. If doppler is present significantly the signal time cell is itself changing with time.

Fig. 3–14 also shows a typical noncoherent code–frequency search detector. The search operation essentially scans all frequency cells in the uncertainty region, measures the output power in the IF bandwidth, and integrates the power and compares with a fixed or variable threshold. When a cell is found which exceeds threshold, and it can be checked, e.g. 3 out of times, then an in–lock condition is declared and search is stopped.

Fig. 3–15 shows the power spectra for the noncoherent lock detector where P_s represents the power in the bandwidth compressed signal.

Code search must really be performed in half chip increments or be of that order in order to avoid missing the correlation peak as shown in Fig. 3–16. If one searches in half chip increments then even at worst the cross–correlation is at least 0.75 of its maximum voltage.

For a probability of detection $P_D = 0.9$ and false alarm probability 0.005, the search rate, S_R in cells/sec is approximately

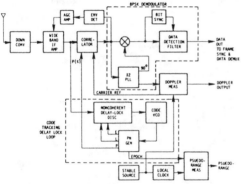

Fig. 3–13—Simplified Block Diagram of a GPS Spread Spectrum Receiver.

$$S_R = C/22N_0 \text{ with a IF bandwidth of } 22S_R \quad (3\text{–}?)$$

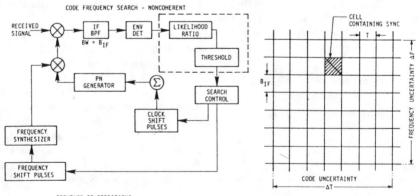

SEQUENCE OF OPERATIONS

1) SENSE "OUT-OF-LOCK" CONDITION AND BEGIN CODE AND FREQUENCY SEARCH
2) SEARCH CONTINUOUSLY OR IN STEPS (FRACTION OF A CHIP) FOR SYNC
3) SENSE CODE SYNCHRONIZATION AND HALT SEARCH
4) BEGIN CARRIER RECOVERY IF COHERENT DATA DEMODULATION IS TO BE UTILIZED
5) SENSE CARRIER ACQUISITION AND STOP CARRIER SEARCH

Fig. 3–14—Acquisition of Spread Spectrum Signals.

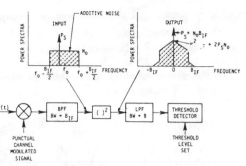

Fig. 3-15—*Noncoherent in-Lock Detector-Power Spectra.*

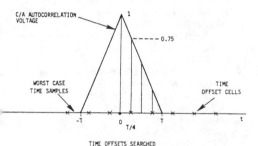

Fig. 3-16—*Acquisition Code Search.*

Thus if $C/N_0 = 33$ dB or 2000 then $S_R = 90$ or 45 chips/sec. The doppler uncertainty tolerated is approximately ±1 kHz or 2 kHz total. Thus it takes approximately 22 sec to search the entire C/A code period with a single 2 kHz frequency segment. Search of additional frequency uncertainty, e.g. ±4 kHz would take 88 sec. Thus acquisition of the C/A code even with significant frequency uncertainty can be accomplished in 90 sec max. or with an expected acquisition time of 45 sec.

The total acquisition time for 4 satellites can be this same value if 4 parallel receivers are employed or 4 times this large if a single receiver is time sequenced over the four satellites.

3.7 Multipath and Interference Effects

Multipath Reflection

Multipath signals can have a significant amplitude relative to the desired direct ray, particularly when the user is over water. Fig. 3-17 shows the dependence of multipath differential delay on elevation angle θ and user altitude h. This relationship is

$$\Delta T \simeq \frac{2h}{c} \sin \theta \frac{h}{5c} \text{ for } \theta > 0.1 \text{ rad.} \quad (3\text{-}3)$$

The multipath signal acts the same as noise of the same power if the delay difference ΔT is > 1.5 μsec for the C/A code or 150 nsec for the P-code and the user receiver is already tracking the desired signal.

Fig. 3-18 shows the P-code multipath tracking error for ratios of multipath signal-to-desired signal of 0.2, 0.6, 1.0. Region 1 is the normal operating region where the signal is initially properly tracking the desired signal. Re-

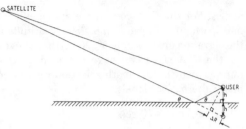

Fig. 3-17—*Multipath Delay vs Elevation Angle and User Altitude h.*

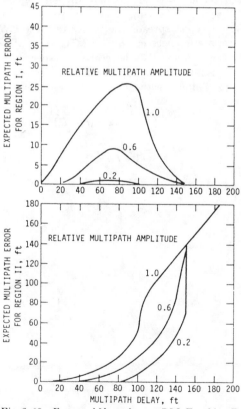

Fig. 3-18—*Expected Noncoherent DLL Tracking Error, 20 dB Carrier Tracking Margin (Haggerman, 1972).*

gion 2 shows the performance where the receiver is offset to track the multipath rather than the desired signal. Note that for a multipath ratio of 0.6 the worst case error is only about 8 nsec in Region 1.

Note that the multipath effects for the P–code are rather unlikely since one has to have a combination of low altitude and low elevation angle. For example, in order to have $c(\Delta T) = 150$ nsec $\geq \dfrac{h}{5}$ or $h < 750$ nsec even at low elevation angles. For the C/A·code there are significant multipath effects even at $h \leq 7500$ ft altitude if the elevation angle is only $5°$. Nevertheless even for the C/A signal we have obtained a large improvement in multipath rejection relative to many alternative signals.

CW Interference Effects

Unintentional narrowband CW interferences of very low power are a likely occurrence. These signals could severely degrade any narrowband CW signal at the same frequency. However the GPS receiver spreads the power in these CW tone interferences out over 2 MHz or 20 MHz for the C/A and P–code receivers, respectively.

Thus if we have a narrowband interference of power P_I the effective C/N_0 of the receiver is

$$(C/N_0)_{eff} = \frac{1}{(N_0/C(+ (P_I/CR_c)}$$
$$= \frac{C/N_0}{1 + P_I/R_c N_0}$$

$$(3\text{--}4)$$

where R_c is the code clock rate. Thus in order for the interference power to be significant it must be 60 dB or 70 dB above the receiver noise density for the C/A and P codes, respectively. Thus there is a substantial tolerance to these low level CW interferences.

REFERENCES

1. Headquarters, USAF Space and Missile Systems Organization, Systems Specification for the NAV-STAR Global Positioning System, 1 Sept. 1977.
2. R. L. Easton, L. C. Fisher, D. W. Hanson, H. W. Hellwig, L. J. Rueger, "Dissemination of Time and Frequency by Satellite," Proc. of the IEEE, October 1976, pp. 1482–1493.
3. J. J. Spilker, Jr., *Digital Communications by Satellite*, Prentice-Hall, Engelwood Cliffs, N.J., 1977, pp. 495–608.
4. R. Gold, "Optimal Binary Sequences for Spread Spectrum Multiplexing," IEEE Trans. on Info. Theory, Oct. 1967, pp. 619–621.
5. B. D. Elrod, "Correction for Ionospheric Propagation Delay in ASTRO-DABS—The Dual Frequency Calibration Method," Mitre Report, MTR-6896, April 1975.
6. L. Hagerman, Private Communication, 1972.
7. A. H. Bogen, "Geometric Performance of the Global Position System," Aerospace Corporation, AD-783-210, 1974.
8. H. Chang, Private Communication, 1976.
9. D. Kleppner, Vessot, R. F. C., and Ramsey, N. F., "An Orbiting Clock Experiment to Determine the Gravitational Red Shift," Astrophysics and Space Sciences vol. 6, 1970, pp. 13–32
10. H. D. Block, "An Easily Implemented Algorithm for Tropospheric Range Correction," Journal of Geophysical Research, April 1978, pp. 1825–1828.

The GPS Navigation Message

A. J. VAN DIERENDONCK, S. S. RUSSELL, E. R. KOPITZKE and M. BIRNBAUM

ABSTRACT

THE GPS USERS CONTINUOUSLY receive navigation information from the GPS Space Vehicles in the form of data bits modulated on the received signals. This information, which is computed and controlled by the GPS Control Segment, includes the vehicle's time, its clock correction and ephemeris parameters, almanacs and health for all GPS Space Vehicles, and text messages. From this information the Users compute the Space Vehicle's precise position and clock offset and less precise positions and clock offsets of Space Vehicles yet to be acquired.

The GPS Navigation Message design process included numerous trade studies which weighed various representations and algorithms against variables such as message size, accuracy, update frequency, User computational requirements, and legacy for the operational GPS. Other factors such as graceful degradation and future User requirements were also considered. Finally, upon selecting the appropriate design structure, the design was fine tuned to its final form and User algorithm implementation trade-offs were performed. The representation algorithms and User algorithms were jointly tested using a simulated Space Vehicle ephemeris trajectory and Space Vehicle clock. The results of these tests demonstrate that the User models represent the simulated ephemeris and clock to within 0.01 meters with precise parameters,

and to within 0.1 meters with truncated parameters.

I. INTRODUCTION

The GPS Navigation Message is the information supplied to the GPS Users from a GPS Space Vehicle. It is in the form of a 50 bit per second data bit stream that is modulated on the GPS navigation signals. This signal data allows the User to navigate successfully with the GPS. It carries Space Vehicle ephemerides, system time, Space Vehicle clock behavior data, transmitter status information and C/A (Clear/Acquisition) to P (Precision) signal handover information. The data stream is common to both the P and C/A signal on both the L_1 and L_2 frequencies.

The data message is contained in a data frame that is 1500 bits long. It has five subframes, each of which contains system time and the C/A to P handover information. The first subframe contains the Space Vehicle's clock correction parameters and ionospheric propagation delay model parameters. The second and third subframes contain the Space Vehicle's ephemeris. The fourth subframe contains a message of alphanumeric characters. The fifth subframe is a cycling of the almanacs of all Space Vehicles (one per frame) containing their ephemerides, clock correction parameters and health. This almanac information is for User acquisition of yet to be acquired Space Vehicles.

The purpose of this paper is to present the design of this GPS Navigation Message, the rationale behind the design and its impact on the Users.

II. GPS NAVIGATION MESSAGE REQUIREMENTS

The User Navigation Solution

A GPS User three-dimensional navigation fix

Dr. Van Dierendonck is with AVAND Systems Engineering, San Diego, CA; Mr. Russell is with General Dynamics Electronics Division, San Diego, CA; Mr. E. R. Kopitzke is with Magnavox Advanced Products Division, Torrance, CA; and, Major Birnbaum is with Space and Missile Systems Organization, Los Angeles, CA.

requires pseudo–range measurements from four GPS Space Vehicles, with time being the fourth solution variable. The concept of these pseudo–range measurements is simplified and illustrated in Fig. 1. These measurements are defined as the transit times of the Space Vehicle's generated signals as observed by the User and scaled by the speed of light (c). Using GPS time as a reference, the true transit times are those between the GPS transmit times and the GPS receive times. They represent the true slant ranges except for propagation delays, described by

$$R_i = c(t_R - t_{T_i}) - c\Delta t_{A_i}; \quad i = 1, \ldots, 4 \quad (1)$$

where t_R is GPS receive time, assumed to be simultaneous from all Space Vehicles i, t_{T_i} are the GPS times of transmission and Δt_{A_i} are the propagation delays.

The corresponding pseudo–ranges are

$$\begin{aligned}\bar{R}_i &= R_i + c\Delta t_{A_i} + c(\Delta t_u - \Delta t_{s_i}) \\ &= c(UT - t_{T_{s_i}}); \quad i = 1, \ldots, 4\end{aligned} \quad (2)$$

where Δt_u is the User's clock offset from GPS time, the Δt_{s_i} are the Space Vehicle i clock offsets, UT is User receive time defined as

$$UT = t_R + \Delta t_u \quad (3)$$

and $t_{T_{s_i}}$ are the Space Vehicle i transmit times defined as

$$t_{T_{s_i}} = t_{T_i} + \Delta t_{s_i}; \quad i = 1, \ldots, 4 \quad (4)$$

The User must solve for four unknowns. These are his position coordinates X, Y, and Z (earth–fixed earth–centered) and his clock offset

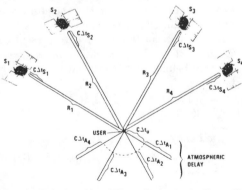

Fig. 1—Relationship of Times Between the Space Vehicles and User and their Respective Range.

Δt_u. Expanding equation (2) expressing the pseudo–ranges in terms of these unknowns yields

$$\begin{aligned}\bar{R}_i &= \sqrt{(X_{s_i} - X)^2 + (Y_{s_i} - Y)^2 + (Z_{s_i} - Z)^2} \\ &\quad + c\Delta t_{A_i} + c(\Delta t_u - \Delta t_{s_i}); \quad i = 1, \ldots, 4\end{aligned} \quad (5)$$

There are twenty other unknowns in these four equations that must be defined before X, Y, Z and Δt_u can be found.

The Δt_{A_i} are estimated by the User by measuring the pseudo–ranges at two frequencies (ionosphere delay corrections) and estimating troposphere delays based on geometry and altitude. The X_{s_i}, Y_{s_i}, Z_{s_i}, and Δt_{s_i} must be computed by the User from information provided to him via the GPS Navigation Message. This is one purpose of the GPS Navigation Message.

Space Vehicle Signal Acquisition

If a user has an a priori knowledge of the pseudo–range to a Space Vehicle to within about 10,000 to 20,000 meters, he can acquire the Space Vehicle's "P" signal *directly* in a specified amount of time. *Direct P* code acquisition is possible for the User who has a stable time reference and has an approximate knowledge of his position. It is useful if he doesn't have time to *normally* acquire the Space Vehicle's Clear Acquisition "C/A" signal so as to handover to P code tracking. It is also useful for reacquisition or when the User is navigating and wishes to change Space Vehicles. In fact, *direct* acquisition is the normal mode in these cases.

Equation (5) will yield this approximate pseudo–range provided that the User has a knowledge of his position and time as well as the knowledge of the Space Vehicle's position and time. The atmospheric delays could be neglected. The Space Vehicle's position and time must be computed *before* acquisition. Therefore the information for this computation must be collected from other Space Vehicles or from the same vehicle at a previous time. This information is provided to the User via the GPS Navigation Message. Each Space Vehicle provides an almanac for *all* Space Vehicles. This is another purpose of the GPS Navigation Message.

Specified Requirements

The GPS System Level Specification[1] spec

fies the signal data of the GPS Navigation Signal Structure. This specification was the basis for the GPS Navigation Message design. However, it has evolved through Specification Change Notices as the message design has evolved.

Originally, the specification was written in fairly general terms with respect to some of the contents of the data, while quite specific on other contents. It is not surprising, however, that only the more general specifications still apply. The first sentence is still intact except for an addition of the word "shall." It states: "The signal data shall allow the User to navigate successfully with GPS." Of course, this statement is *the* top level requirement. All the other requirements of the original specification were only guidelines for the design along with some constraints imposed by completed signal structure or Space Vehicle design. These constraints were:

1) The data rate shall be 50 bps.
2) Each data frame shall have lengths of 600, 900, 1200, 1500, or 1800 bits. (It is now fixed at 1500 bits.)
3) Each data frame shall contain handover words (HOW), and telemetry words (TLM). The HOW and TLM shall be generated on-board the Space Vehicle. Parity bits shall be generated by the Space Vehicle. Each HOW shall be spaced 6 seconds apart uniformly throughout the frame and shall contain system time. The TLM shall be used to indicate the status of the data uploading operation while it is in progress. A synchronization pattern and a within-frame identifier shall be in the HOW and/or TLM words. (The synchronization pattern was specified to be in the HOW, but ended up in the TLM.)
4) The total number of bits required in Space Vehicle memory shall be approximately 100 K bits.

There were many other "thought to be" constraints that were changed during the design process. As a result, the current system specification reflects "derived" requirements rather than specified requirements. This set of "derived" requirements is really the Navigation Message design presented here.

III. THE TLM AND HOW WORDS

Originally, the content of the TLM and HOW, their order of appearance (HOW first, followed by TLM) and their size were specified. The HOW was specified at 56 bits and the TLM at 24 bits for a total of 80 bits not including parity. They have been compacted to two 24 bit words plus parity, thus allowing more space in the message for navigation data.

The data frame is now made up of five subframes of 300 bits each. Each subframe consists of 10 words of 30 bits each. The first two words are the TLM and HOW, which are generated by the Space Vehicle. The remaining eight words of each subframe are User navigation data generated by the Control Segment.

The TLM contains an eight bit preamble (the synchronization pattern), 14 bits of TLM message, 2 non-information bearing bits and 6 bits of parity. The TLM message contains, at the appropriate time, primary upload status messages, diagnostic messages, and other messages, including roll momentum dump Z-count (Space Vehicle time of roll momentum dump).

The HOW contains a 17 bit Z-count (Space Vehicle time at the leading edge of the next subframe), a one-bit synchronization flag, a three bit subframe identification, two non-information bearing bits, and six bits of parity. The synchronization flag is an indicator to the User that the data frame may not be aligned with the X1 Code Epoch. The probability of this occurring is quite remote.

The Space Vehicle generates the parity on these two words. The Phase I Space Vehicles will not generate the parity on the other eight words; later Space Vehicles may. The parity is a (32, 26) Hamming Code, thus the parity overlaps the words. To account for this, the Space Vehicle "wastes" two bits each in the TLM and HOW so they are not linked with the other words. In later Space Vehicles, these 4 bits can contain information.

The parity algorithm will not be discussed in this paper. It is described in detail in Ref. 2.

IV. DATA BLOCK 1—SPACE VEHICLE CLOCK CORRECTIONS

Data Block 1 appears in the first subframe, repeating itself every 30 seconds. It is generated by the Control Segment and contains frequency standard corrections, an associated Age of Data (AODC) word and ionospheric propagation delay model coefficients. The ionospheric delay model is for single frequency Users and will not be discussed in this paper, as it is presently an experimental model. A discussion of the Space Vehicle clock corrections follows.

Space Vehicle Clock Drift Characteristics

The purpose of the clock correction parameters is to provide the Users with a description of the Space Vehicle's time offset from GPS time. This offset is not constant because the Space Vehicle's frequency standards have definite drift characteristics. These drift characteristics determine (in part) how the time offset should be represented and presented to the Users. Ref. 3 presents a detailed description of GPS time and its relationship to Space Vehicle time.

During Phase I of GPS the frequency standards will be of the Rubidium type and of the Cesium beam type. The Rubidium standards exhibit deterministic drift characteristics on the order of a first derivative of frequency (drift rate) or a second derivative of phase (phase = time offset). At times in transient situations (caused by temperature variation, frequency adjustment or turn-on) they exhibit higher order derivatives. However, these higher order effects can be neglected over short intervals of time. Random drift characteristics are not predictable. They only corrupt one's ability to estimate and predict the deterministic drift and cause some of the higher order derivatives of drift. Cesium beam standards normally don't exhibit higher order deterministic drifts in frequency over the time periods of interest. They can be characterized as a frequency offset plus random variations in frequency. Any other characteristics are only observable over very long periods of time (a day or two).

General Relativistic Effects on Space Vehicle Clocks[4, 5]

It is necessary to correct Space Vehicle time for drift due to general and special relativity. These drifts arise from the fact that the Space Vehicle clocks are located at different gravitational potentials than the GPS Users and are traveling at much higher velocities. The relativistic effects cause apparent shifts in the frequencies of the clocks.

Considering the orbits of the Phase I GPS Space Vehicles, there is the possibility of two relativity drift effects—a secular drift and a periodic drift. A large secular drift can be, and will be removed by offsetting the frequency standard frequency prior to launch. Smaller secular drift is due to an off nominal semi-major axis of the orbit. A periodic time variation is caused by a non-zero eccentricity.

User Algorithm Considerations

The model for representing the corrections for the Space Vehicle's time offset must be compatible with drift characteristics and relativistic effects described above. It must also be computationally efficient for the User (including storage requirements). This consideration would suggest the use of a polynominal expansion representation of a minimum degree, with coefficients that required a minimum multiple of 8 bit bytes. It should also represent the corrections over a long enough time interval to minimize changes in the data being transmitted, and overlapping intervals to allow time for the User to collect the change in data.

Space Vehicle Clock Correction Representation Model

A second order polynomial expansion is ideal to represent the drift characteristics of a Space Vehicle clock. It would certainly also absorb any secular relativistic effect. In fact, for reasonable time periods a first order representation would probably suffice to describe a Cesium beam frequency standard's drift, but not a Rubidium frequency standard's drift.

The primary problem in using a polynomial expansion is to include the periodic relativistic effect, which for the Phase I GPS orbits could have an amplitude of up to 70 nanoseconds (considering a maximum eccentricity of .03) with a period of approximately 12 hours. The expression for this periodic effect is

$$\Delta t_r(t) = (-4.443 \qquad (6)$$

$$\times \ 10^{-10} \ \text{sec}/\sqrt{\text{meter}})e \ \sqrt{A} \ \sin E(t)$$

where e is the eccentricity, A is the semi-major axis and $E(t)$ is the eccentric anomaly. A polynomial (Taylor's series) expansion of this equation for a Phase I GPS orbit with an eccentricity of .03 is approximately

$$\Delta t_r(t) \approx 6.869 \times 10^{-8} \sin E(t_o)$$

$$+ [1.002 \times 10^{-11} \cos E(t_o)](t - t_o) \qquad (7)$$
$$- [7.307 \times 10^{-16} \sin E(t_o)](t - t_o)^2$$
$$- [3.552 \times 10^{-20} \cos E(t_o)](t - t_o)^3 + \ldots$$

where t_o is the reference time of the representation. t_o is at the midpoint of the time interval to maximize the length of the interval.

To maintain an accuracy of about a nanosecond, the second order term can't be neglected for a time interval longer than 0.65 hours. The third order term can't be neglected for periods over 1.69 hours. This is certainly a reasonable time interval even allowing for an overlap. In fact, the nominal period of applicability has been chosen to be one hour with one-half hour of additional applicability after the data has changed.

Thus, the representation model for the Space Vehicle clock corrections is a second order polynomial described by three coefficients a_0, a_1, and a_2 and a reference time t_{oc}.[2] More specifically, the User will correct the time received from the Space Vehicle with the equation (in seconds)

$$t = t_{SV} - \Delta t_{SV} \qquad (8)$$

where

$$\Delta t_{SV} = a_0 + a_1(t - t_{oc}) + a_2(t - t_{oc})^2 \qquad (9)$$

where t is GPS time in seconds, t_{SV} is the Space Vehicle code phase time at *message transmission time* in seconds, t_{oc} is the Data Block 1 reference time in seconds, measured from the GPS time weekly epoch (which is approximately Greenwich Mean Time Saturday night/Sunday morning midnight), and a_0, a_1, and a_2 are Data Block 1 parameters.

Note that equations (8) and (9) as written are coupled. As it turns out, however, the sensitivity of Δt_{SV} to t in equation (9) is negligible. Thus, the User may approximate t by t_{SV} in equation (9). However, since GPS time spans only 1 week, the value of t must account for beginning or end of week crossovers. That is, if the quantity $t - t_{oc}$ is greater than 302,400, subtract 604,800 from t. If the quantity $t - t_{oc}$ is less than $-302,400$, add 604,800 to t.

The parameters a_0, a_1, a_2 include all general relativistic effects on the Space Vehicle clock. The Control Segment does not even correct for the secular effects, since they appear to be frequency offsets, and thus absorbed in the a_1 term.

The only restriction is that the a_1 term have a range large enough to absorb the effect. For other reasons it has been chosen to be an order of magnitude larger than even the nominal secular effect accounted for in the Space Vehicles prior to launch (a frequency correction of -4.484 parts in 10^{10}).

The polynomial approximation of the periodic relativistic effect does not provide a model with graceful degradation after its period of applicability. Graceful degradation may be desirable for a User if jamming prevents him from receiving new data, or if the Space Vehicle fails to transmit new data.

The User has the option, however, to subtract the correction from the coefficients, and replace it with the more exact correction of equation (6). That is, compute the Space Vehicle clock offset as

$$\Delta t_{SV} = (a_0 - a_{0r}) + (a_1 - a_{1r})(t - t_{oc}) \qquad (10)$$
$$+ (a_2 - a_{2r})(t - t_{oc})^2 + \Delta t_r(t)$$

where a_{0r}, a_{1r}, and a_{2r} are

$$a_{0r} = \Delta t_r(t_{oc}) \approx K \sin M(t_{oc}) \qquad (11)$$

$$a_{1r} = \left. \frac{d\Delta t_r(t)}{dt} \right|_{t = t_{oc}} \approx Kn \cos M(t_{oc}) \qquad (12)$$

$$a_{2r} = \left. \frac{1}{2} \frac{d^2 \Delta t_r(t)}{dt^2} \right|_{t = t_{oc}}$$
$$\approx -\frac{K}{2} n^2 \sin M(t_{oc}) \qquad (13)$$

where

$$K = (-4.443 \times 10^{-10} \text{ sec}/\sqrt{\text{meter}}) e \sqrt{A} \qquad (14)$$

$M(t_{oc})$ is the mean anomaly at time t_{oc} and n is the mean motion of the Space Vehicle. The required orbital parameters for the computations are part of Data Block 2, which will be discussed later. The angle approximations in equations (11), (12), and (13) (M instead of E) are sufficiently accurate for these corrections.

Other Data Block 1 Parameters

In addition to the parameters described above, Data Block 1 also includes the Space Vehicle clock correction parameter age of data word (AODC), an $L_1 - L_2$ correction parameter for the single frequency Users (T_{GD}) and eight ionospheric correction parameters.

The age of data word (AODC) provides the User with a confidence level in the Space Vehicle clock correction. It represents the time difference (age) between the Data Block 1 reference time (t_{oc}) and the time of the last measurement update (t_L) used to estimate the correction parameters. That is,

$$\text{AODC} = t_{oc} - t_L \qquad (15)$$

Based on a knowledge of the Space Vehicle frequency standard's stability and the Control Segment's ability to predict its drift, the User can model a "deweighting" function which deweights a clock correction computed with relatively old data.

T_{GD} is provided to the single frequency Users as a correction term to account for the Space Vehicle's group delay differential between L_1 and L_2. This group delay differential is the difference in the propagation times of the two signal paths prior to radiation from the Space Vehicle's antennae. It is of no consequence to the two frequency Users because their ionospheric delay corrections are identical to that of the Control Segment. Thus, any differential is absorbed in the Space Vehicle's clock correction coefficient a_o. Because of this, it is of consequence to the single frequency User who does not observe this differential.

This differential is specified (in Ref. 2) to have a mean value that will not exceed 15 nanoseconds with random variations about that mean that will not exceed 1.5 nanoseconds (one-sigma). The a_o coefficient, however, absorbs an amplification of the mean value through the ionospheric delay correction which multiplies the differential by a factor of 1.546 (approximate). Therefore, the value of T_{GD} could be as large as 23.2 nanoseconds. The random variations will not be included in T_{GD}. They would only be part of the error budget for the a_o coefficient (2.32 nanoseconds one-sigma).

T_{GD} is estimated by the Control Segment from long-term observations of the ionospheric delay corrections. At certain latitudes and at certain times of the day and year, the ionospheric delays are near zero. A consistent residual at these times is defined to be due to the group delay differential and assigned to T_{GD}.

The ionosphere correction parameters are for an experimental model for single frequency Users and will not be discussed in this paper. They are described in detail in Ref. 2.

Data Block 1 Format

Data Block 1 occupies the third through tenth thirty bit words (including parity) of the first subframe. The third and fourth words are spares. The number of bits, the scale factor of the least significant bit (LSB), which is the last bit received, the range and the units of the parameters are as specified in Table 1.

The last word in the subframe, the one containing a_0, has two non-information bearing bits, for the same reason as given for those in the TLM and HOW words. In this way, a_0 is not linked with the TLM word of the next subframe through the parity algorithm. Eventually, a_0 may have two additional bits of accuracy.

The scale factors of the LSBs were determined from the maximum sensitivities with respect to the parameters

$$\frac{\partial \Delta t_{SV}}{\partial a_0} = 1 \qquad (16)$$

$$\frac{\partial \Delta t_{SV}}{\partial a_1} = t - t_{oc} \leq 2700 \text{ seconds} \qquad (17)$$

$$\frac{\partial \Delta t_{SV}}{\partial a_2} = (t - t_{oc})^2 \leq 7.29 \times 10^6 \text{ seconds}^2 \qquad (18)$$

The RSS of the maximum errors per term due to truncation is 0.59 nanoseconds. This is well below the expected prediction error for Δt_{SV}.

The LSB of t_{oc} has a somewhat different meaning as it is defined to be exactly GPS time. Its accuracy need only be about 0.267 seconds to provide a Δt_{SV} accurate to one nanosecond. t_{oc} is always selected to be a reference time of a multiple of 16 seconds from GPS weekly epoch prior to the definition of the coefficients. The range of t_{oc} is one week less 16 seconds since one week is the range of GPS time. The range of the coefficients are worst case expected values, or in the case of a_0, the largest value that will be allowed. Space Vehicle code phase adjustments will be performed via uploaded command from the Control Segment to maintain all Space Vehicles' times to within 976.6 microseconds of GPS time. This insures that all Space Vehicles will be transmitting the same subframe, the preamble and the same Z Count at the same time to within

Table 1—Data Block 1 Parameters

Parameter	No. of Bits	Scale Factor (LSB)	Range*	Units
Spare	24	—	—	—
Spare	24	—	—	—
α_0	8	2^{-31}	$\pm 2^{-24}$	seconds
α_1	8	2^{-31}	$\pm 2^{-24}$	seconds
α_2	8	2^{-29}	$\pm 2^{-22}$	seconds
α_3	8	2^{-28}	$\pm 2^{-21}$	seconds
β_0	8	2^{8}	$\pm 2^{15}$	seconds
β_1	8	2^{9}	$\pm 2^{16}$	seconds
β_2	8	2^{10}	$\pm 2^{17}$	seconds
β_3	8	2^{12}	$\pm 2^{19}$	seconds
T_{GD}	8	$2^{-31} \simeq 4.66 \times 10^{-10}$	$\pm 2^{-24} \simeq \pm 5.96 \times 10^{-8}$	seconds
$AODC$	8	$2^{11} = 2048$	$2^{19} = 524288$	seconds
t_{oc}	16	$2^{4} = 16$	604,784	seconds
a_2	8	$2^{-55} \simeq 2.78 \times 10^{-17}$	$\pm 2^{-48} \simeq \pm 3.553 \times 10^{-15}$	sec/sec^2
a_1	16	$2^{-43} \simeq 1.14 \times 10^{-13}$	$\pm 2^{-28} \simeq \pm 3.725 \times 10^{-9}$	sec/sec
a_0	22	$2^{-32} \simeq 4.656 \times 10^{-10}$	$\pm 2^{-10} \simeq \pm 9.766 \times 10^{-4}$	seconds

* ($\pm$) indicates that sign bit will occupy the most significant bit (MSB).
NOTE: All binary numbers will be two's complement.

one twentieth of a data bit. These adjustments should be required no more than 3 times a year for a normal frequency standard.

The range of a_1 represents the worst case frequency offset expected, even if all redundancies have been exhausted to the point of using the crystal oscillators. Frequency adjustments via the S–band telemetry are possible, however, they will not be normally utilized.

The range of a_2 is primarily $2^7 (= 128)$ times the LSB. It is only 4.87 times larger than the periodic relativity effect described in equation (7). Drift rates of Rubidium standards should never be that large. The backup crystal oscillators may have drift rates that large.

V. DATA BLOCK 2 SPACE VEHICLE EPHEMERIS REPRESENTATION

Data Block 2 appears in the second and third subframes, repeating itself every 30 seconds. It is generated by the Control Segment and contains a representation of the transmitting Space Vehicle's ephemeris and associated Age of Data (AODE) words. A discussion of this ephemeris representation follows.

GPS Space Vehicle Orbit Characteristics

The characteristics of the GPS Space Vehicle orbits are only summarized here. A more detailed discussion appears in Ref. 6.

The final orbits of the GPS Phase I Space Vehicles are characterized by an orbital ground trace which repeats once each sidereal day. These orbits have a near one-half sidereal day period. The nominal period, including nodal regression effects, will be 11.9661 hours which corresponds to a semi–major axis value of 26560.123 Km. The inclination angle will be 63 degrees and a nominal eccentricity of less than 0.005 (with an upper limit of 0.015).

Even though the orbits are nominally circular, they must be described as elliptical orbits. The radial variation in the orbit (with respect to the earth) varies from

$$r_{min} = A(1 - e) < 26427.322 Km \qquad (19)$$

to

$$r_{max} = A(1 + e) > 26692.924 Km \qquad (20)$$

for eccentricities greater than .005. This is a variation of 265.602 Km.

The eccentricity causes the greatest perturbation from a circular orbit. However, there are other perturbations from even the elliptical orbit that are significant. These are due to perturbing accelerations that will act on the GPS Space Vehicles. The approximate values of these accelerations are given in Table 2. Over a short period of time, these forces could be considered as linear perturbations to estimate their effects on the ephemeris. These effects are also listed in Table 2 for a one hour time period. Because of the nature of these effects and their magnitude, it is desirable to represent the GPS ephem-

Table 2—Summary of the Approximate
Perturbing Forces For GPS Space Vehicles

Source	Maximum perturbing acceleration	Maximum excursion growth in one hour
	m/sec^2	meters
Earth-mass attraction	5.65×10^{-1}	—
Second zonal harmonic	5.3×10^{-5}	300
Lunar gravity	5.5×10^{-6}	40
Solar gravity	3×10^{-6}	20
Fourth zonal harmonic	10^{-7}	0.6
Solar radiation pressure	10^{-7}	0.6
Gravity anomalies	10^{-8}	0.06
All other forces	10^{-8}	0.06

erides over periods of time no longer than a few hours.

The second zonal harmonic provides the major perturbing force to the two body elliptical orbit with a dominant period of half the orbit period (that is, 5.98305 hours). There also exists some secular drift in the ephemeris.

The next most predominant forces are the gravities of the Sun and Moon. These forces vary as a function of the position of the Space Vehicle in its orbit. They are nearly constant over short intervals of time. However, when the Space Vehicle is at a position of its closest approach to the moon, there are some pronounced variations in its ephemeris.

All other forces can essentially be considered constant over short intervals of time, or they have a negligible effect. Any residuals would be reasonable representation errors.

In summary, the GPS Space Vehicle ephemerides are characterized by elliptical orbits with both periodic and secular perturbations. The predominant periodic perturbations have a 5.98305 hour period. Other perturbations are smaller and might be represented over short intervals of time as simple functions of time (i. e., constant or linear).

Ephemeris Representation Trade Studies and Results

The final GPS ephemeris representation evolved through numerous trade studies. There were many criteria to be considered. Some of these are (not necessarily in order of importance):

1) Users Time-To-First-Fix (TTFF)—This basically is a function of how many subframes are required to transmit and collect the ephemeris representation. Does the clock and ephemeris representations data fit in two, three, or four subframes? There was a time when it was thought that two subframes would suffice.

2) User Computational Time—complexity of algorithm to compute earth–centered earth–fixed Space Vehicle position; the number of sines, cosines, square roots, multiplies, divides, etc. This is only critical if User computational through–put is a problem.

3) User Storage Requirements—a function of how many subframes of data must be stored and the computer code required for the User algorithm. There is also a requirement for an almanac algorithm to compute the positions of all Space Vehicles. Thus, commonality of algorithms impacts the storage requirements.

4) Refresh Rate—How long is one set of parameters valid before they must be replaced? This impacts the memory required in the Space Vehicle as well as how often the User must collect a new set of parameters.

5) Overlap in Time of Applicability—This directly impacts the refresh rate.

6) Accuracy—How well is the ephemeris *and* the rate of change of ephemeris represented? Accuracy is usually directly proportional to the number of parameters required and how many bytes are needed to store them. Almanac accuracy is also important.

7) Orbital Tolerance—How well does the representation represent off–nominal orbits? What is the range of the parameters? Orbital tolerances are hard to pin down. That is, how off–nominal can an orbit get before the Space Vehicle is no longer useful? Large tolerances require more bytes of information.

8) Degradation—Does the representation degrade gracefully after its period of applicability, or does it degrade abruptly? Degradation of representation was discussed earlier for the clock correction pa-

rameters. It would be desirable to navigate in a degraded mode with "old" parameters if new ones are not obtainable.

9) Clock Relativity Compensation—Does the representation aid graceful degradation of Space Vehicle clock corrections?

10) Time for User to Receive Almanac—Related to criteria 1 and 3. How much data is required to represent a common algorithm almanac? In order to keep the almanac data to a minimum, the almanac representation should represent multiple orbits. To do that plus have a common representation with the precise ephemeris constrains that representation considerably.

11) Clarity of the Representation—Is it clear to facilitate debugging and interpretation and can the algorithm be extended to future considerations, to other computers, etc.? For the representation to have some physical meaning enhances the understanding of its design.

Considering the above criteria, three representations or variations thereof were investigated. Candidate representations were:

1) Polynomials in time
2) Harmonic expansions
3) Keplerian parameters plus perturbations (polynomials, harmonics)

Polynomials were considered because the User algorithm would be simple, minimizing the processing time. Algorithm storage requirements are also minimal, however, polynomials could never by themselves represent total orbits or multiple orbits. Thus, a separate algorithm would be required for the almanac computations. Thus, other than the minimal processing time, polynomial representations had no clear advantage over other candidates, and had some definite disadvantages.

Harmonic expansions around a circular orbit were also considered but not investigated in depth. This was because they didn't appear to have any clear advantages over a Keplerian type representation with the main disadvantages of not having a clear physical meaning, making it difficult to determine the range of the coefficients for data word sizing. The coefficients would be sensitive to position in an elliptical orbit and to unknown orbital tolerances.

Keplerian parameter representation provided advantages in all criteria except for User computation time and possibly, User storage requirements. The storage requirement disadvantage tends to be offset because this representation handles the almanac very well. A definite advantage was the fact that the Keplerian representation has a physical meaning—at least a familiar one. This made it relatively easy to size the data words, even for off nominal orbits. However, perturbations about the Keplerian orbit require additional parameters. Representation candidates for the perturbations were polynomials (in time) and harmonic coefficients. The harmonic coefficients have a more familiar physical meaning, therefore they provided a better representation when combined with two secular drift terms. They also provided a more graceful degradation using "old" parameters.

It should be clear by now that the choice of representation was that of Keplerian type parameters plus secular drift terms and harmonic coefficients. Table 3 summarizes the candidates versus the selection criteria described above. A detailed description of the exact choice of parameters follows.

User Algorithm Considerations[7]

Because the Keplerian representation could have had a severe impact on the User's computation time, extensive algorithm manipulations were considered to optimize the User algorithm and to determine the impact. The primary emphasis was in the solution of Kepler's equation.

$$E(t) = M(t) + e \sin E(t) \qquad (21)$$

and subsequent solutions for the true anomaly

$$\sin v(t) = \frac{\sqrt{1 - e^2} \sin E(t)}{1 - e \cos E(t)} \qquad (22)$$

$$\cos v(t) = \frac{\cos E(t) - e}{1 - e \cos E(t)} \qquad (23)$$

to a defined accuracy. Other manipulations and approximations were investigated, consisting mostly of the selection of the best order of computation to minimize operations, using appropriate trigonometric identities and using small angle approximations for the sines and cosines of the harmonic perturbations.

Table 3—Ephemeris Representation Candidates Versus Selection Criteria

	Polynomials	Harmonic* Expansion	Keplerian with Polynomials	Keplerian with Harmonics
No. of subframes	3+	2+	2+	2−
User computation time	short, simple	sines, cosines	sines, cosines	sines, cosines
User storage requirements	3 + Subframes Small algorithm Need almanac	2 + Subframes Med. algorithm Same as almanac	2 + Subframes Large algorithm Same as almanac	2 Subframes Large algorithm Same as almanac
Refresh rate	Once per hour	Once per hour	Once per hour	Once per hour or longer
Refresh overlap	½ hour	½ hour	½ hour	½ hour or longer
Accuracy	≺1 ft. error	Probably OK	<1 ft. error	<1 ft. error
Orbital tolerance effects	Not clear	Not clear	Handles any orbit	Handles any orbit
Degradation	Abrupt	Unknown	Marginal	Graceful
Clock relativity compensation	Not compatible	Not compatible	Compatible	Compatible
Almanac subframe	Not compatible	1+	1−	1−
Clarity	Not clear	Not clear	Orbit—clear Perturbations—not clear	Clear

* Estimated characteristics.

In these equations, e is given and $M(t)$ is computed easily from given data. In general, equation 21 is nonlinear in $E(t)$. It is impractical to solve for $E(t)$ in any way except approximately because, for $e \leq 0.663$, the exact solution is

$$E(t) = M(t) + 2 \sum_{k=1}^{\infty} \frac{1}{k!} J_k(ke) \sin[kM(t)] \quad (24)$$

where the J_k are Bessel functions of the first kind of order k. Therefore, a number of methods of solution were considered in evaluating the Keplerian representation and in choosing the appropriate algorithm. Four factors were considered (in order of importance):

1. Accuracy
2. Legacy and Clarity
3. Duty Cycle
4. Memory

The guidelines followed relative to these factors were:

Accuracy. The algorithm was to introduce an error of less than 1 centimeter for eccentricities of less than 0.03.

Legacy and Clarity. The algorithm was to be suitable for implementation on digital computers with a broad range of architectures, word lengths, instruction sets and internal speeds. The algorithm structure was to be clear to facilitate debugging and interpretation.

Duty Cycle. The execution time of the algorithm was to be minimized subject to the accuracy and legacy constraints.

Memory. Memory was not to be wasted but was to be traded for duty cycle, legacy and accuracy. If it becomes necessary to save memory at the expense of other factors, clarity was to be sacrificed.

There are two basic approaches in solving the total set of equations 21 through 23. One solves for $E(t)$ explicitly and then solves for sine and cosine of $v(t)$, while the other solves the "equation of the center" which contains an implicit solution of Kepler's equation and yields the true anomaly $v(t)$ directly. The "equation of the center" algorithms generally yield shorter duty cycles, where the explicit solutions generally require less memory.

There are also both iterative or closed form approximations for each approach. Closed form approximations are faster but use more memory than iterative methods for the same level of accuracy. They are also usually easier to debug, maintain, size, scale and schedule.

Ten different methods were evaluated. Six of these methods were discarded by inspection.

The remaining four were tested against the four factors given above. Two of these were tested with modifications and/or different coding methods to produce results with different orderings of the factors. The results of these seven tests are summarized in Table 4. The numbers are typical for an HP21M20 computer programmed in a higher order language. They do not necessarily reflect relative efficiency in other processors and/or languages.

Algorithms 1 and 2 are differently coded versions of a closed form approximate solution to the "equation of the center." Basically, sine $v(t)$ and cosine $v(t)$ are solved as series expansions of powers of e and sines and cosines of $M(t)$ (sixth or seventh power). Algorithm 3 consists of an iterative solution of Kepler's equation of the form

$$E_k(t) = M(t) + e \sin[E_{k-1}(t)] \qquad (25)$$

where

$$E_o(t) = M(t) \qquad (26)$$

until a desired accuracy is achieved (about 3 iterations).

Algorithm 4 is a variation of Algorithm 3 where first and second differences are used to accelerate convergence. Because Algorithm 3

Table 4—Memory and Duty Cycle Requirements of Several Candidate Ephemeris Algorithm Implementations

Algorithm	Relative Order of Importance	Memory Required for Four Space Vehicles (words)	Cycle Time Per Call (milliseconds)*
[1] Using modified Lagrange solution of equation of center	Accuracy Clarity Speed Memory	2203	22.3
[2] Using modified Lagrange solution of the equation of the center	Accuracy Speed Memory Clarity	1496	12.5
[3] Using classic successive substitutions to solve Kepler's equations	Accuracy Memory Speed Clarity	1145	40.9
[4] Using Stephenson's successive substitution method to solve Kepler's equations	Accuracy Speed Memory Clarity	1202	46.4
[5] Using classic Newton Raphson method to solve Kepler's equations	Accuracy Clarity Speed Memory	1515	55.0
[6] Using modified Newton Raphson method to solve Kepler's equation	Accuracy Clarity Memory Speed	1755	35.9
[7] Using modified Newton Raphson method to solve Kepler's equation	Accuracy Memory Speed Clarity	1319	20.6

* HP21M20 Computer—FORTRAN IV.

converges so fast, Algorithm 4 was actually inferior.

Algorithm 5 uses a classical Newton Raphson method as an iterative solution to Kepler's equation by searching for an $E(t)$ that minimizes the function

$$f[E(t)] = M(t) - [E(t) - e \sin E(t)] \qquad (27)$$

with

$$E_o(t) = M(t) \qquad (28)$$

Algorithms 6 and 7 are simply differently coded versions of an approximation of the combined first two iterations of Algorithm 5, which was shown to be sufficiently accurate.

There were two results of this trade study. First of all, it demonstrated that the Keplerian approach to ephemeris representation was a viable approach with regard to user algorithm considerations. The memory requirement for any of the algorithms was not excessive nor was the cycle time. Considering eight calls to the routine for each navigation cycle (to evaluate range and delta-range), the total cycle time would be in the order of 100 to 200 milliseconds for this more desirable algorithm. User navigation cycles would occur every 1 to 10 seconds depending on the user set or type. Although a 100 to 200 millisecond period is a good portion of a one second navigation cycle, it is not an unreasonable portion.

The other result was a selection of the most desirable algorithms. These were either Algorithms 1 or 2, depending on whether or not the clarity factor would have to be waved for better speed and less memory.

The Space Vehicle Ephemeris Representation Model

The Space Vehicle ephemeris representation model is characterized by a set of parameters that is an extension to the Keplerian orbital parameters describing the Space Vehicle ephemeris during the interval of time (at least an hour) for which the parameters are transmitted. They also describe the ephemeris for an additional interval of time (at least one-half hour) to allow time for the User to receive the parameters for the new interval of time. The definitions of the parameters are given in Table 5. The age of data word (AODE) provides the User with a confi-

Table 5—Ephemeris Representation Parameters

M_o	Mean anomaly at reference time
Δn	Mean motion difference from computed value
e	Eccentricity
$\sqrt{A}$	Square root of the semi-major axis
Ω_o	Right ascension at reference time
i_o	Inclination angle at reference time
ω	Argument of perigee
$\dot{\Omega}$	Rate of right ascension
C_{uc}	Amplitude of the cosine harmonic correction term to the argument of latitude
C_{us}	Amplitude of the sine harmonic correction term to the argument of latitude
C_{rc}	Amplitude of the cosine harmonic correction term to the orbit radius
C_{rs}	Amplitude to the sine harmonic correction term to the orbit radius
C_{ic}	Amplitude of the cosine harmonic correction term to the angle of inclination
C_{is}	Amplitude of the sine harmonic correction term to the angle of inclination
t_{oe}	Ephemeris reference time
AODE	Age of Data (Ephemeris)

dence level in the ephemeris representation parameters. AODE represents the time difference (age) between the reference time (t_{oe}) and the time of the last measurement update (t_L) used to estimate the representation parameters. That is,

$$\text{AODE} = t_{oe} - t_L \qquad (29)$$

The AODE word also provides a linkage between Subframes 2 and 3 because it appears in both subframes. This is to ensure the User that the subframes he collected do not apply to different intervals of time, as he may collect those subframes at different times.

The user computes the earth-fixed coordinates of the position of the Space Vehicle's antenna phase center with a variation of the equations shown in Table 6. The parameter values are obtained via a nonlinear iterative least squares curve fit of the predicted Space Vehicle's antenna phase center ephemeris (time-position quadruples; t, x, y, z) over the interval of time $t_{oe} - T$, $t_{oe} + T$. T is 5 minutes longer than half the transmission interval plus half the overlap period into the next interval. For example, if the transmission interval is one hour, and the overlap period is 30 minutes, T is 50 minutes.

Table 6—Ephemeris Representation Definitions

$\mu = 3.986008 \times 10^{14}$ meters^3/sec^2	WGS 72 value of the earth's universal gravitational parameter
$\dot{\Omega}_e = 7.292115147 \times 10^{-5}$ rad/sec	WGS 72 value of the earth's rotation rate
$A = (\sqrt{A})^2$	Semi-major axis
$n_o = \sqrt{\dfrac{\mu}{A^3}}$	Computed mean motion
$t_k = t - t_{oe}{}^*$	Time from epoch
$n = n_o + \Delta n$	Corrected mean motion
$M_k = M_o + nt_k$	Mean anomaly
$M_k = E_k - e \sin E_k$	Kepler's equation for eccentric anomaly
$\cos v_k = (\cos E_k - e)/(1 - e \cos E_k)$ $\sin v_k = \sqrt{1 - e^2} \sin E_k/(1 - e \cos E_k)$	} True anomaly
$\phi_k = v_k + \omega$	Argument of latitude
$\delta u_k = C_{us} \sin 2\phi_k + C_{uc} \cos 2\phi_k$	Argument of latitude correction
$\delta r_k = C_{rc} \cos 2\phi_k + C_{rs} \sin 2\phi_k$	Radius correction
$\delta i_k = C_{ic} \cos 2\phi_k + C_{is} \sin 2\phi_k$	Correction to inclination
$u_k = \phi_k + \delta u_k$	Corrected argument of latitude
$r_k = A(1 - e \cos E_k) + \delta r_k$	Corrected radius
$i_k = i_o + \delta i_k$	Corrected inclination
$x_k' = r_k \cos u_k$ $y_k' = r_k \sin u$	Positions in orbital plane
$\Omega_k = \Omega_o + (\dot{\Omega} - \dot{\Omega}_e)t_k - \dot{\Omega}_e t_{oe}$	Corrected longitude of ascending node
$x_k = x_k' \cos \Omega_k - y_k' \cos i_k \sin \Omega_k$ $y_k = x_k' \sin \Omega_k + y_k' \cos i_k \cos \Omega_k$ $z_k = y_k' \sin i_k$	} Earth fixed coordinates

(2nd harmonic perturbations, bracketing the δu_k, δr_k, δi_k equations)

---

* t is GPS system time at time of transmission, i.e., GPS time of reception corrected for transit time (range/speed of light). Furthermore, t_k must be the actual total time difference between the time t and the epoch time t_{oe}, and must account for beginning or end of week crossovers. That is, if t_k is greater than 302,400, subtract 604,800 from t_k. If t_k is less than $-302,400$ add 604,800 to t_k.

The equations given in Table 6 provide the Space Vehicle's antenna phase center in earth-centered earth-fixed Cartesian coordinates. The system is characterized as follows:

1) x is in the true equatorial plane in the direction of the Greenwich meridian
2) z is along the true earth spin axis, positive in the northern hemisphere
3) y completes the right hand system

$$y = (z) \times (x) \qquad (30)$$

It must be emphasized that these representation parameters are the result of a curve fit and are only Keplerian in appearance. They only describe the ephemeris over the period of applicability and not for the total orbit, however, they do describe the true Keplerian orbit to within a few thousand meters.

There are usually only six Keplerian parameters if the reference time is the time-of-perigee. However, in this case seven are needed (M_o, t_{oe}, e, $\sqrt{A}$, Ω_o, i_o, ω), replacing the time-of-perigee with the pair (M_o, t_{oe}). The net effect of this replacement requires no increase in the number of words. This results because of the decrease in sensitivity of the time derivative parameters since t_{oe} is always within a few minutes of the evaluation time. It also improved the stability of the curve fit algorithm for near circular orbits.*

The additional parameters in Table 5 do not adequately describe an ephemeris with its many perturbations over long periods. They do, however, describe it to the required accuracy over

---

* Incidentally, a least squares curve fit algorithm would be ill-conditioned for a perfectly circular orbit with no perturbations because M_o is redundant with ω. However, there is no such thing as a perfectly circular orbit other than instantaneously. The algorithm converged for values of e as small as 10^{-8}, although it converged to negative values of e depending on the initial selection of M_o and ω. This condition was easily corrected by adding (or subtracting) π to both M_o and ω and then converting to a positive e. Eccentricities of less than 10^{-8} could not be generated over the appropriate time intervals. If e were zero, either M_o or ω could be fixed, while letting the other vary in the fit.

intervals of 1.5 to 5 or more hours. They primarily describe the second zonal harmonic effects while absorbing all other effects during those intervals of time. Table 7 lists the major contributions that justify each of the additional parameters.

These additional parameters add very little to the user's computation requirement because they either add to total angles before sines or cosines are computed; or, if they represent angle perturbations, it suffices to use small angle approximations.

The figure of merit used to measure the quality of the curve fit is User Equivalent Range Error (UERE). UERE is the projection of the curve fit error onto the user's range. The curve fit results in a UERE of less than .01 meter, one sigma. This is, of course, considerably less than

Table 7—Contributions Justifying Parameters in Addition to Keplerian Parameters

Parameter	Justification[K]
Δn	For near circular orbits, there is very little difference between Δn and $d\omega/dt$ over the time intervals of interest. Absorbing the effects of either in Δn rather than in $d\omega/dt$, simplifies the User's algorithms by reducing sine and cosine computations. Primarily secular drift in $d\omega/dt$ due to the second zonal harmonic. Also absorbs effects of sun and moon gravity and solar radiation pressure over the interval of fit.
$\dot{\Omega}$	Primarily secular drift in right ascension due to the second zonal harmonic, but also includes effect of earth wobble and polar wander.
$C_{uc}, C_{us}, C_{rs},$ $C_{rc},$ $C_{ic},$ C_{is}	Second zonal harmonic. The theoretical solutions to Lagrange's equations for the 2ϕ perturbations do not always indicate the necessity of both the cosine and sine terms. However, experimentally they were quite helpful as they account for non-zero phase angles introduced due to perturbations attributed to other than second zonal harmonics. The parameters also absorbed short-term effects of the moon's gravity during the closest approach of the Space Vehicle to the moon.

the ephemeris prediction error, which is specified to be less than 12 feet in UERE (3.658 meters) one sigma, for the Phase I GPS or 5 feet in UERE (1.524 meters) one sigma for the Phase III GPS.

The UERE described above is for the results of an algorithm where the parameters are double precision floating point numbers (32 bit machine) and only represent the curve fit algorithm errors. The parameters are, of course, truncated for the GPS Navigation Message. The effect of that truncation increases the one sigma error to 0.1 meters over the time period of the fit. As stated earlier, it is desirable that the representation also degrades gracefully after its period of applicability. The parameters described in the preceeding paragraphs exhibit a reasonable degradation if used beyond their period of applicability. In fact, it is exceptional relative to other candidate representations. The relationship between the curve fit error, the truncation error and the degradation error is presented in Fig. 2.

Data Block 2 Format

Data Block 2 occupies the third through the tenth thirty bit words (including parity) of the second and third subframes. The number of bits, the scale factor of the least significant bit (LSB), which is the last bit received, the range and the units of the parameters are as specified in Table 8. The last word of subframe 2 is a six bit spare word and the last word of subframe 3 is a 14 bit spare word. They are both part of the tenth thirty bit word of a subframe that has two

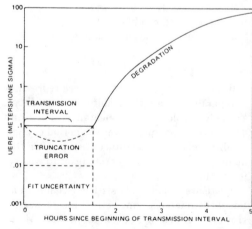

Fig. 2—Expected Ephemeris Representation Errors.

non-information bearing bits. Thus, it does not link with the TLM word of the next subframe through the parity algorithm.

The scale factors of the LSBs were determined through a sensitivity analysis. This analysis computed the sensitivity of the User's range to the Space Vehicle due to truncation of the ephemeris parameters. Defining the truncation as a vector

$$e_T = x^* - x_T \qquad (31)$$

where x^* and x_T are vectors of ephemeris parameters without and with truncation respectively. At a given time, the User's range R to the Space Vehicle can be expanded in a Taylor's series as

$$R = R^* + \left.\frac{\partial R}{\partial x}\right|_{x^*} e_T + O[e_T^2] \qquad (32)$$

or

$$\Delta R = R - R^* \approx \left.\frac{\partial R}{\partial x}\right|_{x^*} e_T \qquad (33)$$

It was required that the range error due to truncation be less than 0.3 meters. That is

$$\left.\frac{\partial R}{\partial x}\right|_{x^*} e_T < 0.3 \text{ meters} \qquad (34)$$

It was assumed that the contribution to range error is uniform over the fourteen components (e_{T_j}) of e_T. The jth contribution of inequality 34 is then

$$\left.\frac{\partial R}{\partial x_j}\right|_{x^*} e_{T_j} < \frac{0.3}{14} \text{ meters} \qquad (35)$$

or

$$e_{T_j} < \frac{.0214 \text{ meters}}{\left.\dfrac{\partial R}{\partial x_j}\right|_{x^*}} \qquad (36)$$

This inequality was used to determine the most significant bit of e_{T_j}. The LSB scale factors of the components of x_T were chosen to be one bit larger. Fractions of bits were dropped. Testing of the algorithm with truncated parameters proved the LSB scale factors to be satisfactory. (See Fig. 2)

VI. DATA BLOCK 3–THE ALMANAC

Data Block 3 appears in the fifth subframe, appearing every 30 seconds. However, it does not repeat itself every 30 seconds as the other two data blocks do. There are twenty-five subframes of data in Data Block 3, appearing in sequence in the fifth subframe; one every 30 seconds. Thus, each of these twenty-five subframes repeats every 750 seconds.

Table 8—Data Block 2 Parameters

Parameter	No. of Bits	Scale Factor (LSB)	Range*	Units
$AODE$	8	$2^{11} = 2048$	524,288	seconds
C_{rs}	16	$2^{-5} = .03125$	± 1024	meters
Δn	16	$2^{-43} \approx 1.14 \times 10^{-13}$	$\pm 3.73 \times 10^{-9}$	semicircles/sec
M_o	32	$2^{-31} \approx 4.66 \times 10^{-10}$	$\pm 1.$	semicircles
C_{uc}	16	$2^{-29} \approx 1.86 \times 10^{-9}$	$\pm 6.10 \times 10^{-5}$	radians
e	32	$2^{-33} \approx 1.16 \times 10^{-10}$	$.5$	dimensionless
C_{us}	16	$2^{-29} \approx 1.86 \times 10^{-9}$	$\pm 6.10 \times 10^{-5}$	radians
$\sqrt{A}$	32	$2^{-19} \approx 1.91 \times 10^{-6}$	8192	meters$^{1/2}$
t_{oe}	16	$2^4 = 16$	604,784	seconds
Spare	6	—	—	—
C_{ic}	16	$2^{-29} \approx 1.86 \times 10^{-9}$	$\pm 6.10 \times 10^{-5}$	radians
Ω_o	32	$2^{-31} \approx 4.66 \times 10^{-10}$	$\pm 1.$	semicircles
C_{is}	16	$2^{-29} \approx 1.86 \times 10^{-9}$	$\pm 6.10 \times 10^{-5}$	radians
i_o	32	$2^{-31} \approx 4.66 \times 10^{-10}$	$\pm 1.$	semicircles
C_{rc}	16	$2^{-5} = .03125$	± 1024	meters
ω	32	$2^{-31} \approx 4.66 \times 10^{-10}$	$\pm 1.$	semicircles
$\dot{\Omega}$	24	$2^{-43} \approx 1.14 \times 10^{-13}$	$\pm 9.54 \times 10^{-7}$	semicircles/sec
$AODE$	8	$2^{11} = 2048$	524,288	seconds
Spare	14	—	—	

* ($\pm$) indicates that the sign bit shall occupy the most significant bit (MSB).
NOTE: All binary numbers will be two's complement.

Data Block 3 is generated by the Control Segment and contains almanacs for up to twenty-four Space Vehicles. The twenty-fifth subframe is a dummy almanac with a Space Vehicle Identification (ID) set to zero. This subframe is present because of a User requirement to have an odd number of almanac subframes to aid in their Data Block 3 data collection. Prior to the availability of twenty-four Space Vehicles, certain Space Vehicle Almanacs will be repeated.

The Space Vehicle Almanacs contain ephemeris representation parameters, clock correction parameters, Space Vehicle ID and Space Vehicle health. The purpose of the almanacs is to provide the Users with less precise Space Vehicle position and clock correction information (relative to Data Blocks 1 and 2 precision) and vehicle health to aid in their *direct* acquisition of the Space Vehicles' signals. Both the ephemeris representation and clock correction representation in the almanacs are truncated versions of the respective representations in Data Blocks 1 and 2.

Almanac Representation Models

The representation model for the Space Vehicles' clock corrections in the almanacs is identical to that given in equation 9 with a_2 assumed to be zero. That is,

$$\Delta t_{SV} = a_0 + a_1(t - t_{oa}) \qquad (37)$$

where t_{oa} is the Data Block 3 reference time in seconds. a_1 is the same as given in equation 9 except that it is truncated because less accuracy is required. a_0 can easily be found by integrating equation 9 to the almanac reference time t_{oa}. That is, neglecting a_2,

$$a_0 \Big|_{\text{Data Block 3}} = a_0 \Big|_{\text{Data Block 1}} \\ + a_1 \Big|_{\text{Data Block 1}} (t_{oa} - t_{oc}) \qquad (38)$$

The representation model for the Space Vehicles' ephemerides in the almanacs is identical to that given in Tables 5 and 6 with certain parameters assumed to be zero. The parameters not assumed zero are the basic seven Keplerian parameters (M_o, t_{oa}, e, $\sqrt{A}$, Ω_o, $i_o + \delta i$, ω) and

one perturbation parameter, the rate of change of the right ascension $\dot{\Omega}$. For the almanac, a nominal inclination angle i_o of 60 degrees is defined, and a perturbation δi is used for the sake of saving data bits.

The almanac reference time, t_{oa}, is the multiple of 4096 seconds just prior to 3.5 days after the time that the almanac begins transmission. The almanac will be renewed every six days at a minimum rate. Therefore, the reference time is not ambiguous even though GPS time never spans more than one week. GPS time t will never differ from t_{oa} by more than 3.5 days. The time from epoch t_k of Table 6 should be computed as described in that table, except that t_{oc} is replaced with t_{oa}. However, if the User wishes to extend the use time of the almanac beyond the time span during which it is being transmitted, he must account for crossovers into time spans where these computations of t_k are not valid.

This may be accomplished by computing t_k at the GPS time t_c that the almanac was collected, and storing it as t_{kc}. That is,

$$t_{kc} = t_c - t_{oa} \qquad (39)$$

corrected for end of week crossover. The time of year t_{cy} corresponding to t_c should also be computed and stored as

$$t_{cy} = (D_{tc} - 1) \times 86,400 + t_c \bmod 86,400 \qquad (40)$$

where D_{tc} is the day of year at the Greenwich Meridian at time t_c. If the GPS time of its use is t_u, the time of year t_{uy} corresponding to t_u is then

$$t_{uy} = (D_{tu} - 1) \times 86,400 + t_u \bmod 86,400 \qquad (41)$$

where D_{tu} is the day of year at the Greenwich Meridian at time t_u, corrected for crossovers into new years since the time of collection (i.e., add 365 or 366 for each crossover). The time from epoch t_k at that time is simply

$$t_k = t_{uy} - t_{cy} + t_{kc} \qquad (42)$$

which is valid even during the time span during which the almanac is being transmitted. For almanacs that are not collected, but are furnished from an external source, it suffices to define the time of collection t_c as the recording time and the day of year as the recording day of year. This time and day of year will accompany the almanac and will always be within 3.5 days of the reference time t_{oa}.

Almanac Representation Accuracy

For *direct* P code acquisition in a specified period of time, the desired combined accuracy for the almanacs, including both the ephemeris and the clock corrections, is about 3000 to 6000 meters for up to one week of applicability. However, for *direct* P code acquisitions in larger periods of time, or for normal C/A code acquisitions, almanacs that are more than one week old, and thus with degraded accuracy, may be used.

The accuracy of this ephemeris representation, including truncation errors, is given in Table 9 for up to five weeks of application. The accuracy of the clock correction parameters is primarily affected by the truncation of the parameters, which may be computed for all time as

$$\text{UERE}_c = \frac{c}{\sqrt{3}} \sqrt{2^{-34} + 2^{-70} t_k^2} \text{ meters} \quad (43)$$

one sigma, where c is the speed of light in meters per second and t_k is as given in equation 42.

Therefore, for one week of applicability, the combined accuracy is about 3200 meters one sigma, and at 5 weeks the combined accuracy is about 24,300 meters one sigma. This is about 828 P code chips or 82.8 C/A code chips, and may be as accurate as, or more accurate than, the User's knowledge of his own position and time, and thus, an excellent aid for faster acquisition.

Data Block 3 Format

Data Block 3 occupies the third through the tenth thirty bit words of the fifth subframes. The number of bits, the scale factor of the least significant bit (LSB), which is the last bit received, the range and the units of the parameters are as specified in Table 10. The last word of the subframe is a six bit spare word and is part of the tenth thirty bit word that has two non-information bearing bits. Thus, it does not link with the TLM word of the next subframe through the parity algorithm.

The scale factors of the LSBs were determined through a sensitivity analysis similar to that described for the Data Block 2 parameters. Equation 34 was changed to reflect the increased tolerance and to reflect only seven parameters.

The reference time t_{oa} has an LSB worth 4096 seconds. This has no impact on accuracy since it is a defined parameter. Its range is the largest multiple of 4096 seconds less than 604,800 seconds.

Table 9—Almanac Ephemeris Representation Performance

Time Past Initial Transmission	Estimated UERE (Meters)
1 day	1,000
1 week	2,500
2 weeks	5,000
3 weeks	10,000
4 weeks	15,000
5 weeks	20,000

Table 10—Data Block 3 Parameters

Parameter	No. of Bits	Scale Factor (LSB)	Range*	Units
ID	8	1	255	discretes
e	16	$2^{-21} \approx 4.77 \times 10^{-7}$	0.03125	dimensionless
t_{oa}	8	$2^{12} = 4096$	602,112	seconds
δi	16	$2^{-19} \approx 1.91 \times 10^{-6}$	± 0.0625	semicircles
Health	8	1	255	discretes
$\dot{\Omega}$	16	$2^{-38} \approx 3.64 \times 10^{-12}$	$\pm 1.19 \times 10^{-7}$	semicircles/sec
$\sqrt{A}$	24	$2^{-11} \approx 4.88 \times 10^{-4}$	8192	meters$^{1/2}$
Ω_o	24	$2^{-23} \approx 1.19 \times 10^{-7}$	±1.	semicircles
ω	24	$2^{-23} \approx 1.19 \times 10^{-7}$	±1.	semicircles
M_o	24	$2^{-23} \approx 1.19 \times 10^{-7}$	±1.	semicircles
a_o	8	$2^{-17} \approx 7.63 \times 10^{-6}$	$\pm 9.77 \times 10^{-4}$	seconds
a_1	8	$2^{-35} \approx 2.91 \times 10^{-11}$	$\pm 3.73 \times 10^{-9}$	sec/sec
SPARE	6	—	—	—

* (±) indicates that the sign bit will occupy the most significant bit (MSB).

$i_o = 0.333333333$ *semicircles*

NOTE: All binary numbers will be two's complement.

Space Vehicle Health

The health word in the almanacs provides the Users with a priori information about the applicable Space Vehicle before they attempt to acquire it. The health words are generated by the Control Segment based on its assessment of the vehicle's health. The contents of this word are partly of a preliminary nature and will not be described in this paper. They are described in detail in Ref. 2.

Space Vehicle Identification (ID)

The Space Vehicle ID word specifies the PRN code assignment of the Space Vehicle. There are only 32 such codes assigned to Space Vehicles (1 through 32). The 0th Space Vehicle is a dummy Space Vehicle whose almanac occupies the 25th subframe of the almanacs. With this ID, there are 33 possible IDs requiring six bits of the eight bit word. The other two bits will be used specifying numbers between 0 and 3. These bits will indicate modifications to the standard Navigation Data structure that might occur in the future. At present there are no modifications and zero will be used.

VII. THE MESSAGE BLOCK

The Message Block occupies the third through tenth thirty bit words (including parity) of the fourth subframe. This block provides space for the transmission of twenty-three eight bit ANSC II characters. The remaining eight bits will be non-information bearing.

This Message Block will be generated by the Control Segment. The purpose of the message is to convey alphanumeric information to the Users. It was included in the GPS Navigation Message for future operational applications.

VIII. THE GPS NAVIGATION MESSAGE FRAME FORMAT

The preceeding discussions describe five subframes of signal data that make up the GPS Navigation Message, which is called the data frame (1500 bits). The format of the frame was described in part throughout these discussions as the formats for the TLM and HOW words, Data Blocks 1, 2, and 3 and the Message Block. The GPS Navigation Message Frame Format brings these parts together, which is summarized in Fig. 3.

This frame repeats itself every 30 seconds, except that Data Block 3 rotates through 25 subframes of data. Periodically (nominally every hour), the data in Data Blocks 1 and 2 are refreshed with data that applies to the new period. Data Block 3 is refreshed by Space Vehicle upload only.

The subframes will always be synchronized to GPS time (within one millisecond). That is, the subframe being transmitted can always be determined from the expression

$$\text{Subframe No.} = \left[\frac{t}{6} \text{ modulo } 5\right] + 1 \quad (44)$$

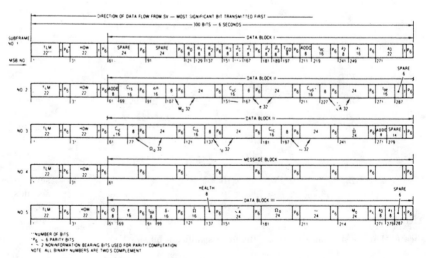

Fig. 3—The GPS Navigation Message Format.

where [a] indicates greatest integer less than a. Furthermore, the word and bit being transmitted within a subframe can be determined from the expressions

$$\text{Word No.} = \left[\frac{t}{0.6} \text{ modulo } 10 \right] + 1 \quad (45)$$

$$\text{Bit No.} = \left[\frac{t}{0.02} \text{ modulo } 300 \right] + 1 \quad (46)$$

IX. FUTURE CONSIDERATIONS

The design, contents and format of the GPS Navigation Message were presented. During the design process, great emphasis was placed on legacy requirements to insure that the design would extend to the operational GPS. Therefore, there is little left for future considerations. There are, however, some parts of the message where changes can be expected in the future. These are as follows:

1) Ionospheric delay correction model
2) Some contents of the TLM and HOW words
3) The health word
4) The non-information bearing bits

Since there are a limited number of Users during Phase I, changes of these parts have essentially no impact if they would occur during Phase I. For instance, the ionospheric delay correction model is only a candidate model being evaluated mostly by the Control Segment. Most Phase I Users who aren't receiving two frequencies will be ignoring the model.

Some contents of the TLM and HOW words are of no interest to the User and are quite Space Vehicle design dependent. They are primarily used by the Control Segment. Also, since the non-information bearing bits may become information bearing bits, additional information can be conveyed via the HOW and TLM. The preamble or system time information should never change.

The health word will be mostly ignored by Users during the early Phase I tests since they will be under complete control of individuals knowing the exact health of the Space Vehicles. It is expected that the contents of this word will evolve during Phase I testing.

The non-information bearing bits may become information bearing bits since future Space Vehicles may generate all of the parity. For now this only impacts the TLM and HOW, the a_0 term in Data Block 1, and the last byte in the Message Block. The reinstatement of these bits will make a_0 more accurate and will allow the Message Block to have another character.

Although it is hoped that all other data will not change, it will not be impossible to change certain parameters during Phase I. All uses of these parameters are programmed in software or firmware. Thus, if changes do occur, only load tapes or the like would have to be changed. Of course, the TLM and HOW words cannot be changed once a Space Vehicle is launched.

X. REFERENCES

1. System Specification for the NAVSTAR Global Positioning System, Phase I, SS-GPS-101B, 15 Apr 74.
2. Space Vehicle Nav System and NTS PRN Navigation Assembly/User System Segment and Monitor Station, Interface Control Document MH08-00002-400, Revision F, 25 July 1977.
3. Van Dierendonck, A. J. and Birnbaum, M., "Time Requirements in the NAVSTAR Global Positioning System (GPS)," Proceedings of the 30th Annual Frequency Control Symposium, June 1976.
4. System/Design Trade Study Report for Global Positioning System Control/User Segment, Trade Study No. 9, General Dynamics Electronics Division Report R74-034, June 1974.
5. Vessot, R. F. C., "The Relativistic Effects on Clocks and Frequency Standards," Lecture Notes for NBS Seminar on Time and Frequency: Standards, Measurements, Usage, Boulder, Colorado, 22-26 August 1977.
6. Kopitzke, E., "NAVSTAR Global Positioning System Satellite Navigation Ephemeris Algorithm," Magnavox Research Laboratories Report R-5226, 19 Dec 75.
7. Memory and Duty Cycle Requirements for Various GPS User Ephemeris Algorithms, Magnavox Interoffice Communication GPS#76-228, E. Kopitzke to G. Eckley, 29 March 1976.
8. Roy, A. E., The Foundations of Astrodynamics, The Macmillan Co., New York, 1967.

Control Segment and User Performance

S. S. RUSSELL and J. H. SCHAIBLY

ABSTRACT

THE CONCEPT VALIDATION PHASE (Phase I) of the Navstar GPS program will evaluate the performance of User receiving equipment and the Control Segment. The purpose of this paper is to describe how the Control Segment supports the User test program, and how Control Segment prediction errors in satellite ephemerides and atomic frequency standard behavior are propagated into User error. A summary of projected performance is also presented based on simulation results.

GPS PHASE I OVERVIEW

Phase I of the GPS navigation satellite effort will evaluate the performance of User receiving equiment on predetermined test ranges. To support this testing, six Space Vehicles (SVs) will be launched to provide a pilot space configuration. The satellite orbits and spatial locations are such that a maximum test period is provided over Yuma Proving Ground (YPG), which is the primary test area for GPS evaluation.

Phase I GPS is composed of the Space System Segment, the Control Segment, and the User Segment. A representation of the system is shown in Fig. 1. The satellites provide highly stable, timebased spread-spectrum signals and navigation data to the User. The ground Control Segment (CS) tracks the satellites to determine their ephemerides and atomic frequency standard (clock) errors. The CS then predicts the ephemeris and atomic clock model parameters for each satellite. These predictions are reformatted into User navigation data and uploaded into the navigation processor of the satellite.

Messrs. Russell and Schaibly are with General Dynamics/Electronics Division, Mail Zone 7-05, P. O. Box 81127, San Diego, CA 92138.

The User navigation data is then transmitted by the satellite to the User. The User equipment demodulates this data from the spread spectrum signal and utilizes it in the computation of User position. The primary function of the Control Segment is to generate precise navigation data for the User. Additional information regarding the Control Segment system software architecture may be found in Reference 1.

USER DATA REQUIREMENTS FOR NAVIGATION SOLUTION

A nominal three–dimensional navigation fix by a GPS User requires measurements from four GPS satellites. Four satellites are required because precise GPS time is assumed to be unknown to the User. The measurements obtained by the User are referred to as pseudoranges. Pseudoranges represent the true slant ranges (between User and satellite) plus propagation delays and time biases. The pseudorange to the ith satellite is:

$$PR_i = R_i + c\Delta t_{A_i} + c(\Delta t_u - \tau_{st_i}), i = 1,\ldots 4 \quad (1)$$

where R_i is the true slant range, c is the speed of light, Δt_{A_i} is signal propagation delay due to atmospheric effects, Δt_u represents the time offset between the User and GPS time, and τ_{st_i} is the satellite atomic clock time offset from GPS time.

As stated previously, the User must solve for four unknowns. They are earth–fixed, earth–centered coordinates X, Y, and Z, and time offset Δt_u. Equation (1) can be written in terms of these unknowns as:

$$PR_i = \sqrt{(X_{s_i} - X)^2 + (Y_{s_i} - Y)^2 + (Z_{s_i} - Z)^2}$$
$$+ c\Delta t_{A_i} + c(\Delta t_u - \tau_{st_i}), i = 1, \ldots 4 \quad (2)$$

Therefore, the Control Segment must provide a

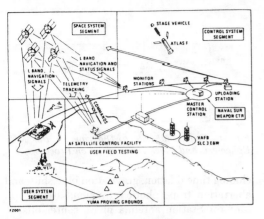

Fig. 1—GPS Phase I Overview.

minimum of X_{s_i}, Y_{s_i}, Z_{s_i}, and τ_{st_i} to the User. In addition, the Control Segment also provides data to permit the User to estimate ionospheric delay, receive special messages, and determine all satellite orbits. Ionospheric delay data permits the User to estimate propagation delay if he is not capable of making two–frequency corrections. The purpose of special messages is self-evident. The availability of the almanac of all satellite orbits enables the User to determine satellites in view, aid in satellite selection, and simplify signal acquisition. Because of the importance of satellite position and time offset, this paper will consider the Control Segment role in providing these variables.

CONTROL SEGMENT

The Control Segment consists of four Monitor Stations (MS), an Upload Station (ULS), and a Master Control Station (MCS). The Monitor Stations are located at Hawaii; Elmendorf AFB, Alaska; Guam; and Vandenberg AFB, California. The remote Monitor Stations are unmanned data-collection centers under direct control of the MCS. Each MS contains a four–channel User-type receiver, environmental data sensors, an atomic frequency standard, and a computer processor. The receiver measures the pseudo-range and delta pseudorange (integrated doppler) of the satellite spread–spectrum signal with respect to the atomic standard. It also detects the navigation data on the spread–spectrum signal. The environmental sensors collect local meteorological data for later tropospheric signal delay corrections at the MCS. The computer

processor controls all data collection at the MS, and provides the data interface with the MCS. All data obtained by the MS is buffered at the MS and then relayed upon request to the MCS for processing.

The ULS, located at Vandenberg AFB, provides the interface between the Control Segment and the satellites. Its function is to utilize an S–band command-and-control uplink to upload data into a satellite navigation processor. This upload data can be User navigation data, requests for processor diagnostics, or commands to change the satellite time provided to the User.

The MCS is also located at Vandenberg AFB, and completely controls the operation of the Control Segment. It performs the computations necessary to determine satellite ephemeris and atomic clock errors, generates satellite upload of User navigation data, and maintains a record of satellite navigation processor contents and status. The MCS also has interfaces with the Satellite Control Facility (SCF) and Naval Surface Weapons Center (NSWC). The SCF provides a backup upload capability in case of ULS failure and also provides satellite telemetry and command information. NSWC generates a predicted reference ephemeris from MCS-smooth pseudorange measurements for use by the MCS in the ephemeris estimation process. Fig. 2 shows the interfaces between the satellites, User equipment, and the Control Segment.

Ephemeris and Clock Computations

The ephemeris determination technique used by the Control Segment is a two–step process which makes use of an off–line least–squares batch fit using approximately one week of measurement data to produce a reference ephemeris,

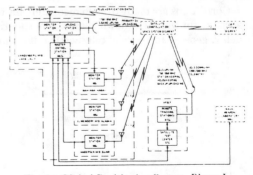

Fig. 2—Global Positioning System, Phase I.

and a first–order correction computed on–line by the Kalman estimator using additional measurement data. The reference ephemeris provides initial estimates of the satellite trajectory around which perturbations are computed by the estimator, and the time dependent state transition matrix (partial derivatives) also used in the estimator. The batch fit for the reference ephemeris is performed at the Naval Surface Weapons Center (NSWC/DL) at Dahlgren, Virginia, using the CELEST program and measurement data transmitted daily to them from the MCS at Vandenberg AFB. A reference ephemeris is subsequently sent weekly from NSWC to the MCS for the on–line processing of new measurements. A time line for the two-step ephemeris determination process is shown in Fig. 3 for one reference ephemeris span.

MCS Ephemeris Determination

The on–line Kalman Estimator processing is summarized functionally in Fig. 4, and is characterized by the following elements.

Ranging Measurements

Ranging measurements (nominally every 6 seconds) are sent from each MS to MCS for each satellite in view. The measurements include:

   a. L_1 pseudorange measurements
   b. $L_1 - L_2$ pseudorange difference measurements
   c. Delta pseudorange measurements on L_1 over the measurement reporting interval (integrated doppler measurement)

Satellite and MS health and status data as well as meteorological data are also received.

Corrector

Corrections are made to each measurement to account for various known biases: ionospheric delay; general and special relativistic effects in-

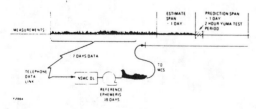

Fig. 3—Time Line for Ephemeris Determination.

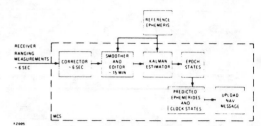

Fig. 4—Functional Block Diagram of the MCS Ephemeris and Clock Deterimination Processer.

cluding time dilation, gravitation blue shift, and aberration; tropospheric refraction; satellite and Monitor Station antenna phase center offsets, earth rotation, and time tag correction.

Smoother

The smoother processes the 6–second measurements contained within a 15 minute Kalman interval for each satellite–monitor station pair. It edits the measurements by discarding points lying outside (nominally) three times the standard deviation of the remaining points. The accepted pseudorange and delta pseudorange measurements are then fit by least squares to a polynomial from which smoothed range and delta range measurements are evaluated.

Kalman Estimator

The smoothed measurements are processed by the Kalman Estimator to produce estimates of the following states:

   a. satellite position ⎤ six orbital element
   b. satellite velocity ⎦ perturbations
   c. three solar pressure constants per satellite
   d. satellite clock bias, frequency offset, and drift rate
   e. clock bias and frequency offset for three Monitor Stations (by definition, one clock is perfect)
   f. tropospheric residual bias states for all Monitor Stations
   g. three polar wander residual states

For the Phase I system with six satellites and four Monitor Stations, 85 states are estimated.

The six orbital element states, ΔP_o, are perturbations from the reference ephemeris at some time, t_o, (Epoch). The ephemeris state transition matrix includes elements for the orbital element and solar pressure perturbation states,

$$\Phi\,(t,\,t_o) = \left(\frac{\partial \bar{R}(t)}{\partial P_o},\,\frac{\partial \bar{V}(t)}{\partial P_o}\right) \qquad (3)$$

which are integrated at NSWC and provided to the MCS as part of the reference ephemeris. The state transition matrix for the other states is generated at the MCS.

Predictor

The satellite clock states are propagated throughout the prediction span and a time polynomial representation is uploaded to the satellite. The satellite reference ephemeris is corrected by the estimated perturbation states by the equations

$$\bar{R}(t) = \bar{R}_{Ref} + \frac{\partial \bar{R}(t)}{\partial P_o}\,\Delta P_o \qquad (4)$$

$$\bar{V}(t) = \bar{V}_{Ref} + \frac{\partial \bar{V}(t)}{\partial P_o}\,\Delta P_o \qquad (5)$$

The polar wander residual states enter the predictions through the earth fixed components of $\bar{R}$ and $\bar{V}$.

Uploading Satellites for User Navigation

During the Phase I User testing, the satellites are uploaded at least once per day. Multiple uploads of User navigation data can also be performed to support special testing requirements. During the uploading of six satellites, the CS (and in particular the MCS) is operating at nearly full capability. In addition to collecting ranging data from Monitor Stations and performing Kalman estimates, the MCS must generate satellite uploads, provide them to the ULS for transmission, and verify the satellite upload process by collecting Telemetry (TLM) verification data from the Monitor Stations. This TLM verification data is contained in the User navigation data modulated onto the spread-spectrum signal by the satellite. The verification process is shown in Fig. 5.

The nominal satellite upload scenario consists of uploading the satellite just prior to entering the testing area at Yuma Proving Ground (YPG). Depending upon the accuracy of satellite clock data desired for testing, the new User navigation data can also be provided to the satellite during the test period. Because of the importance and time criticality of the uploading process to User testing, the priority of satellite

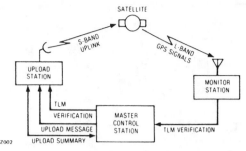

Fig. 5—GPS Satellite Upload Verification Process.

uploading in the Control Segment is much higher than any other activity. It also requires CS resources such as devoted MS receiver channels for verification and MCS computer assets for generating upload messages and verifying the satellite upload process. Therefore, during the upload period, normal range data collection may be delayed and total CS resources must be allocated accordingly.

There are two navigation message uploads used to support User testing. They are referred to as the 6–hour and 26–hour upload. The 6–hour upload consists of satellite ephemeris and clock error parameters for only 6 hours. The 26–hour upload contains sufficient data for 26 hours of satellite orbit and consists of satellite ephemeris, satellite clock, all satellite almanacs, and a special message. Either upload can contain satellite navigation processor diagnostic requests. The 6–hour upload will be used to initialize or refresh User navigation data for testing. The 26–hour upload supports once-a-day uploading and final uploading before loss of satellite visibility to the ULS.

The upload process is completely controlled by the MCS. As shown in Fig. 6, the MCS generates the upload message, maintains an image of the satellite navigation processor, monitors the uploading process, and verifies the satellite's transmission of the User navigation message. The upload generation is initiated and completely controlled by the satellite processor manager module. This module initiates the generation of predicted ephemeris and clock parameters for the upload. Almanac, special messages, and diagnostics are added, if required. The processor manager module then selects the portion of processor memory and formats processor control tables. These tables control the starting time and duration of individual data messages. The

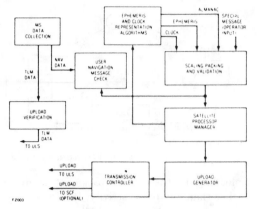

Fig. 6—MCS Upload Message Processing.

upload generator formats the upload message into a satellite-compatible data form. The transmission controller then sends the data to either the ULS or SCF for normal or backup uploading of the satellite, respectively.

The upload data is checked for transmission errors during the ULS upload process and upon transmission via satellite to the User. The upload verification is accomplished in the MCS by collecting TLM words from at least one MS receiver channel. These words are presented to the MCS operator and relayed to the ULS for the formal verification of the satellite uploading. The navigation message radiated by the satellite to the User is also systematically checked by the MCS every time it is changed by the satellite. This data is collected by the Monitor Stations either automatically or upon command from the MCS, and relayed to the MCS for verification when requested.

PREDICTED EPHEMERIS AND CLOCK ERRORS

The accuracy of the navigation and clock behavior predictions depends on error sources related to each function within the MCS processing chain (see Fig. 6).

Measurement Errors

Table 1 gives the predicted errors in the measurements as received from the Monitor Stations, the Corrector, and the Smoother.

The receiver measurement noise includes a component that is inversely proportional to the signal-to-noise ratio, and truncation error of the

signal processor used at the MS. The Corrector adds noise to the pseudorange measurements due to the ionospheric correction using the noisy L_1-L_2 measurement. The inaccuracies of the Corrector model are expected to result in approximately a .6 meter pseudorange bias error which is unchanged by the Smoother. The delta pseudorange measurements have very little noise from the receiver, and this is unchanged by the Corrector since no ionospheric correction is made. On the other hand, the ionospheric delay variation is expected to be .03 meters over each 6-second interval, which would result in a 4.5 meter error over the 15 minute Smoother interval. The Smoother, however, deweights the delta pseudorange measurements so that the effect of this bias is reduced to approximately .1 meter.

Estimation Error

Estimation error is defined as the error in the Kalman state estimates during the estimation span, i.e., when there are measurements. Estimation errors result in part from the measurement bias errors discussed above. At worst, they cause line-of-sight position errors as large as the measurement errors. Since the measurements are along the line-of-sight vectors to the Monitor Station, the time dependence of these errors will tend to appear in the satellite clock states. Additional estimation error arises from the transient nature of the problem. When satellites are out of view (as long as 8 hours), model error accumulates and an error transient occurs when measurements begin again. The degree to which this transient estimation error affects the prediction errors depends on the estimation time span available before prediction and upload.

Table 1—Receiver, Corrector, and Smoother Errors (Based on 6 second measurement interval and 15 minute Kalman Estimator interval)

Function	Pseudoranges L_1 and L_1-L_2		Delta Pseudoranges L_1	
	Noise (1σ)	Bias	Noise (1σ)	Bias
MS Receiver	.3m	0	.01m	0
Corrector	.6m	.6m	.01m	.03m
Smoother	.2m	.6m	.4m	.1m

Prediction Errors

Prediction errors consist of the propagation of the estimation error at the end of the estimation span throughout the prediction span (i.e., when there are no measurements), and the accumulation of additional modeling error during the prediction span. Estimation errors propagate into both time periodic and secular errors. Modeling errors include errors in the reference ephemeris force model and clock modeling errors. Another modeling error is due to nonlinearities which can occur if the reference ephemeris is outside of the linear range of the current ephemeris. The Kalman estimator provides a linearized estimation for the satellite ephemeris, where the quantity, if assumed to be small, may be interpreted as the deviation of the reference ephemeris from the actual satellite trajectory. If the reference ephemeris is far from reality, the ability to predict accurately is impaired even if there is no estimation error. To evaluate this nonlinearity error, the following prediction error can be evaluated

$$\epsilon_{pred} = |\bar{R}_{truth}(t_p) - \bar{R}_{ref}(t_p) - \Phi(t_p, t_0)\Delta P_0| \quad (6)$$

for reference ephemerides which depart from the truth by different amounts. Assuming that the estimation error is zero at the beginning of the prediction period, it is necessary only to evaluate

$$\epsilon_{pred} = |\bar{R}_{truth}(t_p) - \bar{R}_{ref}(t_p) - \Phi(t_p, t_e)\Delta P_e| \quad (7)$$

where ΔP_e are the (perfectly) estimated states at the end of estimation, t_e. This error was evaluated for the radial, in-track and cross-track directions for a family of reference ephemerides with perturbed initial conditions over the time span $t_p - t_e = 24$ hours. The reference position $\bar{R}_{ref}$ and $\Phi(t_p, t_e)$ were generated using the CELEST integrator program and compared to $\bar{R}_{truth}$ which was also generated by the same integrator (unperturbed). Reference ephemeris errors, ϵ_{ref}, at t_e which lead to nonlinearity errors, ϵ_{pred}, of 1 meter after a 24 hour prediction span are shown in Table 2.

These tolerances define the so-called Linear Range for the trajectories.

The reference ephemeris generated by NSWC is expected to have less than 80 meters cross-track and in-track error and less than 20 meters radial error over a two week span. There-fore, nonlinearity errors are expected to be smaller than .1 meter under normal conditions.

USER ERROR

The expected User error is related to error in the predicted satellite position, error in the predicted satellite clock drift, and error in the User's measurement of pseudorange. The expression for the User navigation–time error covariance matrix using four satellites is

$$E\{\delta\bar{U}\delta\bar{U}^T\} = G^{-1}E\{ZZ^T\}G^{-T} \quad (8)$$

where

$$\bar{U}^T = (u_1, u_2, u_3, T_u)$$
$u_i = i^{th}$ component of User position
$T_u =$ User time
$E\{ZZ^T\}ij =$ component of pseudorange error covariance matrix between ith and jth satellite (4 × 4)
$$= E\{(\delta p_i - l_i \cdot \delta\bar{r}_i + \delta\tau_{sc_i})(\delta p_j - l_j \cdot \delta\bar{r}_j + \delta\tau_{sc_j})\}$$

where

$\delta\bar{r}_i =$ position prediction error for i^{th} satellite
$\delta\tau_{sc_i} =$ clock offset prediction error for i^{th} satellite (meters)
$\delta p_i =$ User error in measuring pseudorange to i^{th} satellite
$l_i =$ line-of-sight unit vector from User to i^{th} satellite
$$= (l_{i1}, l_{i2}, l_{i3})$$
$$G = \begin{pmatrix} l_{11} & l_{12} & l_{13} & -1 \\ l_{21} & l_{22} & l_{23} & -1 \\ l_{31} & l_{32} & l_{33} & -1 \\ l_{41} & l_{42} & l_{43} & -1 \end{pmatrix}$$

If the User required his navigation solution in a frame of reference unrelated to the earth's actual pole position (non–PW frame), error in the predicted polar wander states need not be of concern. GPS Users, on the other hand, require their position in earth crust fixed coordinates, (PW frame) i.e., in a system with polar wander.

Table 2—Reference Ephemeris Error Tolerance, ϵ_{ref}, Leading to 1–Meter Prediction Errors, ϵ_{pred}, After 24 Hours

radial	175 meters
in track	1.5 km
cross track	1.5 km

Let the matrix A be defined as the 4×4 error matrix of the polar wander transformation matrix A augmented to be 4×4 to include identity User clock offset transformation. Then, if $\bar{U}$ in equation (8) is defined in a non–PW frame,

$$\delta \bar{U}_{PW} = A\delta \bar{U} + \delta A \bar{U} \qquad (9)$$

where $\delta \bar{U}_{PW}$ = User position–time error vector in PW frame.
Therefore,

$$E\{\delta \bar{U}_{PW}\delta \bar{U}_{PW}^T\} = AE\{\delta \bar{U}\delta \bar{U}^T\}A^T \qquad (10)$$

$$+ E\{\delta A \bar{U} \bar{U}^T \delta A^T\}^{\cdot}$$

The first term is the transformation of the error covariance to the PW frame.

Polar wander uncertainty then gives an additional error (the second term) which is dependent on User position. If polar wander were not estimated at all in the Kalman Estimator, this component of error could be as large as the polar wander change over the reference ephemeris time from epoch, 11 days, i.e., an error of approximately 2.3 meters.

Ignoring polar wander for the moment, it is assumed that, to a good approximation, range errors are uncorrelated between satellites. Thus, evaluation of the prediction errors for one satellite at a time is needed and the error depends on the position error, $E\{(\bar{l}\cdot\delta\bar{r})^2\}$, the clock error $E\{\delta\tau_{st}^2\}$, and the covariance, $E\{\delta\tau_{st}\bar{l}\cdot\delta\bar{r}\}$ of each satellite (satellite index has been suppressed). Our simulation experience, however, shows that the clock–position correlations are small after steady state is reached (after three or four passes).

SIMULATED CONTROL SEGMENT PERFORMANCE

Control Segment performance has been simulated for a one SV system (NTS–II) using simulated smoothed measurement data generated at the Aerospace Corporation and reference ephemerides generated at NSWC. Reference 2 reports on these tests. The Phase I MCS Kalman

Table 3—Summary of Predicted Ephemeris and Clock Errors

	2 Hours (During Yuma Test Period)	24 Hours
Ephemeris prediction error	.818m radial	1.69m radial
	6.31m along track	15.0m along track
	3.01m cross track	2.8m cross track
Clock prediction error	7.7 ns	41.0 ns
UERE$_R$ at Yuma	.74m	—
UERE total at Yuma	2.2m	—

filter and Predictor programs were used to produce daily predictions during a two–week span. The measurement errors included receiver noise, satellite ephemeris and cesium clock errors, tropospheric errors, geopotential errors, and solar pressure errors.

The entries presented in Table 3 were computed as the RMS of the daily prediction error over the two week simulation period. The clock and ephemeris errors are assumed to be uncorrelated.

Using a typical G in Equation (8) for the Yuma Test Site, an estimate of User's position error is approximately 11 meters.

If polar wander were not successfully modeled by the MCS, an additional error will appear in the earth crust fixed User horizontal position. The magnitude of this error can be as great as 2.3 meters, depending on the User's location.

REFERENCES

1. Thornburg, D. D., et al, "The GPS Control Segment and Its Service to the GPS User," Record of the IEEE 1976, Position Location and Navigation Symposium, San Diego, CA, 1–3 November 1976, pp. 196–202.
2. Schaibly, J. H., et al, "Simulated and Projected Performance of the NAVSTAR GPS Control Segment," Proceedings of the AIAA Guidance and Control Conference, San Diego, CA, 16–18 August 1976, pp. 1–9.

GPS Receiver Operation

B. G. GLAZER

ABSTRACT

DIFFERENT RECEIVER configurations are suitable for applications having differing levels of dynamics of the Host Vehicle and interference environments. All configurations must be capable of accomplishing certain fundamental operations: satellite selection, signal acquisition, tracking and measurement and data recovery. After correction for propagation effects, the signal time-of-arrival measurements are used to obtain the nagivation solution. Limits of performance of receivers are described.

I. ARCHITECTURE

A GPS User Equipment is comprised of four principal components: antenna, receiver, computer and input/output devices.

The antenna in most cases is a relatively simple element providing approximately isotropic gain from the zenith to the horizon at one or both of the GPS frequencies. Since the signals are circularly polarized, a conical spiral or variation thereof is suitable. Where high performance is required, particularly near sources of interference, a more elaborate antenna system such as a steered-beam phased array or null steering adaptive array may be used. Antenna placement on the Host Vehicle is important in two regards. There should be a clear view of the whole sky; shadowing of some of the satellites can result in degraded performance. A potentially significant error source is multipath, particularly of the stationary sort produced by reflections from surfaces near the antenna. In the

Mr. Glazer is Vice President and Director of Engineering and Research, Magnavox Government & Industrial Electronics Co., Advanced Products Division, Torrance, CA 90503.

extreme, measurement errors of tens of meters on the P signal and hundreds of meters on the C/A signal can arise from such reflections. Both of these considerations favor antenna placement at the highest point on the vehicle. In the majority of vehicles it is impractical to locate the receiver there, and so a preamplifier must be used to drive the signal to the receiver.

The primary decision in the selection of receiver architecture for each application is the number of signals to be processed simultaneously by the receiver. Each satellite transmits three signals (C/A and P on the L1 frequency and P on the L2 frequency) and in the fully deployed system there will be as many as eleven satellites in view at a time. While a thirty-three channel receiver capable of tracking and measuring all of these signals simultaneously might be useful for a monitor station, users can obtain nearly optimum performance with one to five channels. The minimum receiver provides only a single channel capable of recovering one C/A signal at a time. More elaborate receivers process five signals at once, where each may be chosen to be a C/A or a P signal on the L1 frequency or a P signal on the L2 frequency. The number of channels and elaborateness of the receiver structure is primarily dependent upon the maneuverability of the Host Vehicles and secondarily upon the accuracy and interference resistance required.

A computer is a necessary part of a GPS user equipment. In ground based radio navigation systems (LORAN, VORTAC, OMEGA) after making the signal measurements, the navigation computation may be completed manually using charts overprinted with lines of position corresponding to measured values of phase or time difference. This is not the case for satellite-based navigation systems; the charts would have to be reprinted every millisecond.

Of interest is the division of functions between the receiver and the computer. Such functions as carrier tracking loop filtering and data bit detection have been accomplished sometimes in the receiver, sometimes in the computer. It has been seriously suggested that the signal be sampled and quantized prior to correlation and that all subsequent processing be accomplished in a high speed computer. Computer functions always include control of the receiver, selection of satellites and signals to be utilized, correction of measurements for propagation effects, computation of position and velocity in the desired coordinate system and communication with other systems and the operator through the input/output devices.

Input/output devices are as widely varied as the applications of GPS. GPS sets can drive cockpit instruments or generate data link messages for position reporting by radio. The GPS set does require certain information to facilitate start-up: approximate satellite and Host Vehicle locations and time. Various methods of introducing this data such as keyboards, cassettes, radio links or data busses may be used. If antenna beam steering is to be accomplished, or the location of a point on the vehicle other than the GPS antenna is desired, then attitude information must be fed to the set. Although the GPS set produces elevation above a geodetic reference as an output under normal operating conditions, it is considered useful to provide barometric altitude as an input to assist in obtaining the first fix.

The "Z-Set", shown in Fig. 1, provides a current example of a nearly minimal GPS user receiver suitable for non-combat military aircraft. Unit manufacturing cost in small-scale production is about $15,000. This set utilizes only the C/A signals on the L1 frequency to provide position accuracies superior to all existing medium and long-range radio or inertial navigation systems.

The major modules of this set are indicated in Fig. 2. The antenna/preamplifier unit is best located either in a tail cap or on the top of the fuselage, just aft of the cockpit. The preamplifier incorporates pre-selection filters and about 30 dB of gain at the L1 frequency, 1575 MHz. The overall noise figure is about 4 dB. The receiver/processor unit may be located in any convenient place. The reference oscillator is a

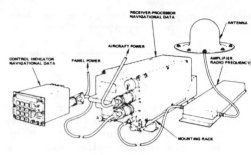

SET Z NAVIGATIONAL SET

Fig. 1—Z-Set.

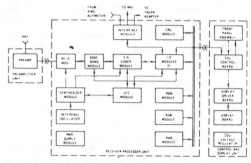

Fig. 2—Major Modules of Z-Set.

good quality crystal oscillator in an oven, with particular care to minimize sensitivity to vibration since phase noise and short-term drift can adversely affect performance. From this oscillator are synthesized the several local oscillator frequencies required by the receiver and the basic time pulses to be counted by the User Time Clock (UTC) module. This count is the time reference against which the signal arrival times are noted. In the RF-IF module, the signal is further filtered, amplified and translated down in frequency. In part, the translation is determined by a voltage controlled oscillator which is driven by tracking loops in the baseband module to offset the doppler shift. This VCO frequency, suitably scaled for the ratio of the C/A code rate to the L-band carrier frequency, also contributes to the synthesis of the clock which drives the C/A coder. This is done in such a way that if the receiver is phase or frequency locked to the L-band carrier, the C/A coder clock will be correct in frequency, requiring only a correct initial phasing to the incoming signal to remain aligned with it thereafter. The baseband module contains the detector circuits for carrier frequency, phase and C/A code error sensing as well as power detection circuitry for recognizing initial alignment and a data demodulator. Upon the occurrence of certain events in the C/A code generator, the UTC time count is strobed and transferred to the computer via an I/O module. The I/O modules contain various buffers, drivers and handshaking logic needed to process the digital signals into and out of the computer. The computer is comprised of four modules: a CPU and three memory modules. This CPU is designed around the LSI-11 central processor, but is augmented beyond that well known computer by the addition of microprogrammed instructions to facilitate high precision floating point computations. Through an interface module, this set can accept a digital altimeter reading, drive cockpit instruments or provide information to other navigation equipments.

II. STARTING OPERATIONS

The first operating function is the selection of the satellites to be used in the navigation solution. Fundamentally, the set is to determine the values of four unknowns: three position coordinates and time. Accordingly, four measurements will be needed, usually the time-of-arrival of signals from four different satellites. In some situations, as when altitude or time is very accurately known, fewer measurements will suffice.

The set must be provided with information regarding the location of each of the satellites as a function of time. For the purposes of selection and signal acquisition, this "almanac" need be accurate only to a few kilometers, and it is estimated that almanacs will be usable for a week or more, so that a set which is regularly used can retain the almanac in a nonvolatile memory from one usage to the next. Each satellite transmits the current almanac as part of the nagivation data message, allowing users to update their stored almanac. For a truly cold start in which the set does not contain a valid almanac, two approaches are possible. The almanac may be transferred from an active GPS receiver via data link, cassette or the manual keyboard. Alternatively, a "search-the-sky" approach may be used in which the set simply tries to acquire the C/A signal of each satellite in turn, without prior knowledge of satellite visi-

bility or doppler. Unless the receiver includes a matched filter for expediting the synchronization process, the search-the-sky process can take many minutes to complete.

When provided with a valid almanac, an approximate knowledge of its own position and time-of-day, the computer can execute a satellite selection algorithm. To minimize the sensitivity of the position solution to measurement errors, the satellites as viewed from the user should have the largest possible angular separations. After excluding those satellites which are or soon will be below the horizon, subsets of four can be tested for angular separation. Other criteria may also be introduced in the selection process such as satellite signal quality or avoidance of the use of low elevation satellites whose observation is most subject to propagation error sources. Subsequent to the selection of the initial subset of satellites, or "constellation", the selection should be reviewed every few minutes and revised when necessary to maintain minimum navigation error as the geometry of the constellation changes.

The next process is the acquisition of the signals from the selected satellites. The normal method of signal acquisition is to synchronize to the C/A signal and then, when necessary, transfer to the P. The computer must designate to the receiver not only the satellite to be acquired, but also an estimate of the expected doppler shift on the signal. This is useful because the doppler range of ± 5 KHz (for a slow moving user) is so large that the signal-to-noise ratio in the corresponding bandwidth is less than unity. Under this condition, it is more effective to subdivide the frequency uncertainty and search sequentially; thus an estimate of doppler can significantly reduce search time. The usual method is to correlate the incoming signal against a local replica consisting of the chosen C/A sequence modulated on the receiver local oscillator. The time phasing of the C/A sequence is varied slowly until the post-correlation power exhibits a rise above that which might be attributable to noise alone.

Having established synchronization of the pseudonoise sequences, tracking is begun in both code sequence timing and carrier phase. Once the tracking loops pull in, the data format features (bit edges, word starts, subframe starts and Z counts) may be recognized to provide unam-

biguous time–of–arrival and time–of–day indication. While the almanac is sufficiently accurate for acquisition, much more accurate information on satellite position and the offsets of its
clock is needed to achieve the desired navigation
accuracy. These data, called the ephemeris, are
contained in about twenty 24–bit words which
are part of the data format transmitted by each
satellite. Having recognized the format identi-
fiers, the ephemeris can be recovered. Although
the 6 parity checks accompanying each of the
24–bit words provide sufficient redundancy for
error correction, it is advisable to use the redundancy for error detection only.

III. MEASUREMENTS

The primary measurements made by a GPS
receiver are the times of arrival of the satellite
generated signals. Arrival time is measured with
respect to the receiver clock which is a stable
oscillator and counter. The time and frequency
offsets of this clock from GPS system time and
true frequency are not critical, since these will
be determined from the navigation solution. Of
considerable importance is the stability of the
oscillator, particularly in receivers which observe the signals sequentially.

Signal–to–noise considerations preclude direct
measurement of the arrival time of a particular
PN code element edge. A replica PN sequence
generator is caused to run in phase with the
modulation of the incoming signal by a tracking
loop. Simultaneously or alternately, the powers
recovered by correlation of the incoming signal
against slightly advanced and delayed versions
of the local replica are compared to provide the
tracking error indication. The arrival time may
then be observed by comparing the replica code
timing with the receiver clock timing. Either the
clock time can be observed upon the occurrence
of certain events of the replica (such as the first
PN edge of a data word) or the phase of the
replica relative to a hypothetical replica driven
by the receiver clock can be observed at certain
events of the receiver clock, such as 1 second
ticks. While substantially equivalent, there are
significant hardware and computational differences between the two schemes. The first technique appears to be slightly more economical for
single channel receivers, the second technique is
preferrable for multi–channel or aided receivers.

These measurements, loosely called pseudo-
ranges, are next adjusted for propagation effects.
The delay in traversing the ionosphere is best
estimated by observing the difference in arrival
time of the P signals on the L1 and L2 frequencies. Since along a given path through the ionosphere at a given time, the group delay varies
inversely as the square of the carrier frequency,
the two frequency observations suffice to determine the proportionality factor. The delay
changes rather slowly, at most about a nanosecond per minute, so that only occasional dual
frequency observations are required. Because
two measurements are needed to compute the
delay correction and the two frequencies are
close, there is a magnification of measurement
noise in obtaining the correction, and so some
filtering of this measurement is desirable. Tropospheric delay also requires correction. The use
of a simple altitude and elevation angle dependent model is sufficient to reduce the error to
negligible levels. While there are some techniques for avoidance of multipath effects and for
recognition that a reflected signal rather than
the direct signal is being tracked, in those cases
when the multipath signal is within 1 or 1–½ PN
chips of the direct signal there is no practical
way to correct the resulting erroneous measurement.

In some sets incremental as well as whole
values of pseudorange are measured. When signal–to–noise ratios permit phase locked tracking
of the received carriers, it is possible to count
beats of the difference frequency between each
received carrier and a hypothetical carrier synthesized from the receiver's frequency standard.
While this sort of observation is sometimes
called a doppler measurement, it is really a
differential pseudorange measurement in which
the change in pseudorange from the start to the
end of the counting interval is observeable with
accuracy and resolution of a fraction of a carrier
wavelength. These measurements are useful
when a fast velocity measurement is wanted.

IV. POSITION COMPUTATION

Each raw pseudonoise measurement is first
compensated for propagation delay and then for
the satellite clock offset. Tropospheric delay
may be estimated from the simple refraction
model using standard atmosphere values. Iono-

sphere delay is most accurately based upon dual frequency measurements. At the present state of knowledge, simple models of the ionosphere do not yield very accurate results: ten or twenty meters error under very bad conditions. There is some hope that improved knowledge, obtained in the next few years from GPS itself, will give rise to an improved ionospheric prediction technique. The satellite clock error (against system or universal time) is modeled by the Control Segment and the coefficients for a correction computation become part of the transmission from the satellite to the user. When the raw pseudorange has been thus compensated, the result is the sum of the user clock offset and the propagation time in vacuum of the signal over the distance from satellite to user.

The position of the satellite is computed from the ephemeris parameters received from the satellite. The parameters appear to describe a Keplerian ellipse with some correction terms for oblateness of the earth and rotation of the orbit plane. To have a complete analytical expression for a whole orbit to the desired accuracy (better than 1 meter) would take far more parameters and impose a huge computational load on the users. The transmitted parmameters, precomputed by the Control Segment, are actually a best fit of the corrected ellipse to the true orbit which meets the desired accuracy over one hour. When a satellite is first acquired, this data is collected. In the event that the satellite remains in the constellation for more than sixty or ninety minutes, a new ephemeris should be collected. At each time of pseudorange measurement, the corresponding position of the satellite is computed by inserting the value of time in the equations of the corrected ellipse and converting to a more convenient coordinate system. For most purposes, we prefer a Cartesian earth centered, earth fixed coordinate frame for performing the basic position solution.

At this point, in the simplest case, we have four unknowns (three coordinates of user position and user clock time offset) and four equations each involving the measured, compensated pseudorange (the scalar distance of user to the satellite plus the clock bias) all units adjusted to meters. The equations are non–linear, but capable of solution by any of a number of techniques suitable for computer execution.

Usually, and always to some advantage, a more sophisticated viewpoint is taken which allows for utilization of additional (or fewer) inputs and thereby improving the solution in terms of accuracy or reliability under unfavorable conditions. Even in the absence of external inputs there is a benefit to be obtained if the GPS user clock is stable. If after a few of the four equation solutions, it becomes possible to predict what the time offset of the user clock will be, the number of unknowns is reduced to three. If four measurements are still available, the redundant measurement can be used to improve the accuracy of the solution. Alternatively, the fourth measurement could be sacrificed to allow the associated hardware (in a multichannel receiver) or time (in a sequential receiver) to be used for other purposes such as dual frequency measurements or acquiring a new satellite when the constellation is to be revised.

The usual formulation is to make the position solution part of a Kalman filtering operation. The user state vector might usefully contain nine terms (give or take a few) such as the three position coordinates, the three components of velocity, clock time offset, clock frequency offset and altitude. The observation vector might include pseudoranges, differential pseudoranges, altimeter and other air data, accelerometer outputs, or position indications from other nagivation systems.

V. NAVIGATION COMPUTATION AND OUTPUTS

User position in Cartesian earth centered coordinates is rarely the acceptable end product. Each application has its own preferences. Latitude, longitude, and MSL altitude for position is commonly desired, but sometimes easting and northing in the military grid reference system is demanded. For navigation, the preference is often for steering instructions to a specified destination in terms of range and bearing of crosstrack error and time to go or other forms. All of these involve additional computation and program, parameter and data storage but contribute greatly to the utility of the set.

The form of outputs is also application dependent. Alphanumeric displays in incandescent, LED or LCD form is often adequate. In survey work, hard copy is desired. In airborne use, the choice may be for moving needle indicators. For aircraft and ships, automatic position reporting via digital data link is a likely future requirement.

VI. ACCURACY

In GPS there are many error sources, some of which are difficult to characterize and simple one-figure accuracy statements must be carefully interpreted.

From the Space and Control Segments come satellite position uncertainties and satellite clock drift. These are projected to be 1.5 meters and 1.0 meter (equivalent) respectively, in their contribution to pseudorange error.

If the ionosphere effect is predicted with current knowledge, the error is very much dependent on time of day, solar activity, geomagnetic latitude and other factors determining the condition of the ionosphere. On a bad day, the errors may be 30 meters, although on an overall average it may be only 3 meters. The dual frequency measurement method will give 1 to 3 meters depending upon signal conditions and receiver design. The residual after tropospheric correction will be 1 meter.

Characterization of multipath errors is virtually impossible, since it depends upon specific antenna locations and the location and surface conditions of nearby objects. It is possible to create situations with multipath induced errors of tens of meters for P code (hundreds of meters for C/A code), but with reasonable care and luck, 1 meter or less will be far more typical.

Receiver measurement error is very much a function of the level of interference at the antenna and to some degree upon the Host Vehicle dynamics, both the actual and the design values. Under benign conditions the measurement error will be under 1 meter for P code (10 meters for C/A) and twice that as the noise and dynamic limits are approached, beyond which point no measurements are available at all.

Receiver mechanization errors arising from such sources as offsets in measurement circuits, quantization noise, computational approximations and truncation errors can be held to 1 meter with careful design.

Without being precise about operating conditions or confidence levels, these errors add (in the square root of the sum of the squares) to 4 to 6 meters in pseudorange for the case of P code, dual frequency sets. In solving for position from the pseudoranges these errors are multiplied by a factor of 1.5 to 2 for most times and places, assuming no substantial blocking of the antenna. A projection of "10 meters rms or better, almost always" is supported by early field test results utilizing the first experimental GPS satellite.

For a minimum cost set such as the Z which uses only C/A code on one frequency, the dominant error source is the ionosphere when it is bad, and receiver measurement noise when it is good. Position accuracy will be about 30 meters under most conditions, but double that under extreme ionosphere situations.

The error analyst has often been asked whether there is benefit to be derived from using more than the minimum three or four satellites. Certainly more measurements are helpful, but under the practical constraint (due to receiver hardware or computational limitations) of allowing only a given number of measurements per minute, the question is more interesting. If all of the error sources were unbiased and independent of the choice of satellite then the best approach would be to select the minimum number of satellites which are geometrically well spaced and whose signal strengths are good and then to use all of the measurement capacity on them. If, on the other extreme, the errors were dominated by sources associated with particular satellites, such as satellite ephemeris errors or multipath reflections which were strong in certain directions, then the best strategy would be to gather measurements on most of the satellites in view.

Texas Instruments Phase I GPS User Equipment

M. J. BOREL, J. N. DAMOULAKIS, DENNIS R. DELZER, T. D. FUCHSER,
J. H. HINDERER, C. R. JOHNSON and D. J. PINKOS

ABSTRACT

THIS PAPER EMPHASIZES the importance of the manufacturer's reaching a proper balance between utility (capacity of equipment to satisfy performance requirements) and affordability (life—cycle cost to the user). The approach used is to produce in sufficient quantity to reduce cost. The demand for quantity is created by designing the equipment so that it will solve problems for large numbers of users. Where different configurations of the same basic equipment are needed, cost can be kept to a minimum by maximum use of common modules.

This philosophy is illustrated by a box–by–box description of the three user equipment sets that Texas Instruments is developing for the NAVSTAR Global Positioning System: the High Dynamic User Equipment, Missile–Borne Receiver Set, and Manpack/Vehicular User Equipment.

I. INTRODUCTION

Historically, sophisticated equipment was designed and fabricated to meet its specific requirements. Although such an approach may be the simplest to undertake, it provides only minimum production advantages to each user. Cost and risk for each configuration are high. In an attempt to offset some of these disadvantages, there is an inclination toward the development of three or four standard system configurations, one of which may be selected for a specific user

Messrs. Borel, Damoulakis, Delzer, Fuchser,
Hinderer, Johnson and Pinkos are with Texas
Instruments Inc., 13500 N. Central Express-
way, P.O. Box 226015, Dallas, TX 75266.

application. Such an approach does afford some advantages as a result of the potential increase in production of each configuration, but, in most cases, it will result in compromises of performance and physical characteristics.

A more effective approach for achieving utility and affordability can present perhaps the more difficult initial design and development issues. This approach requires establishing user equipment commonality, not at the system level, but at the subsystem level. These building blocks or common modules can be used to satisfy every user equipment requirement and consequently, provide the maximum production volume advantage. Because of the flexibility and commonality established at this level, performance and physical characteristics are not compromised for specific user requirements. Component technology improvements can be incorporated with minimum perturbations to other functional elements. What results is an approach that permits a concentration of efforts in subsequent development phases aimed toward minimum cost improvements that are beneficial to all users and not encumbered with the difficulties of the "slight" variations of system performance that all too often result in a major rework or redesign.

II. GLOBAL POSITIONING SYSTEM (GPS) USER EQUIPMENT IMPLEMENTATION

The design of common modules must be preceded by a careful definition of the functions to be performed by each module. This definition is evolved through an iterative evaluation process centered upon variables such as GPS equipment functions to be performed, current and projected component technology, performance and physical characteristics, and cost. Basically, this process follows the general steps listed below (illustrated in Figs. 1 and 2):

Definition of functions to be performed by GPS user equipment

Separation of these functions into two categories: those sensitive to applications and those not sensitive

Subdivision of application-insensitive functions into elements grouped to provide maximum commonality over the identified user requirements

Design of common modules that provide the performance required of these elements.

The design of each common module was guided by imposing constraints defined by the requirement containing the worst case condition applicable to the module. For example, the design requirement for size, weight, and power may be driven by a man-portable requirement while performance and environmental constraints may be driven by missile and satellite requirements. In addition, other constraints and controls were established that guided the common module

life-cycle cost efforts.

The system concept and design resulting from this effort permit maximum commonality between various system designs through the use of different quantities of common modules to satisfy specific performance requirements. Also, because of the functional nature of the modules, improvements to accommodate performance requirements were incorporated with minimum impact. Texas Instruments GPS user equipment consists of three different system types: the High Dynamic User Equipment (HDUE), the Missile Borne Receiver Set (MBRS), and the Manpack/Vehicular User Equipment (MVUE). The applications of these three systems are, respectively, in high-performance aircraft, the Minuteman missile test program, and manned vehicles such as trucks, tanks, and jeeps. A comparison of the major performance requirements of these systems is shown in Table 1, while a comparison of other characteristics is shown in Table 2. These systems are shown in Figs. 3, 4, and 5.

Additional information regarding the three

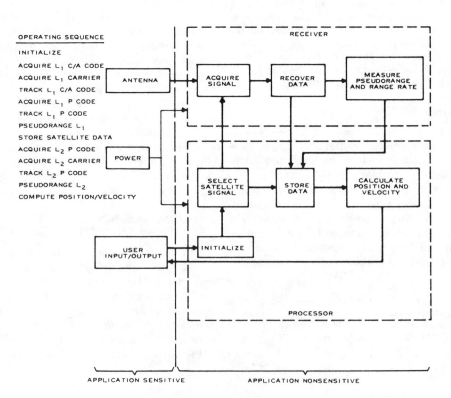

Fig. 1—Functional System Operation.

systems is presented following a discussion of the receiver section, the processor section, and the navigation filter section.

III. RECEIVER

A. Block Diagram

A receiver may be configured with one to five channels, depending on user dynamics and performance requirements. A block diagram showing one of these channels is presented in Fig. 6. Each channel contains two or three narrowband modules and one each wideband, output, code, and frequency synthesizer modules. Each receiver has a single master oscillator, clock mod-

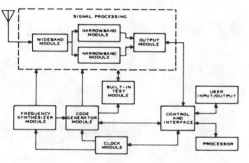

Fig. 2—General Block Diagram.

ule, built-in test module, and data processing unit, regardless of the number of channels. Both code and carrier loops are contained in each RF channel. The input signal of L_1 (154 f_0) and L_2 (120 f_0) is received at the antenna (f_0 is a reference frequency of 10.23 MHz). The code tracking is implemented in the narrowband modules (where correlation occurs), the output module and data processing unit (offset detection), and the code module (code generation and adjustment).

The carrier tracking loop is implemented in the wideband and narrowband modules (RF down–conversion and phase/frequency detection) and in the frequency synthesizer module (loop filter and VCO). The clock for the code generator module is tuned by the carrier tracking loop. Thus, the code loop tracking is aided by the carrier tracking loop.

B. Module Description

The input signal is doppler shifted in frequency and contains the biphase code and data modulation as shown in Fig. 6 as an input to the antenna. The antenna signal may be amplified in a low–noise preamplifier before reaching the wideband module. The wideband module ampli-

Table 1—Phase I GPS Systems—Requirement Comparisons

Parameter	HDUE	MBRS	MVUE
SV carrier signal from antenna L_1 and L_2 (dBW)	−166 to −156	−176 to −166	−166 to −156
Code demodulation	P-code C/A code	P-code C/A code	P-code C/A code
User velocity (maximum) (meters/second)	1,100	7,620	25
User acceleration (maximum) (meters/second^2)	80	100	6
User jerk (maximum) (meters/second^3)	50	9	NA
Jamming levels, J/S (dB)			
Acquisition	24 (C/A)	NA	25 (C/A)
Track/lock	40 (P)	NA	40 (P)
Weak signal hold on	47 (P)	NA	NA
Time to first fix (seconds)	152	120	240
Pseudorange accuracy at (C/No)	1.5 meters (30 dB-Hz)	1.34 meters (25 dB-Hz) 2.4 meters (20 dB-Hz)	1.67 meters (30 dB-Hz)
Pseudorange rate accuracy (meters/second)	0.2	0.012	NA
Mean time between failures (hours)	500	Ps = 0.995	2,000
Temperature range	−20° to +55°C	+25° to +50°C	−40° to +70°C

fies the signal at L–band, down–converts to the first intermediate frequency (IF) of $18 f_0 (1 + V/C)$, and amplifies further in the IF. The IF bandwidth is 15 MHz to allow the code spectrum to pass. Some of the doppler is removed from the signal in all down–conversions in this receiver. When the carrier is locked, all local oscillator frequencies tune and track with the signal doppler offset in a coherent manner. The wideband module contains an AGC to control its gain and a pulse blanker to minimize the effects of pulse jamming. The output of this module offsets the IF by 10 MHz and introduces a receiver internal code (T–code) to enhance rejection of CW jammers. The wideband module output is split to feed either two or three narrowband modules.

The narrowband module has a second down–conversion and an IF at $f_0 + 10$ MHz. Final IF amplification and filtering occur before conversion to baseband in a Costas phase detector. The code is correlated or removed at this module's input, so the IF bandwidths are reduced to 50 kHz and eventually to 4 kHz to

Fig. 4—Missile-Borne Receiver Set.

Fig. 5—Manpack/Vehicular User Equipment.

Table 2—Phase I GPS Systems—Hardware Comparisons

Parameter	HDUE	MBRS	MVUE
No. of LRUs	4	1	1
No. of receiver channels	5	4	1
Size (ft³)	3.5	1.6	0.75
Weight (pounds)	200	77	25
Power (watts)	529	208	45
Design-to-cost goal (1,000 units)	25K	NA	15K
Receiver modules/channel	6	7	6
Total common modules	65	50	12
Total unique units	13	13	6
Memory size (maximum capability)	68K	82K	48K
Memory size required	62.3K	62K	40K
Bits/word	16	16	16

prevent noise power saturation in the IF amplifiers. Baseband circuitry in this module includes phase detection, frequency detection, envelope detection of the input signal, signal–to–noise ratio detection, and a second AGC circuit.

The phase or frequency detector output of the narrowband module is used to drive the carrier tracking network in the frequency synthesizer module. The network or loop filter output tunes a voltage–controlled crystal oscillator (VCXO) which tunes the frequency of all the local oscil-

Fig. 3—High Dynamic User Equipment.

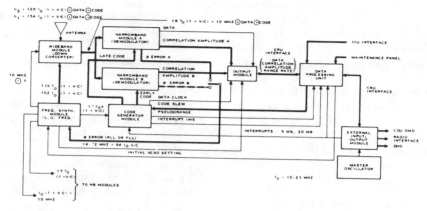

Fig. 6—Manpack Receiver Functional Block Diagram.

lators (LOs) used throughout the receiver. All LOs and the tracking network are in the synthesizer module. A digital loop filter and oscillator are used for these carrier tracking functions in the MBRS system to accommodate tracking the higher doppler frequency and provide the more stringent accuracy in range rate measurements.

The code module generates the receiver's replica of the input signal code. Early, late, and prompt code versions are generated and output to the narrowband modules for code correlation and alignment. As described earlier, the code tracking is aided by the carrier tracking loop to remove the doppler. This is accomplished through $17 f_0 (1 + V/C)$ input to the code module used as the code clock after division by 17. In addition, the code can be slewed by division by 16 or 18 to center the code alignment. A code discriminator is formed in the data processing unit and is used to drive the code centering circuitry in the code module. The code module also contains the pseudorange measurement circuitry that measures the code state at a reference time mark.

The clock module uses a 10–MHz reference oscillator clock signal to provide timing marks needed in the rest of the receiver. Both hardware counters and processor interrupts are obtained from this module.

The output module serves as an interface between the RF hardware and the digital processor receiver control unit. The output module provides analog-to-digital (A/D) conversion of the envelope detectors in the narrowband modules

and control decoding to set latches in the other hardware modules. The 50–Hz signal data are also detected in this module. Finally, a range rate counter is included in this module to count the frequency of the VCXO in the frequency synthesizer module. When the receiver is locked to the input signal, its output is the pseudorange rate used in navigation computations.

A separate built-in test (BIT) module provides a coded L_1 and L_2 test signal and an $18 f_0$ test signal for testing the receiver. It allows calibration of time delays in multichannel systems and provides health checks for all the receiver channels.

C. Performance

The receiver provides pseudorange and pseudorange rate measurements for navigation computations. Table 3 shows the accuracy of these measurements for normal and jamming conditions.

IV. PROCESSOR

The various common processor system configurations are illustrated in Fig. 7. All configurations use the same basic set of common processor modules (e.g., microprocessor module, memory modules, I/O modules). The single processor configuration uses fewer of each module type than the more sophisticated multiple processor configurations.

The microprocessor module (MPM) provides computational and functional control capability for the various system configurations. Each MPM interfaces with program memory modules

(PMMs), data memory modules (DMMs), and a communication register interface module (CRIM) on its local memory bus. The components of the MPM, as shown in Fig. 8, are the microprocessor unit, address decode logic, programmable read–only memory (PROM), PROM power switching circuitry, random–access memory (RAM), clock circuitry, and buffer logic.

The basic functional component of the MPM is the single–chip 16–bit I^2L SBP 9900 microprocessor unit. The 9900 is software compatible with the TI 990 minicomputer family. General operational characteristics the microprocessor unit exhibits are:

- 16–bit instruction word
- 3–MHz basic clock
- Memory-to-memory architecture
- Memory address capability for up to 32,768 sixteen–bit words or 65,536 eight–bit bytes
- Separate memory, I/O, and interrupt bus structure
- Use of 16 workspace registers in memory
- Up to 16 prioritized interrupts
- Instruction–driven communication register unit (CRU) and direct memory address (DMA) I/O capability.

The MPM address decode logic performs memory address recognition and decode for the memory (read–only or read/write) contained within the MPM. The PROM on the MPM provides the microprocessor unit with 512 words of nonvolatile storage for program instruction and data constants. The PROM switching circuitry minimizes MPM power by disabling the power source from all MPM PROM devices not

Table 3—Receiver Accuracies

	Pseudorange Accuracy (meters)	Pseudorange Rate Accuracy (meters/second)
Phase lock		
Normal	1.67	0.046
Jamming		
(J/S = 42 dB)	1.70	0.139
Frequency lock		
Normal	1.70	0.25
Jamming		
(J/S = 45 dB)	1.87	4.7

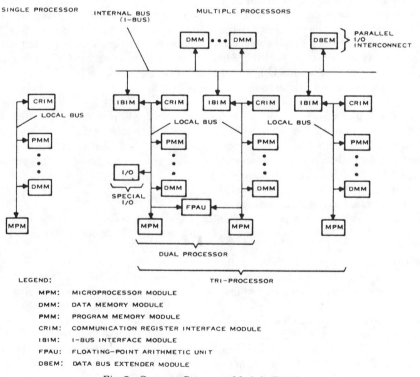

LEGEND:

MPM: MICROPROCESSOR MODULE
DMM: DATA MEMORY MODULE
PMM: PROGRAM MEMORY MODULE
CRIM: COMMUNICATION REGISTER INTERFACE MODULE
IBIM: I–BUS INTERFACE MODULE
FPAU: FLOATING–POINT ARITHMETIC UNIT
DBEM: DATA BUS EXTENDER MODULE

Fig. 7—Common Processor Module Family.

being addressed. The RAM on the MPM provides the microprocessor unit with 256 words of high-speed read/write memory for allocation as work-space memory. The MPM clock circuitry is provided for use as a system clock at the user's option. The buffer logic on the MPM provides the necessary buffering for the microprocessor unit memory bus and CRU bus signals.

The MPM memory bus provides the mechanism for information transfer between the MPM and memory for instruction fetch operations and storage/data retrieval operations. The instruction-driven CRU bus, along with the microprocessor unit DMA I/O feature, provides the MPM with input/output capabilities.

Each DMM provides the system with 4,096 words of random-access read/write memory for temporary storage of 17-bit data words (16 bits for data and 1 bit for parity). Each DMM contains a single-port data and address bus compatible with the MPM local memory bus.

Each PMM provides the system with nonvolatile PROM for program instructions and data constants. Each module contains a maximum of 16,384 words of 16 bits each. The PMM single-port data and address bus is compatible with the MPM local memory bus. The memory bus signal pinouts of the PMM and DMM are assigned so that a PMM can be inserted in any DMM location and replace up to four DMMs. The PMM minimizes power by disabling the power source from any PROM devices not being addressed.

The CRIM consists of:

Communication register unit decoder and buffers
Interrupt circuitry
Parity generator/checker
Reset circuitry.

The CRIM decodes bits 3 through 5 of the address bus into eight register select lines for use by any CRU device. The other address and CRU control lines are also buffered for use by CRU devices. The interrupt circuitry synchronizes the interrupt stimuli, provides interrupt masking/clearing capability, and generates the interrupt request and code signals for the MPM. The parity generator/checker performs parity checks on read operations and generates the parity bit for storage during write operations to read/write memory. Parity errors are signaled to the user as interrupts. The reset circuitry receives the various system reset stimuli (e.g.,

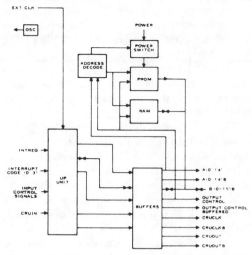

Fig. 8—*Microprocessor Module (MPM) Block Diagram.*

from power supply) and provides corresponding reset signals to the other processor modules.

In Fig. 7, communication between the processors in the multiple processor configurations is accomplished via the internal bus (I-bus). The I-bus is a high-speed, 16-bit parallel data bus. The transfer of data between processors is accomplished through an intermediate DMM interfaced to the I-bus. Each MPM interfaces to the I-bus through its associated I-bus interface module (IBIM). The IBIM controls access onto the I-bus and provides for the bidirectional passage of data between the MPM and the I-bus.

In multiple processor configurations, a floating-point arithmetic unit (FPAU) can be included to provide floating-point arithmetic and conversion capability. The FPAU is a dual-port, high-speed, auxiliary arithmetic unit that performs single and double precision arithmetic operations. The FPAU can be interfaced to a maximum of two processors via their local memory buses. In systems where the FPAU is interfaced to two processors, a software calling sequence has been established to avoid usage conflicts.

Additional input/output capability is provided by the data bus extender module (DBEM) which extends the I-bus to external devices. Other special I/O interface modules may be added on any local bus to satisfy system-unique I/O requirements.

The various processor modules and processor

configurations are shown in Fig. 9. Each module is implemented on a single 4.7- by 5.6-inch multilayer printed wiring board (PWB). The exception is the FPAU, which consists of seven multilayer boards. Interconnection of the various modules to obtain the different processor configurations is accomplished via multilayer mother boards.

The microprocessor unit on each MPM executes a full minicomputer instruction set containing 69 instructions. The arithmetic instructions include add, subtract, compare, negate, absolute value, increment, decrement, shift left/right arithmetic, clear, multiply, and divide. A variety of logical instructions is also provided. Included are set 1's/0's corresponding, compare 1's/0's corresponding, exclusive OR, invert, AND, OR, and shift logical/circular. The set of program control instructions includes jump (13 conditions), load, store, move, swap byte, branch, and return (from interrupt/subroutine).

Seven addressing modes are available for operand derivation. Instruction execution times range from 8 (add) to 124 clocks (divide). Most instructions require 10 to 20 clocks to execute, with variations dependent on the instruction function and the specified operand derivation cycle. Table 4 lists the various processor instruction execution times assuming a 3–MHz system clock.

V. NAVIGATION FILTER

The current user sets (HDUE, MBRS, and MVUE) employ a navigation filter configuration that optimizes the processing of pseudorange and pseudorange rate measurements. The HDUE and MBRS filters process the measurements simultaneously, while the MVUE filter processes the measurements sequentially.

For either type of processing, the system is as shown schematically in Fig. 10. The system uses two computational loops: the fast loop (FL) and the slow loop (SL). The FL consists of the propagation (PR) task and the measurement-incorporation (MI) task. The SL consists of the optimal-filter (OF) task. The operations performed by each task are as follows:

Propagation (PR) task–propagates the dynamic equations forward in time. For this, assume that y is the state of the system. This task performs the operation:

$$y_i = \Phi(t_i, t_{i-1})\bar{y}_{i-1} \tag{1}$$

where y is the state of the system and y_i denotes the state vector of the system at the time t_i, $\bar{y}_{i-1}$ the state of the system at t_{i-1}, and $\Phi(t_i, t_{i-1})$ the system transition matrix from t_{i-1} to t_i.

Measurement-Incorporation (MI) task—incorporates the receivable measurements in the system to correct the existing propagated state y. This task performs the operation:

$$\bar{y}_i = y_i + K_i\Delta z_i \tag{2}$$

where K_i is a set of existing gains at t_i and Δz_i the measurement residual at t_i.

Optimal Filter (OF) task—simultaneous processing (HDUE, MBRS) uses two stages, both of which employ an optimal Kalman filter. Sequential processing (MVUE) uses only one stage and also employs a Kalman filter.

In the HDUE and MBRS systems, the first stage, Stage I, propagates and updates the system error state covariance based on the time interval Δt; while the second stage, Stage II, propagates and updates the system error state covariance based on the time interval $\Delta \tau$. The output of the OF is a set of optimal gains K_i, used by the MI task, and the system error covariance matrix P_i.

In the MVUE system, Stage I, the only stage, propagates and updates the system error state covariance based on the time interval $(\Delta t + \Delta \tau)$. Similarly, the output of OF is a set of optimal gains K_i, used by the MI task, and the system error state covariance matrix P_i.

Basically, the system receives observable data, consisting of the vectors p and Δp, at Δt intervals. The data are processed as they are received by the FL mechanization. The SL mechanization operates in parallel with the FL mechanization, in real time, computing the appropriate gains for the system and updating the system statistics. The execution of SL occurs at $(\Delta t + \Delta \tau)$ time intervals.

A. Detailed System Description

Fig. 10 describes the tasks relative to the processor time line. The process starts at time t_0 and executes one cycle of the OF, which takes

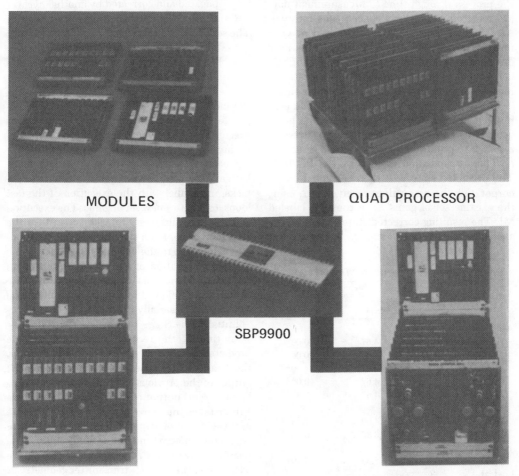

MODULES   QUAD PROCESSOR

SBP9900

SINGLE PROCESSOR

Fig. 9—Processor Common Module Family.

the process through time $t\cdot$. Measurement data are received at regularly spaced time intervals Δt. These measurements are denoted at each instant as p_M and Δp_M. The filter gains used during the execution of OF, denoted by K_o, correspond to the gains used to incorporate the measurements received at the particular times.

The process has available, at time t_0, an estimate of existing state y_0. The process first propagates this state through the interval Δt between t_0 and t_1 to produce a predicted state y_1 at time t_1. This extrapolation is done by the PR task. The predicted state y_1 is then corrected by incorporating the data values received at t_1 using the existing set of gains K_0 in the task labeled MI. The resulting corrected state $\bar{y}_1$ is then the available system state at time t_1. This state will

Table 4—Instruction Times

Instruction Type	Execution Times (microseconds)	
	Minimum	Maximum
Arithmetic		
Add/subtract	4.67	10.00
Multiply	17.33	20.00
Divide	30.67	44.00
Compare	4.67	10.00
Shift (left/right arithmetic)	4.67	17.33
Absolute value	4.00	7.33
Increment/decrement	3.33	6.00
Clear	3.33	6.00
Logical		
Set 1's/0's corresponding	4.67	10.00
Compare 1's/0's corresponding	4.67	7.33
Exclusive OR	4.67	7.33
OR/AND (immediate)	4.67	4.67
Shift (logical/circular)	4.67	17.33
Swap bytes	3.33	6.00
Program control		
Move	4.67	10.00
Jump	3.33	3.33
Branch	2.67	5.33
Return	4.67	4.67
Load	4.00	4.00
Store	2.67	2.67
Input/output		
Single bit	4.00	4.00
Multiple bit	7.33	22.67

be propagated and corrected by another cycle of PR and MI tasks to compute the state $\bar{y}_2$ at t_2. The sequence of these events, that is, an MI task followed by a PR task, constitutes the FL cycle. The FL cycle is repeated every Δt seconds throughout the execution of the OF cycle.

In each of the fast loops, the system is using the most recent set of gains available to incorporate the measurements. However, processor execution load prevents the system from computing a new set of optimal gains for incorporating each received measurement in real time. Instead, the process executes two filtering subtasks, in parallel with the execution of the fast loops, to create a new set of gains. The execution of these two filtering subtasks constitutes the slow loop cycle. Each slow loop is computationally equivalent to the optimal filter task.

The combination of the two subtasks which produces the new set of gains constitutes the State I filter followed by the Stage II filter. The two stages are serially executed.

Initially, the Stage I filter uses the state $z_1 = y_0$ at time t_0, the receiver data at t_0, and the predicted covariance estimate M_o. Thereafter, the Stage I filter uses as starting values the output of the previous Stage II subtask and the last (current) output of the FL cycle. The Stage I filter takes the above information to compute a Stage I set of gains and updates the state covariance matrix and the system states. The resulting covariance P_1 and state vector x_1 are based upon the user–to–transmitter geometry at time t_0 (or, in general, at time $t\cdot$). During the final step of the Stage I filter cycle, the system error state covariance and state are propagated forward at time Δt, producing the matrix P_1 and the state vector x_1 which are valid for time t_1.

Upon completion of Stage I, the Stage II filter subtask begins. Input data for Stage II is the Stage I output P_1 and x_1, plus the observed data p_M and Δp_M valid for time t_1. The filter processes this information to produce a Stage II set of gains and to update the state covariance. Note that, during the next SL filter cycle, the FL filter cycle will use these same optimal gains to incorporate measurements while yet another set of optimal gains is being created. The Stage II subtask is completed with the forward propagation of the state covariance over a time $\Delta\tau$; thus, the state covariance P_2, valid for time $t\cdot$, is generated. This last value of the covariance, P_2

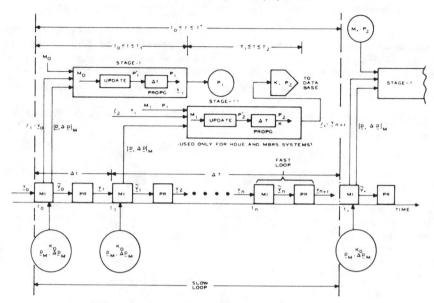

Fig. 10—Schematic Representation of the Navigation Filter Structure.

becomes the *a priori* covariance for the next SL filter cycle. The existing filter state is not propagated to time t^*. Instead, the *a priori* state vector $z \cdot$ is set equal to $y \cdot$ which is the output from the FL cycle at time $t \cdot - \Delta t$.

Thus, the fast loop consists of one execution of the MI task followed by one execution of the PR task using the best estimate of gains. The slow loop consists of one execution of the Stage I subtask followed by one execution of the Stage II subtask to produce the final optimal gains and system statistics. Stage I operates on the measurement and predicted state at time t_0 (or $t \cdot$) and the covariance estimate from the last Stage II to produce an updated covariance valid at time t_1. Stage II operates on the measurements at time t_1, the predicted state at t_1, and the covariance derived from the execution of the preceding Stage I.

The result of this process is an estimate of current system state based on more measurements than could be used if optimal filtering were used on–line. The estimate is more accurate than that obtainable from a single measurement incorporation during an optimal filter loop, or from simple data preaveraging.

For the MVUE sequential processing, the same philosophy as outlined above is followed with the exception that the Stage II filtering procedure is not present. At each fast loop, the measurements from only one satellite are processed. Thus, for four satellites, the fast loop is activated four times before completing one execution of the slow loop. During the execution of each slow loop, the gains and the error state covariance for only one satellite are updated. Therefore, it takes four executions of the slow loop to update the gains and covariance for all four satellites.

B. Simulation Results

Tables 5 and 6 present typical statistics of the errors resulting from implementation of the previously discussed filtering schemes, both simultaneous and sequential. Table 5 presents the results of an F-4 aircraft trajectory for 260 seconds of flight time. The satellite constellation is typical for GPS. As noted, these numbers may vary with the changes in the satellite constellation, trajectory, and measurement errors. Table 6 presents the results for a truck path at Yuma Proving Grounds. The simulation time is about 3,000 seconds. The satellite constellation and errors are the same as in Table 5. Again, it is noted that these results may change as the various error parameters and satellite constellations change. Details on the above simulation results are given in Refs. 1 through 3.

VI. MVUE

The MVUE set consists of a single–channel sequencing receiver with its associated control/navigation data processor. A block diagram of this set is shown in Fig. 11. The MVUE major

characteristics are listed in Table 7.

The MVUE set sequences between satellites every 2 seconds. The major space vehicle (SV) selection, acquisition, and tracking processes are shown in Table 8. The MVUE tracks both L_1 and L_2 satellite frequencies and uses both C/A

Table 5—Typical Statistical Values of the Errors for Simultaneous Processing

Quantity	Average RSS	Spherical Error Probable	Circular Error Probable	Probable Error
Resultant position error in earth-fixed coordinates (meters)	11.74	10.36	—	—
Resultant velocity error in earth-fixed coordinates (meters/second)	4.75	3.47	—	—
Horizontal position error (meters)	—	—	10.50	—
Horizontal velocity error (meters/second)	—	—	2.89	—
Error in range bias (meters)	—	—	—	1.70
Error in range-rate bias (meters/second)	—	—	—	0.02
Error in altitude (meters)	—	—	—	2.90
Error in vertical velocity (meters/second)	—	—	—	1.15

Table 6—Typical Statistical Values of the Errors for Sequential Processing

Quantity	Average RSS	Spherical Error Probable	Circular Error Probable	Probable Error
Resultant position error in earth-fixed coordinates (meters)	20.72	—	—	—
Resultant velocity error in earth-fixed coordinates (meters/second)	1.49	—	—	—
Horizontal position error (meters)	—	—	13.08	—
Horizontal velocity error (meters/second)	—	—	1.18	—
Error in range bias (meters)	11.71	—	—	—
Error in range-rate bias (meters/second)	0.231	—	—	—
Error in altitude (meters)	—	—	—	9.99
Error in vertical velocity (meters/second)	—	—	—	0.634

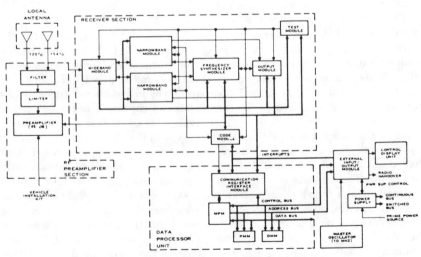

Fig. 11—MVUE LRU Functional Block Diagram.

and P codes during the acquisition process. Navigation calculations are made using an eight-state Kalman filter.

Input initialization data (approximate position and time) are entered by means of a hand-held control/display unit (CDU) calculator-type keyboard. Output data are displayed on the LED display. Various outputs available from the MVUE set are shown in Table 9.

A number of advanced component technologies are used in the MVUE set to reduce size, weight, and power. These include miniature volute antenna, surface acoustic wave (SAW) bandpass filters, custom large-scale integration (LSI) digital circuits for code generation, an I^2L 16-bit microprocessor, and hybrid RF circuits.

The MVUE set can operate from rechargeable or primary batteries (24 Vdc) or vehicle generator power. In the vehicle operation mode, a separate antenna/preamplifier is provided in a vehicle installation kit.

VII. HDUE

The HDUE set consists of four major line replaceable units (LRUs). They are the receiver,

Table 7—Major MVUE Characteristics

Size	23,000 cubic centimeters
Weight	15 kilograms
Major system outputs:	
Present position (MGRS or latitude/longitude)	
Range and bearing to any of 8 waypoints	
Time of day (day of week, hours-minutes-seconds)	
Battery life (with NiCad BB590)	
Continuous mode	2 hours
Periodic (4 fixes/hour)	6 hours
Stationary user CEP	15 meters
Dynamic user CEP (25 meters/second, maximum velocity, 6 meters/second² acceleration)	50 meters
Receiver contribution to range accuracy (1σ)	1.64 meters
C/No thresholds (including jamming effects)	
Acquisition	34 dB-Hz
Accurate navigation	33 dB-Hz
Carrier/code track	30 dB-Hz

Table 8—SV Selection, Acquisition, and Tracking Processes

SV Selection
  Check every 2 minutes
  Track longer to minimize changes
  Fit parabola to orbit for navigation
First SV Acquisition
  Highest SV first
  25 kilometers, 30 seconds, and almanac require two full doppler bins
  C/A "sequential" search
  Code center
  Phase lock
  BIT synchronization
  Frame and HOW synchronization
  Reset time to 0.1 millisecond
  C/A to P while still recovering data
  Recover clock and ephemeris data
  Measure pseudorange and delta range for navigation
Subsequent SV acquisition
  25 kilometers, 0.1 millisecond, and almanac require one doppler bin
  600 C/A chip "sequential" search
  12 seconds during subframes 4 and 5
  C/A to P while still recovering data
  Recover clock and ephemeris data
  Measure pseudorange and delta range for navigation
Tracking
  C/A reacquisition to improve aiding
  P reacquisition every $\Delta\tau$
  Track in deterministic sequence
    Carrier/code track
      Measurements for navigation
    Accurate navigation
      Ionospheric correction
      Data refresh
      New SV acquisition

Table 9—MVUE Outputs

Position Output	Additional Outputs
Coordinates	Time
Grid	Altitude
Geographical	CEP
Timing Options	PE
Automatic mode	Number of SV
Manual mode	Waypoint
Time-to-first-fix mode	Position
Cold start	Range and bearing
Warm start	Audio digital (digital
Direct handover	message device)
Periodic mode	Instrumentation
	Direct handover

data processor, AC/DC converter and CDU. The receiver LRU is composed of five continuous tracking receiver channels and a receiver controller/processor. An existing antenna/preamplifier will be used for tests. The data processor LRU consists of the master state controller and the navigation processor. All GPS controller/processors are designed around the SBP 9900 microprocessor. The CDU has a calculator-type keyboard and an incandescent light alphanumeric display. A block diagram of this set is shown in Fig. 12. Major characteristics of the HDUE are presented in Table 10. The HDUE major modes of operation are shown in Fig. 13.

The HDUE set tracks four satellites continuously using four receiver channels. The fifth receiver channel is used for SV acquisition, L_1/L_2 ionospheric correction measurement, and reading of data. The HDUE tracks both L_1 and L_2 satellite frequencies and uses both C/A and P codes during the acquisition process. Navigation calculations are made using an 11-state Kalman filter.

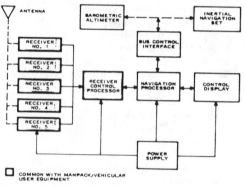

Fig. 12—*High Dynamic User Equipment Block Diagram.*

Table 10—HDUE Major Characteristics

Range measurement accuracy	
(J/S = 30 – 40 dB)	
Coarse (C/A code)	15 meters (1σ)
Fine (P code)	1.5 meters (1σ)
Resulting position accuracy	
Horizontal	10 meters (CEP)
Vertical	10 meters (PE)
Intrinsic maintainability design	
LRU replacement	5 minutes
SRU replacement	10 minutes
	20 minutes maximum

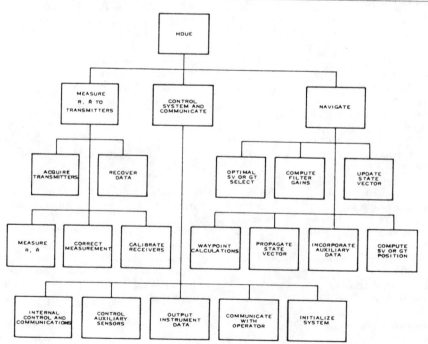

Fig. 13—*HDUE Major Modes of Operation.*

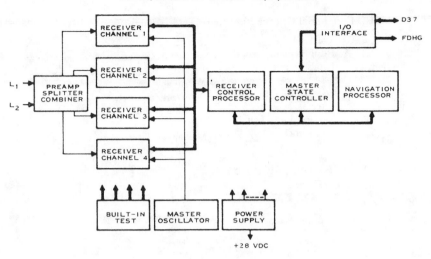

Fig. 14—MBRS Block Diagram.

The HDUE set can handle two antenna inputs (inverted range or satellite antenna) and switch any of these two inputs to any one of the five receiver channels (2 × 5 matrix switch). Input initialization data (position and time) are entered by means of the keyboard on the CDU. Output data (position, velocity, time, etc.) are displayed on the CDU. The same receiver and processor common modules are used in the HDUE as are used in the MVUE. Software is programmed in both Fortran and 990 assembly language.

VII. MBRS

The MBRS consists of one major LRU that contains the receiver, receiver controller, data processors, and power conditioning modules, forming a four–channel, continuous tracking receiver configuration. A block diagram of this set is shown in Fig. 14.

The major characteristics of the MBRS are shown in Table 11 and the operational sequence is shown in Table 12. The MBRS interfaces directly with the digital control unit (DCU) computer on the Minuteman missile. All initial inputs of position and time are entered from the DCU. All outputs of position, velocity, and time from the MBRS are sent to the DCU or telemetry assembly. The MBRS is used to provide

Table 11—MBRS Operational Characteristics (Position, Velocity)

Mission Sequence

Prelaunch
C/N_i = 33 dB-Hz
T_{ACQ} = 120 seconds

Launch
C/N_i = 33 dB-Hz
T_{ACQ} = 10 seconds
Probability of acquisition = 0.95

Powered flight
$\dot{R}_{MAX}$ = 25,000 feet/second
$\ddot{R}_{MAX}$ = 10 g
$\dddot{R}_{MAX}$ = 9 meters/second³ (T_{MAX} > 0.25 second)
σR = 4.4 feet (C/N_i = 29 dB-Hz)
$\sigma \dot{R}$ = 0.012 meter/second (1 second average) (C/N_i = 29 dB-Hz)
σR = 8 feet (C/N_i = 25 dB-Hz)
T_{ACQ} = 10 seconds (C/N_i = 33 dB-Hz)
Probability of acquisition = 0.95
J_{STAGE} = 50 g/second, 100 g/second, and 300 g/second (T < 0.1 second)

Post boost
σR = 4.4 feet (C/N_i = 29 dB-Hz)
$\sigma \dot{R}$ = 0.012 meter/second (1 second average) (C/N_i = 29 dB-Hz)
σR = 8 feet (C/N_i = 25 dB-Hz)
T_{ACQ} = 10 seconds (C/N_i = 33 dB-Hz)

Table 12—MBRS Functional Operations

Turnon	Track GPS signals
Self-test	Read SV data
Receive initialization data	Establish position
Send initialization data for verification	Send R, R, T to telemetry
Acquire selected GPS signals	Perform L_1/L_2 switching sequence

Table 13—Phase I GPS Systems—Common Module Comparisons

Module Name	Number of Units/Modules/Cards		
	HDUE	MBRS	MVUE
Wideband	5	4	1
Narrowband	10	12	2
Output	5	—	1
Frequency synthesizer	5	—	1
Code generator	5	4	1
Clock	1	1	—
MPM	3	4	1
4K—DMM	17	4	1
16K—PMM (MBRS legacy)	—	4	2
IBIM	2	4	—
FPAU	2	2	—
FPAU	1	1	—
FPAU	1	1	—
FPAU	1	1	—
FPAU	1	1	--
FPAU	1	1	—
CRIM	3	4	1
Receiver test	1	1	1
Distribution	1	1	—

navigation instrumentation for postflight test data evaluation of the missile trajectory.

The MBRS has improved features in the receiver area. These include a digital oscillator to track the increased missile doppler frequency and provide increased position and velocity accuracy. Also, the carrier tracking loop circuitry is implemented in a special digital processor.

Table 14—Phase I GPS Systems—Unique Module Comparisons

Module Name	Number of Units/Modules/Cards		
	HDUE	MBRS	MVUE
Antenna	2 (GFE)	—	1
Filter/preamplifiers	2 (GFE)	1	1
Antenna switch	1	—	—
CDU	1	—	1
Master oscillator	1	1	1
Power supply (regulated)	4	1	1
EIOM	—	—	1
TACAN/clock I/O	—	—	—
IFM	—	1	—
SCM	—	1	—
Frequency synthesizer	—	4	—
Output module	—	4	—
DRIM	1	—	—
SBIM No. 1	2	—	—
SBIM No. 2	2	—	—
DBEM	1	—	—

MBRS tracks both L_1 and L_2 satellite frequencies and uses both C/A and P codes during the acquisition process. Navigation calculations are made using an 11-state Kalman filter.

The antenna inputs at both L_1 and L_2 (1575.42 MHz and 1227.6 MHz) frequencies. The missile 28-Vdc prime power is regulated and conditioned for use in the MBRS.

All three GPS Phase I user sets use common receiver/processor modules to the maximum extent possible. The extent of module commonality between sets is shown by the module comparisons listed in Table 13. Unique modules were designed to cover the individual differences and special requirements of each GPS set. These unique modules are listed in Table 14. The greater use of common modules will increase the total production volume for each module and, hence, drive module cost down. Maximum use of standard replaceable modules will continue in the next generation GPS user equipment.

Performance Enhancements of GPS User Equipment

N. B. HEMESATH

INTRODUCTION

Unprecedented accuracy, global coverage, and three dimensional position fixing are GPS features unmatched by any other navigation system in existence today. These characteristics, along with its user passive nature, make the system very attractive for a wide variety of applications, both commercial and military. However, because it is a radio-based system, its potential susceptibility to jamming is a concern in military applications. The relatively low radiated power levels of the satellites and the extreme user-to-satellite distances combine to produce a received signal level of approximately −165 dbw and a signal-to-noise ratio in the 20 megahertz receiver front end on the order of −40 db. Thus, even though the transmitted signal has been carefully designed to provide 70 db of processing gain (by virtue of the 10.23 megabit/second PN code bi-phase modulated on the carrier), it is clear that a jammer in close proximity to a user can overcome the desired signal and thereby deny GPS navigation capability to that user.

The top level partitioning of a GPS user set, shown in Fig. 1, indicates a receiving function and a navigation function. The former acquires the signals and measures ranges along the lines-of-sight to the satellites; the latter manages the overall system and projects the measured range data into the user's navigation coordinate frame. Thus the navigation function is primarily concerned with coordinate conversion and data manipulation and does not significantly affect either system accuracy or tracking thresholds. On the other hand, the receiving function acquires and tracks the desired signals, and its design can be optimized to enhance performance. Thus the performance enhancements discussed in this paper are all associated with the receiving function and are intended to extend receiver operation into deeper and deeper noise (jamming) environments. The techniques addressed include advanced antennas, inertial aiding, and special signal processing.

BASIC RECEIVER PERFORMANCE

GPS is a one-way ranging system wherein the user determines his position by processing range measurements to each of four separate satellites. The receiver is intended to measure the path delay between the user and each of the satellites, but because its clock is not in synchronism with satellite clocks (GPS system time), the time delay which the receiver actually measures includes the user clock time offset with respect to system time. Because the measurements include this clock error, they are called pseudo-ranges. By properly processing these four measurements the user is able to determine his three position coordinates and correct his own clock error.

The receiver measures pseudo-range by correlating a locally generated replica of the PN code with the incoming signal, thereby collapsing the 20 megahertz spectrum of the received signal into the 50 hertz bandwidth associated with the 50 bps downlink data. Further processing by a Costas mechanization detects the 50 bps data and reconstructs the carrier. Because the received signal level is so low, signal-to-noise ratios adequate to make the needed range measurements can be achieved only with system bandwidths of a few hertz. Thus since the combined effect of satellite and

Dr. Hemesath is with Rockwell International, Collins Radio Group (M/S 106–187), Cedar Rapids, IA 52406.

vehicle dynamics can create doppler shifts as large as 10 kilohertz, tracking filters are used in the receiver. The carrier tracking loop centers the reconstructed carrier frequency and the code loop tracks the correlation function peak by controlling the locally generated PN code. Each of these loops can be thought of as a position servo tracking an input signal which varies with the dynamics of the vehicle and the satellite. The narrower the bandwidths of these two loops, the better the system signal–to–noise ratio. However, as illustrated in Fig. 2, there is a trade between dynamic tracking capability and system signal–to–noise ratio or anti–jamming performance. Thus, the design objectives are to choose the minimum system bandwidths that will track the maximum specified dynamics. The following section of the paper addresses the relationship between tracking loop errors and vehicle dynamics, while the remainder of this section discusses RMS tracking errors as a function of loop bandwidth in the absence of dynamics.

The RMS phase error of the Costas implementation of the carrier loop is:

$$\sigma_\phi = \left[\frac{B_L N}{C} \left(1 + \frac{N}{2CT_I} \right) \right]^{1/2}$$

where

B_L = Loop noise bandwidth in hertz

C = Received signal power
N = Noise power in one hertz bandwidth
T_I = Predetection integration period in seconds

This relationship is plotted in Fig. 3 for two different values of B_L as a function of J/S ratio in db where J/S and C/N are related as follows:

$$J/S + C/N = 70$$

This expression is valid for all interference sources well above the thermal noise level of the receiver. As will be discussed in the following, curves A and B of Fig. 3 represent the nominal design points for unaided and aided operation of the carrier loop, respectively. The 20 millisecond predetection integration interval is the largest possible due to the 50 bps data. Using the 0.5 radian carrier loop lock limit indicated in the figure, one can see that the carrier thresholds for the 20 hertz and the 1 hertz loops are approximately 50 db and 59 db, respectively. Implementation of a frequency tracking algorithm extends each of these thresholds several db.

The similar relationship which describes the RMS response of the code loop to noise (jamming) is

$$\frac{\sigma_T}{D} = \left[\frac{NB_L}{2C} \left(1 + \frac{2N}{CT_I} \right) \right]^{1/2}$$

The symbols have the same meaning as above except that D is the width of a single PN code chip. This expression is plotted in Fig. 4 as a

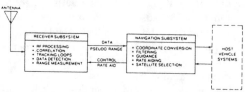

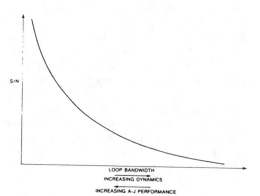

Fig. 1—GPS User Equipment Functional Diagram.

Fig. 2—Dynamics vs. S/N Trade.

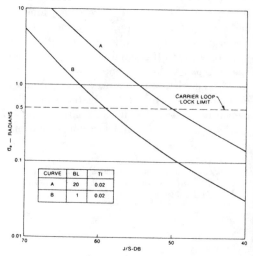

Fig. 3—Carrier Loop Noise Response.

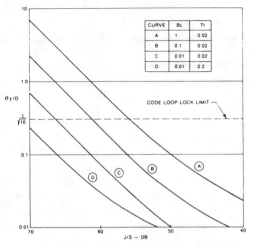

CURVE	BL	TI
A	1	0 02
B	0 1	0 02
C	0 01	0 02
D	0 01	0 2

Fig. 4—Code Loop Noise Response.

function of J/S for several values of B_L and T_I. Curve A, which corresponds to a completed unaided code loop, has a lock threshold of 56 db J/S; Curve C is an inertially aided implementation and thresholds at about 67 db. Curve D, with a threshold of 71 db, is a very special case: an inertially aided loop with T_I equal to 0.2 seconds. This integration interval is achievable only if the 50 bps is known *a priori* and multiplied off just as the 10 megahertz code is. This "data aiding" technique has some special uses but is not generally applicable because the data stream is not usually known in advance. In comparing thresholds it is clear that the phase locked carrier loop loses lock before the code loop.

TRACKING ERRORS UNDER DYNAMICS

Loop tracking errors are a combination of noise effects and loop lags due to dynamics. Fig. 2 illustrates that increasing loop bandwidth reduces dynamic errors but increases errors due to noise while the reverse is true for lowering loop bandwidth. A well designed tracking look achieves a balance between these two error components. The design procedure for either the code loop or the carrier loop is to select a bandwidth which produces tracking errors under maximum dynamics approximately equal to the lock limit of the loop.

Typical vehicle dynamics used for design are 900 m/s velocity, 50 m/s^2 acceleration and 100 m/s^3 jerk. Using a sinusoidal model for the dynamics produces the spectral representation

shown in Fig. 5. For that input spectrum Fig. 5 also shows the tracking errors as a function of frequency for second and third order code loops of 1 hertz bandwidth. The peak error for either loop is on the order of 10 meters, the code loop lock limit as shown in Fig. 4. Thus 1 hertz is about the lowest bandwidth which can be used to implement an unaided code tracking loop. A similar plot for the carrier loop with the tracking error criterion set at 0.5 radian would establish the loop bandwidth to accommodate full dynamics at approximately 20 hertz. Loop bandwidths are chosen based on vehicle dynamics because satellite dynamics as seen at the input to the tracking loops are considerably lower than vehicle dynamics.

PERFORMANCE ENHANCEMENT TECHNIQUES

The previous sections of this paper have established the performance capabilities of a basic GPS receiver. The tolerance to jamming inherent in the PN–coded signal structure has been summarized, and the tracking loop bandwidths dictated by dynamics have been identified. This section describes methods for enhancing performance and shows the amount of enhancement which each technique can be expected to produce. The performance enhancements consist of extending tracking loop thresholds rather than improving range measurement accuracies. The three principal techniques for enhancing performance are directive antennas, inertial aiding, and special signal processing. Each of the three is discussed below.

Antennas

The general antenna requirement for GPS

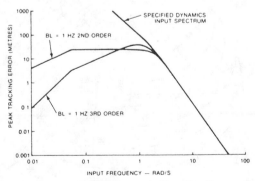

Fig. 5—Code Loop Dynamic Tracking Error.

user equipment is to provide uniform coverage over the upper hemisphere since satellites must be tracked anywhere from the horizon to the zenith. However, if maximum use is made of known user-to-satellite geometries and known or deducible jammer locations, antennas can be a very effective form of spatial filtering by providing selective directional responses. Two quite different antenna approaches which can be used are beam steering and adaptive null steering.

Beam steering involves developing and pointing beams towards each satellite being tracked, thereby providing gain to the desired signals and discrimination against all out-of-beam sources. Fig. 6 displays the beam characteristics. Direction cosine commands, based on user-to-satellite geometries, control each beam. The antenna array would normally lie in the horizontal plane with its aperture facing upward. As the figure shows, beams at or near zenith have a circular cross section while those near the horizon are elongated in the elevation plane. The disadvantages of beam steering are: (1) large array apertures are needed to form narrow beams at L-band, and (2) because beams must be spatially stabilized, beam steering computa-

tions for a high performance vehicle can become a very substantial computational task. Fig. 7 shows a typical set of beam patterns for an 18 × 18 inch array at the L_1 frequency. The 3 db width of the beams near zenith is approximately 30 degrees, and the first sidelobes are down about 15 db. Thus a jamming source anywhere outside of the primary beam would be suppressed 15 db or more with respect to the desired signal by this antenna.

As was previously mentioned, the PN-coded GPS signal is buried deep in thermal noise. Therefore any receiver input that rises above receiver front end noise must be interference. Adaptive null steering antennas use this fact to place nulls over strong interference sources. The outputs of several individual antenna elements are adaptively combined to minimize the total input power to the receiver system. This approach effectively drives a strong jammer down to the thermal noise level. Adaptive antennas need neither large aperture arrays nor computed pointing commands and consequently are potentially simpler and lower in cost than beam steering units. Their disadvantages are that they can create spurious nulls which may suppress the desired signal and that only a small number of jammers can be nulled simultaneously. Fig. 8 shows the characteristic behavior of an adaptive array. A jammer is located 21 degrees off boresight; the adaptive algorithm places the jammer in a deep null while maintaining the boresight gain. As the figure shows, it is possible to adaptively suppress a single jammer by 50 db or more. However, any one of the other deep nulls which are also present could suppress the desired signal as well. This potential difficulty oc-

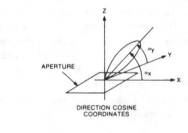

DIRECTION COSINE
COORDINATES

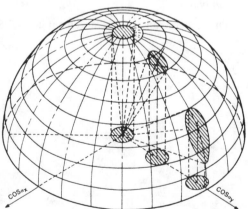

Fig. 6—Beam Steering Geometry.

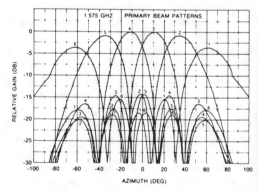

Fig. 7—Steered Array Beam Patterns.

curs because the adaptive system does not know the direction of the desired signal. If the line-of-sight vector to the satellite is provided, the adaptive algorithm can impose gain constraints which keep the spurious nulls from falling on the desired signal.

Inertial Aiding

The use of inertially derived range rate to aid both carrier and code tracking loops can substantially reduce loop bandwidths without the penalty of increased dynamic tracking errors. A generalized block diagram of an inertially aided tracking loop that is applicable for analysis of either carrier or code loops is shown in Fig. 9. Actual signal dynamics along the selected line-of-sight are described by the acceleration A(s). The velocity aiding signal (the dashed lines), although an imperfect measure of the true dynamics, drives the loop VCO in an open loop sense. The transfer function

$$\frac{1 - K}{\tau s + 1}$$

represents the imperfections in the measurement process where K is scale factor error and

τ models sensor or processing lags. Without aiding the loop transfer function is

$$\frac{E(s)}{A(s)} = \frac{1}{s^2 + sF(s)}$$

With velocity aiding it becomes

$$\frac{E(s)}{A(s)} = \frac{1}{s^2 + sF(s)} \frac{\tau s + K}{\tau s + 1}$$

Thus the effect of aiding is to modify the loop transfer function by the attenuation factor $(\tau s + K/\tau s + 1)$. With perfect aiding $(\tau = 0, K = 0)$ the loop tracks all dynamics without error thereby implying that bandwidths can become arbitrarily narrow. However, a more interesting and useful consideration is to ask how tracking bandwidths vary as a function of imperfect aiding. Specifically, assuming that the delay parameter τ is negligible, both carrier and code loop bandwidth variations as a function of scale factor error K have been analyzed.

Figs. 10 and 11 show the results for carrier and code loops, respectively. A sinusoidal dynamics model was used employing the peak values given in Fig. 10. The curves are normalized to the unaided case, i.e., $K = 1$. For the carrier loop $K = 0.001$ reduces the bandwidth needed for full dynamic capability from about 20 hertz to on the order of 2 hertz; for the code loop $K = 0.001$ reduces the necessary bandwidth from 1 hertz to about 0.03 hertz. $K = 0.001$ is roughly the level of performance of today's one nautical mile per hour inertial systems without special calibration. Thus, today's typical inertial systems by virtue of the loop bandwidth reductions they permit due to aiding, improve anti-

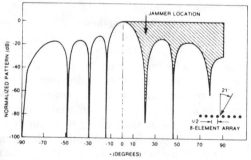

Fig. 8—Adaptive Array Response Pattern.

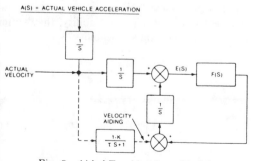

Fig. 9—Aided Tracking Loop Model.

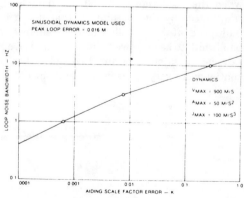

Fig. 10—Carrier Bandwidth vs. Quality of Aid.

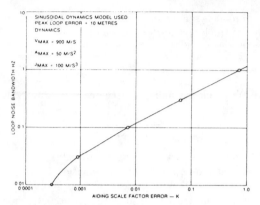

Fig. 11—Code Bandwidth vs. Quality of Aid.

jamming performance on the order of 10–15 db. Special calibration methods could reduce the scale factor error further, but it is unlikely that an order of magnitude improvement can be attained. Even if such a reduction in scale factor error were possible, other error sources would limit bandwidth. Although a detailed discussion is beyond the scope of this paper, some of these are gyro bias, random gyro drift, inertial axes misalignments, frequency standard phase noise, and frequency standard g sensitivity. Theoretically, all of these errors are compensatable via Kalman estimation techniques.

Special Processing

Certain special processing techniques can be used to enhance GPS user equipment performance. These methods apply in special situations or to special types of interference as contrasted to the general applicability of antenna techniques and inertial aiding. Data aiding, which has been mentioned previously, applies only when the user knows the 50 bps data being transmitted by the satellites so that it can be multiplied off thereby allowing the predetection bandwidth to be narrowed. Since switching from satellite to satellite occurs frequently due to continuously varying geometry and since data

must be detected for each newly acquired satellite before data aiding can be employed, the technique can be used for only brief periods—for example, to extend system operation another 5 or 6 db during a weapon delivery run against a target defended by a jammer.

Other processing techniques improve performance by operating on known waveform and spectral characteristics of jammers. These work by estimating the jammer based on an *a priori* model, correlating this estimate with the signal plus jammer, and adjusting the estimation parameter to minimize the correlation. One example is an adaptive notch filter which is effective against a narrow–band jammer. A second technique, also effective against narrow–band jamming, clips narrow–band spectral peaks generated by a frequency domain transform operation.

SUMMARY

Even though the GPS signal is coded to offer substantial processing gain, the great satellite–to–user distances mean that the receiver signal level is very low. Therefore performance enhancements in the form of improved jamming tolerance are desirable. The three principal enhancement techniques are:

1. Antenna methods
2. Inertial aiding
3. Special processing

Antennas offer the most potential improvement in anti–jamming capability. Improvements of 15 db are readily attainable and a gain of 40 db or more appears to be possible. Inertial aiding improves margins approximately 10–15 db; however, inertial systems also have other substantial benefits related to the navigation problem which make them very attractive for complementing GPS in a hybrid configuration. In general, while special processing techniques offer modest improvements in anti–jam capability, they suffer from lack of general applicability.

GPS User Equipment Error Models

E. H. MARTIN

ABSTRACT

THE BASIS FOR ESTABLISHING the fundamental mathematical error models associated with measurements of the Global Positioning System (GPS) signals by various types of user equipments is provided in this paper. The GPS user equipment error models which are described are intended to be utilized for various system performance and mission effectiveness analyses.

GPS PERFORMANCE

The level of navigation performance envisioned for the Global Positioning System is a direct result of the selected waveform characteristics of the GPS satellite signal. Operation with either the P (10.23 MHz) or C/A (1.023 MHz) code modulations to a large extent establishes the basic navigation accuracy level which may be provided to the user. The system level navigation performance accuracy is therefore formulated by error contributor categories for P or C/A signals.

The other significant performance constraint on GPS is the environmental medium or propagation link in which the signals are transmitted and received. Performance in the L–band spectrum is influenced by natural phenomenon and by the mechanization techniques which are employed and discussed in this paper.

Error contributions have been allocated to the various system segment contributors; the Space Vehicle segment, the Propagation Link, and ul-

Mr. Martin is with Magnavox Government and Industrial Electronics Co., Advanced Products Division, 2829 Maricopa St., Torrance, CA 90503. He presented this paper at the 33rd Annual Meeting of the Institute of Navigation in Costa Mesa, CA on June 23, 1977.

timately, the User Segment. These error contributions are shown categorically in Table I.

ERROR CHARACTERIZATION

The navigation error characterizations for GPS follow the definitions utilized by Reference 1. For each user observation of pseudorange toward a specific satellite the uncorrelated portion of the observed range error is termed the "User Equivalent Range Error" or UERE. Equivalently the range rate observed error toward the satellite may be termed the "User Equivalent Range Rate Error" or UERRE.

User navigation error defined in terms of three vector components of position and scalar system time is obtained by utilizing four independent scalar pseudorange observations. This resulting navigation error is thus defined by the UERE multiplied by the Geometric Dilution of Precision (GDOP) which is uniquely established by the geometric relationship between the user's position, and the specific positions of the four satellites utilized for the observations. Similarly the user velocity error and clock error drift rate are derived from the product of GDOP and the four UERRE measurements. These concepts provide a means of defining navigation capability which is not associated with geometric orientations but which instead stipulates fundamental measurement or observational errors inherent to the navigation process of the user equipment receiver and data processor. For performance analysis the specific mission profiles can be formulated in time, and by using specific direction cosines between the user and individual satellites the GDOP functions can be defined in a temporal and spatial sense.

Reference 2 provides an excellent summary of the mathematical derivations and definitions associated with the GPS GDOP term. Fig. 1 from the same reference summarizes the cumulative

Table 1—Categorical Error Sources for GPS

Error Contributor	Category
Satellite Ephemeris	Space Vehicle Segment
Satellite Delay and Clock	
User Receiver Measurement Error	User System Segment
User Mechanization Errors	
Ionosphere Delay	Propagation Link
Tropospheric Delay	
Multipath	

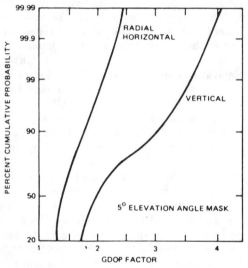

Fig. 1—*Cumulative GDOP Distribution for Operational GPS Phase.*

probability distribution function for the GDOP anticipated during the operational 24 satellite coverage phase. Navigation error in terms of both radial horizontal plane errors and vertical axis errors are indicated for a satellite elevation viewing restriction of 5° above the horizon.

DELTA RANGE CHARACTERIZATION

As a result of both preliminary design studies and subsequent design mechanization implementations, the concept of "Delta Range" has been formulated to characterize the user receiver performance in measuring equivalent pseudorange rates or specifying UERRE. The Delta Range is fundamentally the change in pseudorange toward a particular satellite over a finite time interval. The utility of Delta Range is that it can be readily mechanized by counting

the carrier doppler cycles over the time interval of interest, and secondly it avoids the necessity of formulating an instantaneous value of satellite ephemeris rate of change. Thus, fundamentally, the Delta range is specified for error characterizations, and the measurement of Delta range over the time interval can be thought of as an "average velocity" or pseudorange rate toward the satellite.

SPACE VEHICLE SEGMENT

The Space Vehicle Segment consists of the satellite emitters which provide the basic GPS signals. Satellites for GPS will be positioned into circular 10,900 nautical miles, 12–hour orbits. Commencing with six (6) satellite launches during Phase I, the coverage will expand to an ultimate twenty–four (24) satellite capability for the fully operational Phase III implementation. Since the navigation mechanization for GPS employs the satellite ephemeris and clock states with respect to GPS system time, errors in these terms enter into the navigation solution.

This paper will not establish the space vehicle error models, but it should be noted that the GPS navigation error model for the space vehicles can be expressed as a simple linearized covariance description. Generally, the complexity of the time–varying propagation of the satellite ephemeris and clock error states is reduced to a single constant UERE, whose variance is the square of the standard deviations given in Table II for each individual satellite.

USER PSEUDORANGE MEASUREMENTS

The GPS User System Segment receiving equipment provides the GPS pseudoranging signal measurement. Every nth satellite emitter transmission consists of a unique pseudorandom code which is monitored by the ground segment. Measurements and data are periodically updated to establish the satellite code epochs with

Table 2—GPS Space Vehicle UERE Contributors

Source	Phase I	Phase III
Satellite Ephemeris	3.6 meter*	1.5 meter
Satellite Group Delay and Clock	2.7 meter	0.9 meter

* All expressed in UERE (1σ)

respect to system time as determined at the Master Station. In this manner time synchronization is determined for each of the nth satellite clocks.

User receivers generate similar pseudorandom phase-shift keyed code sequences relevant to the unsynchronized user clocks and by means of a cross–correlation detection process the time shift between the satellite code sequences and the user code epochs is measured. The time shift measurement consists of the delay due to actual range separation; timing uncertainty due to differences in the user clock relative to the satellite clock; and errors introduced by the measurement process.

Ranging Geometry

The exact range scalar between a user and an orbiting satellite is defined by the quantity (see Fig. 2).

$$\bar{R}_n = \bar{E}_n - \bar{P} \qquad (1)$$

where

$\bar{R}_n$ = range vector
$\bar{P}$ = user position vector
$\bar{E}_n$ = nth satellite position vector

From received satellite data the user calculates

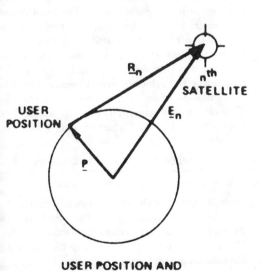

**USER POSITION AND
SATELLITE EMITTER
GEOMETRY**

Fig. 2—User Position and Satellite Emitter Geometry.

an estimate of the nth satellite position vector such that

$\hat{\bar{E}}_n$ = estimate of the nth satellite position vector

and

$$\hat{\bar{E}}_n = \bar{E}_n + \Delta\bar{E}_n \qquad (2)$$

where

$\overline{\Delta E}_n$ = nth satellite position error vector

Each receiver pseudorange measurement can then be expressed in range terms as:

$$S_n = |\bar{R}_n| + c(b_u - b_n) + \Delta L_n + \delta_m \qquad (3)$$

where

S_n = pseudorange measurement to nth satellite
b_n = n^{th} satellite clock error
b_u = user clock delay
ΔL_n = propagation link errors
δ_m = measurement error terms in range
c = speed of light

The following sections of this paper define the magnitudes and functions of the User Segment measurement error, δ_m, for pseudorange and Delta range. These user measurement errors consist primarily of receiver noise and receiver quantization contributions which are functions of the received signal–to–noise ratios and of the user receiver precision.

Additional mechanization processing errors are also allocated to the user measurement error process. It should be noted that user clock delays which are correlated between measurements do not propagate into a GPS User Segment navigation error contribution. These bias user clock delays are estimated by the navigational estimation process and hence user clock biases may be omitted from system error modeling for performance analysis. Time dynamic user clock error variations which may exist due to user clock noise or environmental noise models should be included for analyses which consider sequential receiver operations or missions with extended periods of GPS signal outage. Reference 3 provides an excellent summary of such dynamic user clock error models for GPS systems which employ quartz crystal oscillators.

Environmental error terms encountered by

the GPS system will generally be classified under the propagation link errors, ΔL_n, due to ionospheric and tropospheric delays and multipath signal effects. Propagation link error models and definitions are derived in subsequent sections of this paper.

GPS Receiver Implementations

The heart of any GPS receiver measurement system consists of two interacting tracking loops. For most Magnavox design implementations, a composite Costas/AFC carrier tracking loop is employed in conjunction with a non-coherent τ-dither code tracking loop. Numerous tracking variations and mechanizations are possible in designing the receiver to satisfy different user requirements or performance goals. This paper employs the above design as a basis for quantifying expected performance and also indicates the parametric functional variation about this performance level.

The GPS receiver carrier and code phase measurements are implemented digitally to achieve accurate tracking performance while retaining design flexibility for application to a wide variety of military users.

Because of the digital precision and stability, the receiver performance can be expected to approach ideal theoretical performance limitations, with the only significant performance losses being due to the finite sampling intervals. Another important benefit of the digital implementation is that it can be easily and quickly tailored to fit a particular military application. Alteration of dynamic loop parameters such as tracking loop bandwidths may be accomplished as a function of signal quality, user dynamics, or with aiding from an external source such as an Inertial Measurement Unit.

Pseudorange Measurement Noise

The generic GPS pseudorange measurement is provided by the user receiver code tracking functions. In one mechanization, the code replica phase is dithered between early and late samples separated by one code bit interval and the difference in the cross correlation function is computed.

These differences are a measurement of the code tracking error which establishes the amount of phase correction which is applied to

a code loop filter algorithm. The performance o the PN (pseudo-noise) code measurement of the user receiver depends upon the selected code modulation and the signal quality. It is possible to formulate a generalized measurement noise expression in terms of noise variance for the code loops as:

$$\frac{\sigma^2}{\Delta^2} = \frac{K_1 B_n}{(C/N_0)} + \frac{K_2 B_i B_n}{(C/N_0)^2} \qquad (4$$

where

σ^2 = variance of measurement noise
Δ = code modulation chip width
C/N_0 = carrier-to-noise density ratio
B_n = one-sided code tracking loop noise bandwidth
B_i = one-sided IF bandwidth for non-coherent code tracking mechanizations
K_1 = code mechanization parameter constant, variable with selected design
K_2 = code mechanization parameter constant, variable with selected design and applicable to noncoherent code tracking implementations

From a performance viewpoint, the selection of a dual channel, coherent code tracking, receiver design offers the best theoretical measurement noise since $K_1 = \frac{1}{2}$ and $K_2 = 0$. For τ-dither or non-coherent configurations, the performance degradation ranges from 3 to 6 dB less due to the average power loss in time sharing or to the squaring loss introduced by the IF bandwidth In a sense, the relation given in equation (4) is a normalized error function whose magnitude depends on the selected code chip width. For the codes used by GPS, the following values are defined:

Δ_p = P code chip width = 29.32 meters

Δ_c = C code chip width = 293.2 meters

With definition of the selected code chip width, it is possible to evaluate the error functional. As an example Fig. 3 provides an evaluation for P-code operation for a code loop design using the following parameters:

B_n = 1.0 Hertz
B_i = 150 Hertz
K_1 = 1.0
K_2 = 2.0

For nominal GPS operations the signal density will be in the region of $C/N_0 = 30$ dB–Hz and the rms code measurement error for P–code operation is found to be:

$\sigma_p = 1.05$ meters (1 σ rms)

and for C/A code operation the error is:

$\sigma_c = 10.5$ meters (1 σ rms)

The measurement noise error is plotted in Fig. 3 for the dependency on signal–to–noise ratio in dB–Hertz. Selection of the noise bandwidth is basically an antagonistic compromise between accuracy and the opposing requirements for dynamic motion imposed upon the receiver tracking loops. Reduction of the noise bandwidth to values less than 1.0 Hertz requires velocity aiding from the carrier loop, or from an augmenting Inertial Measurement Unit. Precision carrier tracking of frequency using a coherent Costas loop may be maintained for $C/N_0 \geq 25$ dB–Hz. For lower values of carrier signal the precision tracking mode is obviated, and the carrier loop reverts to AFC mode with degraded accuracy. This operation is termed the HOBYT mode for "Hold on by your teeth". Operation in the HOBYT mode is provided to maintain tracking in low signal environments and is maintained without inertial aiding to levels of $C/N_0 = 20$ dB–Hz. Below this level IMU aiding is required and effects such as oscillator phase noise, vibration–induced phase noise, aiding delays and ultimately IMU accuracy limit code tracking performance.

Code Loop Error Model

The code loop pseudorange error model for covariance error analysis should generally be approximated as a first order Markov process with an exponential autocorrelation function. This approximation is valid for code loop implementations that utilize a first order code loop filter algorithm and may be altered accordingly for higher order mechanization implementations. The correlated nature of the code loop measurement noise must be accounted for in the navigation filter estimation process by an expanded state formulation or by other forms of mechanization compensation.

Receiver Range Quantization

The selection of the receiver pseudorange

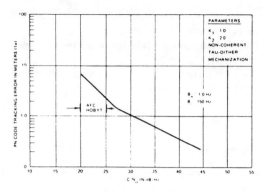

Fig. 3—P-Code Pseudorange Measurement Accuracy.

quantization is a variable parameter which can be chosen to be a negligible error contributor. Present designs with the GPS PN code rates and digital implementations provide a selected code phase tracking resolution which permits tracking accuracies on the order of a few feet. As an example, pseudorange measurements of the code may be quantized to $\frac{1}{64}$ of a PN code chip. Depending upon which code rate is being employed, the following quantization sizes are defined.

Factors	P–Code	C/A Code
Code Rate	10.23 MB/s	1.023 MB/s
Code Chip Size	29.32 m	293.2 m
Quantization Size	0.46 m	4.6 m

Using the assumption that the quantization error is a uniform distribution over the quantization sizes indicated, the resultant errors are:

P Code _____ 0.266 meter (1σ)
C/A Code _____ 2.66 meter (1σ)

The code loop range quantization error is defined as a white noise function which is uncorrelated from measurement to measurement with a variance defined by the appropriate value for P or C/A code operation.•

Delta Range Measurement Noise

The carrier tracking loop of a GPS receiver must function to provide accurate carrier phase tracking, data recovery, and phase rate aiding of the code loops. For Magnavox designs, a composite Automatic Frequency Control (AFC) and Costas loop mechanization is employed to allow rapid phase lock from a large initial frequency error and to provide high accuracy coherent phase tracking measurements.

The classical equation for noise performance in a carrier phase lock loop can be employed to define the Delta range measurement noise. The relationship is given as:

$$\sigma_\phi^2 = \frac{B_L}{C/N_0} \cdot \frac{\lambda^2}{6.28^2} \tag{5}$$

where

σ_ϕ^2 = variance of measurement noise
B_L = one-sided carrier loop noise
λ = carrier wavelength
C/N_0 = carrier-to-noise power density

Depending upon which carrier frequency is being employed, the following phase error characterizes each measurement of phase at C/N_0 = 30 dB Hz with B_L = 20 Hertz:

$\sigma_{\phi 1} = 0.44$ cm at $\lambda_1 = 19$ cm
$\sigma_{\phi 2} = 0.56$ cm at $\lambda_2 = 24.5$ cm

Since the definition of Delta range is that of a change in range over a defined time interval, the effect of the measurement noise will be to increase the noise by the $\sqrt{2}$ (given that the time interval is sufficient to insure independent samples).

So,

$\sigma_{\Delta R_1} = 0.62$ cm at $\lambda_1 = 19$ cm
$\sigma_{\Delta R_2} = 0.80$ cm at $\lambda_2 = 24.5$ cm

The Delta range measurement error is plotted in Fig. 4 as a function of carrier-to-noise density ratio.

Receiver Delta Range Quantization

Delta range measurements are accomplished by counting the number of L_1 or L_2 carrier cycles that occur over a finite interval in the GPS user receiver carrier phase lock loop. Since the carrier tracking loop is phase locked to the incoming signals, the total phase change accumulated over the measurement cycle is equivalent to the integral of the Doppler phase rate (frequency) due to relative motion between the user and the satellites during the measurement interval.

The accumulated phase increments are quantized in the receiver Costas tracking loop to be $\frac{1}{64}$ of a cycle or wavelength of the received carrier frequency. Depending upon which fre-

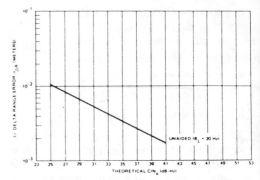

Fig. 4—Delta Range Measurement Accuracy.

quency is being tracked, the following quantization sizes result for the Delta range measurement:

Factor	L_1	L_2
Frequency	1575 MHz	1227 MHz
Wavelength	19 cm	24.5 cm
Quantization Size	3 mm	3.8 mm

From the magnitudes given, the data indicates that the Delta range measurement is extremely precise and for measurement intervals of the order of 0.1 to 0.5 seconds in length that the "average velocity" magnitudes are of the order of hundredths of meters per second. This extreme precision is maintained as long as the carrier Costas loop is locked and tracking. During decreased signal levels when coherent carrier tracking is obviated, the receiver utilizes non-coherent AFC tracking. During this carrier AFC operation mode, or with subsequent carrier signal outage, the Delta range measurement observable is *not* utilized or provided to the navigation processing.

For uniform distributions of the Delta range within the quantization size the quantization error for the two frequencies of operation is:

L_1 Frequency_____ 2.5 mm (1σ)
L_2 Frequency_____ 3.1 mm (1σ)

MECHANIZATION ERROR ALLOCATIONS

The implementation of the GPS navigation solution in any specific navigation computer introduces mechanization errors which can be allocated to pseudorange and Delta range measurements. The source of the mechanization error contributions is due to finite computer bit resolution, mathematical approximations, algorithm uncertainties, and execution or timing delays inherent in the computations.

Utilization of present day computer capabilities for double precision, extended precision, and floating point mechanizations can provide error contributions of the following values:

Scalar Pseudorange
Mechanization error   1.0 meter

Delta Range
Mechanization error   0.1 meter

These error sources (1σ) can be assumed to be white noise error statistics for analysis purposes.

PROPAGATION LINK ERRORS

The propagation link errors have been identified as being due to ionospheric delay, tropospheric delay, and multipath. The following sections of this paper derive and quantify the magnitudes of these error sources, the form of the compensation mechanizations which may be employed, and ultimately the form of the resulting error residuals appropriate to performance analysis.

Ionospheric Code Modulation Delay

The presence of a finite transmission medium produces a pseudorange code modulation delay with a resulting range bias error. The ionospheric delay depends upon the columnar electron content along the line-of-sight between the satellite and user receiver. Data shown in Fig. 5 expresses the ionospheric delay in terms of the maximum possible ionospheric delay error. An analytical expression for the ionospheric delay is given as:

$$\Delta L = \frac{-b}{4\pi^2 f^2} I_v \left[\csc\left(E^2 + 20.3^2\right)\right]^{1/2} \quad (6)$$

where

ΔL = Ionospheric Delay in meters
b = 1.6×10^3 = constant in MKS unit
f = carrier frequency in hertz
I_v = vertical electron content in electrons/meter²
E = elevation angle in degrees

The two prime statistical uncertainties for the above model are the variations of electron content and geometric obliquity as indicated by Fig.

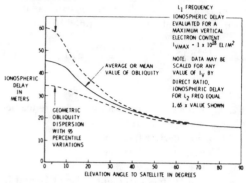

Fig. 5—Frequency Ionospheric Delay Evaluated for a Maximum Vertical Electron Content ($I_{V_{max}} = 1 \times 10^{18}$ el/m²).

5. When the solar cycle is near its maximum value, the mid–day electron content can be as large as 10^{18} electrons/meter² at the mid-latitudes.

Average values of daytime electron content are generally an order of magnitude less, and the diurnal minimum for total electron content can be as low as 10^{16} electrons/meter², which yields an ionospheric delay error of less than 0.5 meter. To provide compensation for the ionospheric delay error, either real–time dual frequency measurements can be employed or apriori modeling estimation of the delay can be used.

Dual Frequency Measurement Error

Military users of GPS that are seeking high system accuracy can make use of real–time dual frequency measurements employing both L_1 and L_2 frequency channels to determine ionospheric delay. The resultant accuracy of the dual frequency measurements is determined by the measurement noise inherent in each code channel pseudorange estimate.

The basis for the two frequency method of correcting for ionospheric group delay is that the delay error is an exactly deterministic function of frequency or

$$\Delta L = \frac{K}{F^2} \quad (7)$$

where

K = constant scale factor
F = L_1 or L_2 carrier frequency

The mechanization uses the difference between L_1 and L_2 pseudorange measurements to estimate the scale factor as defined by:

$$\hat{K} = \frac{[\hat{\Delta}_p - \sigma_1 + \sigma_2]}{(1 - \alpha^2)} (F_1^2) \qquad (8)$$

where

$\hat{\Delta}_p$ = measured pseudorange difference between L_1 and L_2 frequency
F_1 = L_1 carrier frequency
F_2 = L_2 carrier frequency
α = F_1/F_2 = 1.28.
σ_1, σ_2 = code measurement noise at L_1 and L_2

Residual mechanization error for this dual frequency technique yields a dual frequency error variance of

$$\sigma_\Delta^2 = \frac{\sigma_2^2 + \alpha^4 \sigma_1^2}{[\alpha^2 - 1]} \qquad (9)$$

With the assumption of equal noise variances for both L_1 and L_2 frequencies, the dual frequency measurement error is

$$\sigma_\Delta \cong 3.0\sigma \qquad (10)$$

where

σ = rms code loop measurement noise defined in equation (4)

The interesting result of this dual frequency mechanization is that the basic deterministic error function for ionospheric delay given in equation (7) is replaced by a noise–like measurement error whose standard deviation is a 3.0 multiple of the measurement noise given by equation (4). The resultant dual frequency measurement noise is also dependent upon C/N_0 signal density in the same functional manner as indicated by equation (4). This noise–like dual frequency error can be further reduced by multiple measurement time averaging subject to the temporal and spatial ionospheric delay gradients encountered by the user.

Apriori Algorithm Estimation

User classes which do not employ dual frequency ionospheric compensation may be mechanized to utilize apriori mathematical ionospheric models. Numerous prognostication studies and empirical data modeling concepts are being considered to provide apriori modeling

estimates for L–band ionospheric delay. From these studies it is possible to determine the factors that influence the values of electron content and geometric obliquity. The most important of these factors are:

> Diurnal Variation (time of day)
> Latitude Dependency (geographic latitude)
> Seasonal Variation (time of year)
> Solar Cycle Variation (phase of sun spot cycle)

To date the veracity of apriori modeling, even with near real–time parametric data, appears to reduce the ionospheric delay error by only 50 to 75 percent. The residual error effect of such modeling compensation will yield an error that is given as:

$$\Delta L = \Delta K \csc [E^2 + 20^2]^{1/2} \qquad (11)$$

where

ΔK = fractional value of reduced ionospheric delay
= 5 meters to ≤ 0.5 meters

Later phases of GPS operation will undoubtedly improve the modeling estimation technique and a real–time delay model message has been accommodated in the satellite data word format for this purpose.

Tropospheric Delay Error

The finite propagation media of the troposphere results in a code phase delay uncertainty due to the unknown refractivity index alteration on the propagation velocity as it differs from the speed of light. This effect has a very deterministic functional dependency which may be stated as

$$D_t = C \, N(h) \csc (E) \qquad (12)$$

where

C = constant of environmental conditions
$N(h)$ = line integral of user to satellite refractivity function
E = elevation angle of satellite

Evaluation of the air density constants and refractivity line integrals for various natural conditions is well documented in numerous refernces with very specific GPS data considered in Reference 4. With low elevation satellites at 5°, and large surface values of refractivity the tropospheric delay can be approximately 80 feet.

Utilization of an altitude dependent mathematical model for compensation of the fundamental tropospheric delay effect will remove a large portion of the error, and the only remaining error is a residual tropospheric term. This residual error term has the same basic functional dependency as was given in equation (12).

$$\Delta D \cong \Delta C \exp\left[-\frac{0.034}{T} h \right] \csc (E) \qquad (13)$$

where

ΔC = residual compensation magnitude
h = vehicle altitude in meters
T = absolute temperature
E = elevation angle to satellite

From Reference 4 it is estimated that the standard deviation value of ΔC is between 4 to 5 percent of the uncompensated tropospheric delay depending upon the users knowledge of surface refractivity in the area of operation. For performance studies a value of ΔC on the order of 0.1 meters (1σ) appears to be suitable for most users.

Propagation Gradients

Consideration of the rates of changes of the ionospheric and tropospheric delay errors indicates that gradient effects are of the order of meters per hour. For user systems that actually transition through significant portions of the ionosphere or troposphere the geometric gradient can increase by an order of magnitude but the effect can be deterministically evaluated. Evaluation of the combined effects of vertical gradients, spatial gradient, and geometric motion defines a gradient bound of:

$$\frac{d\Delta L}{dt} \leq 10 \, \frac{\text{meters}}{\text{hour}} = 2.75 \times 10^{-3} \, \frac{\text{meter}}{\text{second}}$$

Delta range measurement errors due to the above gradient depend upon the time interval over which the gradient is observed. For nominal 1.5 second intervals the propagation gradients contribute to the delta range error an ensemble rms value which is approximately equal to the measurement noise contributed by the receiver.

This gradient rms value has a functional dependency with elevation angle similar to the basic propagation link error and thus the gradient model for delta range error can be bounded by the following function:

$$\delta = \frac{0.5 \times 10^{-3}}{\Delta t} \csc E \qquad (14)$$

where

Δt = delta range measurement interval
E = satellite elevation angle

Multipath Errors

The pseudonoise code modulation of the GPS signal provides an inherent rejection to multipath interference signals which do not occur within one code width of the direct signal time delay. Analysis of specific multipath signal magnitudes, time delays, and phase relations in conjunction with detailed receiver processing functions is generally too specific and not indicative of the transient and sporadic nature of the dynamic multipath. In user applications, the multipath signal is generally a function of user vehicle attitudes, and antenna pattern alterations with respect to the multipath. Only vehicle surfaces reflection should provide the spectral magnitude required to alter the code delay measurements although certain sea states could be a source of multipath for naval vehicles. An error budget allocation for multipath has been defined to be a noise–like measurement error whose ensemble statistics have an rms value of 1.0 to 3.0 meters for P–code operations.

Since the multipath error magnitude is dependent upon the code rates utilized, the magnitude for C/A code operation should be increased to an rms value an order of magnitude greater. Reference 5 provides a quantitative evaluation of the multipath error magnitudes for specific mission analysis conditions if such performance values are considered to be typical of the user scenario.

ERROR MODEL SUMMARY

Evaluation of GPS NAVSTAR system performance and mission effectiveness analysis requires the incorporation and propagation of a number of functionally dependent and mechanization unique system and user error models.

Table 3—Error Summary

Error Contributor	Pseudorange	Delta-Range	Statistics	Notes
Satellite Ephermeris	1.5 meter		Bias	Uncorrelated between Satellites.
Satellite Group and Clock	1.0 meter		Bias	Uncorrelated between Satellites.
Satellite Clock Noise		3×10^{-3} meter	White Noise	Assumed Cesium clock and 0.5 second interval.
Pseudorange Noise	1.0 meter		Markov	Evaluated at $C/N_0 = 30$ db for P-Code.
Range Quantization	0.266 meter		White Noise	
Range Mechanization Error	1.0 meter		White Noise	
Delta-Range Measurement Noise		6×10^{-3} meter	White Noise	Evaluated at $C/N_0 = 30$ db for P-Code.
Delta-Range Quantization		3×10^{-3} meter	White Noise	
Delta-Range Mechanization		0.1 meter	White Noise	
Ionospheric Dual Frequency	3.0 meter		Markov	Evaluated at $C/N_0 = 30$ db for P-Code. No Averaging.
Tropospheric Residual	1.0 meter		Bias	Evaluated at $5°$ elevation and zero altitude.
Propagation Gradient		1.0×10^{-2} meter	Markov	Spatial and temporal decorrelation. Evaluated at $5°$ elevation.
Multipath Error	1.0 meter		White Noise	

The significant user error contributors which should be incorporated have been presented and defined to be appropriate to a large class of user ensemble statistics or covariance error analyses. Table III provides a summary of these error contributors and is intended to illustrate the terms which may be employed for a P-code user performance analysis.

Simulation and analysis sophistication beyond the degree presented herein is of course anticipated for further more detailed performance studies. Consideration of complex simulation terms related to signal tracking dynamics, sequential data switching and delay transients, and the topic of receiver aiding are appropriate subjects for user model expansion.

REFERENCES

1. System Specification for the NAVSTAR Global Positioning System, Phase I, Specification Number SS-GPS-101B, 15 April 1974.
2. "NAVSTAR/GPS: Operational Status", E. M. Lassiter and Col. B. Parkinson; Proceedings of the International Navigation Congress, Boston, Mass. August 1976.
3. "Clock Error Models for Simulation and Estimation" by J. S. Meditch, Aerospace Report TOR-0076(6474-01)-2, July 1975.
4. "Tropospheric Range Error Corrections for the NAVSTAR System" by E. E. Atlshuler, and P. M. Kalaghan, Air Force Cambridge Research Laboratories, AFCRL-TR-74-0198, April 1974.
5. "Effects of Multipath on Coherent and Noncoherent PRN Ranging Receiver" by L. N. Hagerman, Aerospace Report No. TOR-0073 (3020-03)-3, May 1973.

Test and Evaluation Procedures for the GPS User Equipment

S. K. GUPTA

ABSTRACT

THREE MAJOR CONTRACTORS, Collins Avionics and Missiles Division of Rockwell International, Magnavox, and Texas Instruments are currently involved in the development of a number of GPS user equipments. These will be flight tested to obtain a comprehensive evaluation of the GPS concept in the first phase of the program. However, prior to flight testing, a complete performance evaluation of these systems in the laboratory has been planned and for some systems, it is already in progress. To accomplish this objective, a number of SV signal generators and simulators have been designed and built, either under contract from the various administrative agencies or by the user equipment developers with private funding.

These signal simulator systems provide a precise simulation of the satellite signals as received by the user equipment at its antenna. The effects of user vehicle dynamics, satellite motion and the atmospheric anomalies are precisely simulated. In the case of testing the high performance user equipment like the Generalized Development Model (GDM) system, the signal simulator also provides simulation of other auxiliary subsystems such as the INS system of the user vehicle.

This paper describes the requirements and procedures employed in the pre-flight laboratory testing of the various user systems.

I. INTRODUCTION

NAVSTAR Global Positioning System is about to enter the final stage of its Phase I development–the stage of comprehensive field

Dr. Gupta is with Rockwell International, Collins Radio Group (M/S 107-142), Cedar Rapids, IA 52406.

testing. The three major contractors–Rockwell/Collins, Magnavox, and Texas Instruments (TI)–for the development of the various user set concepts will be required to demonstrate the navigation accuracy expected of a GPS System at the Army Proving Grounds near Yuma, Arizona. Some field tests using inverted range have already been performed successfully with expected results. However, it is expected that GPS signals from four satellites will be available in the second half of 1978 for periods of up to four hours each day for full–fledged field tests. Nonetheless, for development purposes, it is necessary to test and evaluate the performance of the user sets in the laboratory to avoid making time consuming modifications during field tests. A number of test systems and procedures have been developed for this purpose. This paper presents some of these system concepts and test procedures.

Even though the performance characteristics and environmental conditions may be different for the different user sets, the driving signals are the same for all types of GPS receivers. The basic characteristics of these signals are given below.

- —Bi-phase modulated rf signals on two carrier frequencies, L_1 (1575.42 MHz) and L_2 (1227.6 MHz) simultaneously.
- —Each signal modulated with a unique pseudo–random noise (PN) code out of a possible 37 code sequences.
- —Both P (protected, 10.23 MHz, 7 days long), and C/A (clear/acquisition, 1.023 MHz, 1 millisecond long) codes provided on L_1 and only P code modulation on L_2.

Usually a number of additional simulations are required from the test systems used in the laboratory. This may include all or a combination of the following:

—Provide four or more signals simultaneously, each with a different PN code.

—Simulate the effects of satellite and user vehicle dynamics on each test signal. This requires a precise computation of doppler frequencies as a function of relative motion between the user vehicle and the satellite.

—Simulate the influence of atmospheric effects as experienced by the signals while traveling through the atmosphere. In other words, the simulation of tropospheric and ionospheric delays.

—Provide measured S/N ratios for each test signal.

A number of simulator systems capable of providing signals with the above characteristics have in fact been designed and built, some under contract from the various GPS administrative agencies and others by the user equipment developers with private funding. Following is a summary of these systems.

A Satellite Vehicle Signal Simulator (SVSS) designed and built at Rockwell–Collins under contract from AFAL. This simulator provides signals on four parallel channels and includes manual control of attenuators. It is also capable of accepting jammer signals from outside sources.

A Satellite Vehicle Signal Generator (SVSG) developed at Magnavox Corp. under contract from SAMSO. This system incorporates an automatic control of signal attenuators.

A GPS User Equipment Performance Evaluator (GPSE) under development at I.T.T. under contract from AFAL. This system is, in principle, an updated version of the SVSS system. GPSE will provide an automatic control of attenuators as well as dynamic jammers. This system will also provide an automatic switching of PN codes to be modulated on to the test signals. For further details of this system refer to (1).

A NAVSTAR/GPS Simulator developed by Texas Instruments Inc. under private funding. It is a dynamic signal simulator for one rf channel and has the provision for adding more channels as may be necessary. For further details reader is referred to (2).

II. DESIGN CONSIDERATIONS FOR A SATELLITE VEHICLE SIMULATOR SYSTEM

The basic principle of operation of the GPS concept is to provide extremely accurate timing signals to a user system. When four such signals are received from four different satellites, the geographic position of the user in three dimensions along with user clock bias can be determined. Time differential of user position can be computed to obtain its velocity. It is important that the signals used to test the performance of the user equipment be precisely simulated. The following is a brief analysis of the various requirements of a satellite vehicle simulator system.

Basic Characteristics of the Test Signals

The rf hardware subsystem employed in the simulator systems usually provides all the desired characteristics of the signals. The rf assembly employs one code generator for each channel. In case of multi–channel systems, a number of identical code generators equal to the number of channels are employed. For example, the SVSS system employs four identical code generators.

Hardwired logic for the code generators provides the desired basic characteristics of the signals. Each code generator is capable of providing any one of the 37 PN code sequences on receiving an appropriate command. Another control is provided to select the P or C/A code for the L_2 carrier. Once selected, these codes remain fixed throughout the duration of the test. However, the GPSE System will have the provision for real time control of the PN code selection which is similar to satellite switching.

Computation of the Doppler Shift

Doppler shift is a well known phenomenon of Classical Physics. It represents the change in frequency of a signal emitted by a source caused by relative motion between the source and an observer receiving the signal. The GPS signals experience complex doppler shifts. Three components of frequency shifts encountered are: two components for the carrier frequencies L_1 and L_2 and the third for the PN code. These effects become particularly important for the high dynamics user equipments.

The change in frequency due to the doppler effect is proportional to the relative velocity between the source and the receiver (i.e. the satellite and the user antenna respectively). The known dynamics of the satellite and the user vehicle for simulation purposes enable the designer to directly compute the doppler frequencies as a function of time. The computed doppler frequencies are then continuously superimposed upon the nominal frequencies of the signals.

Simulation of Atmospheric Effects on the Signals

The path of the rf signals is considerably modified as they travel through the earth's atmosphere. The resulting two significant effects are due to the troposphere (altitudes of 0–100 Km), and the ionosphere (altitudes of 100–2000 Km). The GPS systems must consider the effects of these two regions on the signals to provide accurate results. The systems on the receiving end must be able to fully compensate for these effects in the acquired signals, while the signal simulator systems must be able to incorporate these effects on the signals generated.

The two atmospheric regions mentioned above cause delays in the propagation of rf signals. The impact of these delays is equivalent to the signals traveling through a longer path. The models employed in the SVSS system to compute the delays in the propagation path are:

1. *Ionospheric Delay Model:*
The interface control document (3) describes a model to compute the time delay of radio signals through the ionosphere. However, since the ionospheric delay is a known function of the frequency, two coherent signals can be used to measure the delay. This mechanism is, in fact, employed in most of the user set designs. Analytically the ionospheric delay can be calculated by the relationship,

$$\Delta R_I = c\Delta t_I = \frac{ck}{(f)^2} \tag{1}$$

where c is the speed of light, f is the frequency of the rf carrier, and k is a constant depending upon time of day, latitude, and longitude of the receiver position. If a GPS receiver measures the relative delay between the two frequencies L_1 and L_2 directly, this measurement can be used in Equation (1) to compute the value of k. This enables the computation of absolute ionospheric delays for the two carrier and the code frequencies. However, for laboratory tests, it may be desired to simulate known and fixed relative

delays of, say, 0, 1/2, 1, or some similar values of P-code chips (1 P-chip = 98 nanoseconds) on to the signals. The GPS receiver under test is then expected to precisely detect the values of the relative and hence absolute delays. For a detailed discussion of ionospheric effects on rf signals refer to (3).

2. *Tropospheric Delay Model:*
In contrast to the ionospheric delay, the path delay due to the troposphere depends upon the altitude of the user above the sea level and is independent of rf frequency. A simple model to calculate this delay is described in (4). The path delay obtained by using this model is given in Equation (2).

$$\Delta R_T = c\Delta t_T = \frac{2.4224}{0.026 + \mathrm{Sin}\,E}\,\mathrm{EXP} \atop [-0.13346 \times H] \tag{2}$$

where H is the altitude (Km) of the user above sea level, and E is the surface refractivity.

Variation of S/N Ratio

The simulator system must provide a control for the signal-to-noise ratios of the simulated signals to account for the loss of signal power during travel through the atmosphere. This control is achieved by providing variable attenuators in line with the output signals.

System Structure

A simplified block diagram showing the overall structure of a simulator system is presented in Fig. 1. In this figure the overall system is shown to consist of two main parts: the software subsystem and the hardware subsystem. System controller is an interface between these two subsystems. Due to the complex nature of some simulation tasks, it is necessary to further divide the software tasks into two programs. The offline program is used to perform the computations which require large execution times. The results of these computations are recorded on a magnetic tape or a disk. The real time program reads

Fig, 1—Block Diagram of a GPS Signal Simulator System.

this data and uses it to generate proper commands to the hardware subsystem.

III. TEST PROCEDURES

Thus far, we have been concerned with the requirements of a GPS receiver system and some of the important features that must be considered during the design of a simulator system to generate GPS signals in the laboratory. In this section we shall discuss the actual use of a simulator system to evaluate the performance of a receiver system. A straight forward method to accomplish this is to design the system to be tested, simulate desired flight pattern on the simulator system and measure the performance of the receiver system using the simulated signals. The accuracy of the receiver system can be evaluated by comparing the outputs of the receiver with the truth data used by the simulator system. Similar tests can be repeated for a number of different user vehicle flight patterns and the performance of the receiver evaluated. The results of these various runs can be analysed and used to make changes or modify designs to improve system performance, if necessary.

The procedure outlined above may be sufficient, but it is not an efficient approach to develop and test a complex system like the GPS receiver. Specifically, it will be extremely difficult to diagnose and isolate an anomaly that may be discovered during such tests. A better approach may be to generate a step by step scheme to design and test the system. The design of the system is divided into a number of stages and at each stage sufficient tests are performed to ensure the performance of the system within permissible tolerances. Such a procedure has in fact been used in the development of the high performance GPS Generalized Development Model of AFAL. The main features of this approach are depicted in Fig. 2 and briefly discussed in the following paragraphs.

The overall development and testing of the system is classified into three major categories:

1. Offline Simulation and Test
2. Closed–Loop Simulation and Test
3. Full-up Integration and Test

Offline Simulation and Test

This is the first step in development and testing. The approach is to formulate a complete analytical design of the system including both the simulator and the receiver systems. The analytical design is then programmed on a sufficiently large computer to accomodate the complete program. The programming language similar to the one selected for the target system configuration is selected for each part of the

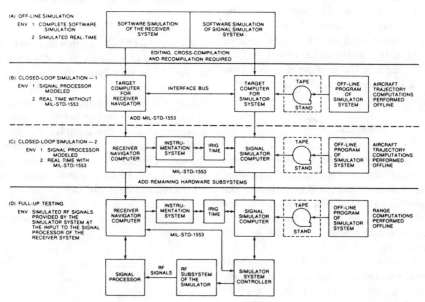

Fig. 2—Evolutionary Development and Test Procedure for a GPS Receiver System.

software system. The system is designed and coded such that the various time channels are clearly distinguished during program execution. However, a simulated real time is used instead of the real time clock to control and execute various program sections. At this stage a detailed diagnosis of system performance is possible due to a less complex nature of the system being tested.

Closed–Loop Simulation and Test

This is an intermediate step between the complete simulation in software and the final full-up system testing. A number of system configurations are possible in this step and the particular configuration selected will depend upon the requirements of particular development group. It is also possible to have a further breakdown of this step into a number of different steps. In the development of the GDM system this step consisted of two steps: Environment-1, and Environment-2.

In Environment-1, the software components of the simulator and the GDM system were moved to the final host computers. However, due to the complex nature of signal processing and navigation functions of the GDM system, the signal processor functions were not brought out as a separate subsystem and were still maintained as part of the simulator system. The transition from the offline to the closed-loop simulator involved some editing and cross-compilation of the programs used in the offline simulation. Since real time clock was used during this phase, a proper synchronization of the two systems was essential. The purpose of this test was to enable the separation of the two major units of the total system without compromising the performance of the system.

Environment-2 of closed-loop simulation does not differ significantly from Environment -1. The only difference is that the interface between the two systems is established via the MIL-STD-1553 Bus.

Full–Up Integration and Test

This is the final stage of testing the system in the laboratory. In this configuration, individual hardware units are included in both the systems. A complete real time interface and timing is established among the various subsystems. The only real time interface provided between the receiver and the simulator systems is via the rf signals generated at the output of the simulator system and input to the receiver system. But, due to the requirements of the receiver system under test, some additional sensor simulations might have to be performed in the simulator system. For example, in the case of GDM system, SVSS was required to simulate models for the IMU and the altimeter subsystems. The interface for these additional sensors is designed so that no special programming is required in the receiver system. This procedure ensures that no modifications will be necessary when field tests are performed with the receiver system.

IV. EVALUATION OF THE PERFORMANCE OF A GPS RECEIVER

In Section II, we presented some ideas about the design of simulator systems which generate GPS signals with known characteristics. Section III presented procedures that can be employed in the development and testing of a GPS receiver system. One important feature of such a testing is the measurement of exact performance of the system. This is possible in a laboratory due to a complete control of operating environment in the hands of the designer. In fact, it is possible to design tests to meet the requirements of testing and evaluation of specific functions of the receiver system.

It is usually necessary to record specific outputs of the system to evaluate its performance, such as, the three positional coordinates of the GPS receiver. At the same time the true position from the simulated dynamics is also recorded in real time. A comparison of these two sets of data as a function of time provides the necessary measure of performance that can be used to analyze and diagnose the discrepancies that may be observed. In more complex systems it may be necessary to record and compare a number of auxiliary outputs.

Field Tests and the Problem of Error Isolation

A comprehensive procedure employed during the laboratory tests should substantially reduce the probability of observing any major errors during the field tests. Nevertheless, the possibility of observing some errors cannot be completely ruled out (for an excellent discussion of various sources of errors in a GPS user equipment, the reader is referred to (6)). During field tests, the test environment is more complex than the laboratory environment. Therefore, the analysis and diagnosis of observed errors becomes more difficult and some elaborate and complex evaluation procedures may have to be designed. These procedures may employ Kalman filtering techniques to separate various sources of errors. For the GDM system an error-isolation system has been developed. This system will provide error isolation among the four major units of the receiver system–the signal processor, IMU, baro altimeter and receiver clock.

V. CONCLUSIONS

This paper has discussed in detail the requirements for the laboratory testing of a GPS receiver system with a brief analysis of important requirements. A number of simulator systems developed for the purpose of testing a GPS receiver have been introduced along with a discussion of some systematic procedures used to test and evaluate a receiver system prior to field tests.

VI. BIBLIOGRAPHY

1. Cooper, B., "A GPS User Equipment Performance Evaluator (GPSE)", ITT Defense Communications Division, Nutley, N.J.
2. Candy, Donald W., "A NAVSTAR/GPS Simulator", Proceedings of *the NAECON 77 Conference* Dayton, Ohio, May 1977
3. Interface Release Notice, Document No MHO8-00002-400, Rev. E, "Space Vehicle Nav System and NTS PRN Navigation Assembly/User System Segment and Monitor Station" Space Division, Rockwell International, Downey California.
4. Samso TR 74-183 Philco-Ford, *Global Positioning System Final Report*, Part II, Vol. A, Report No. 5, "Ionospheric Model Analysis".
5. *A World Atlas of Atmospheric Radio Refractivity*, U.S. Department of Commerce/Environmental Science Services Administration, Monograph 1.
6. Martin, Edward H., "GPS User Equipment Error Models", paper presented at the *33rd Annual Meeting of the Institute of Navigation*, 22-24 June, 1977, Costa Mesa, California.

GPS Phase I User Equipment Field Tests

R. DENARO, V. G. HARVESTER, and R. L. HARRINGTON

INTRODUCTION

The NAVSTAR Global Positioning System (GPS) Program is currently in the first of three phases in the Department of Defense acquisition process. Phase I, Concept Validation, includes building engineering development models of the GPS User Equipment and extensive in–plant and field Developmental Test and Evaluation (DT&E). The overall objectives of Phase I DT&E are to validate the GPS concept, to validate the preferred design, to define system costs, and to demonstrate military value. Field checkout tests are now being conducted at the Army Yuma Proving Ground (YPG), Arizona. The Joint Test Team is managed by the GPS Joint Program Office at the USAF Space and Missiles System Organization. General Dynamics Electronics has had primary responsibility for the test program, especially with User Equipment developed by their subcontractor, Magnavox Advanced Products Division. Texas Instruments and Collins Radio Group will also test their User Equipment later this year. Test operations and data reduction are supported by the Yuma Proving Ground. Host vehicles and crews are provided from several Air Force, Army, Navy, and Defense Mapping Agency units. Phase I field checkout testing has been underway at YPG since March 1977. This paper presents some of the preliminary results from these early field tests.

FIELD TEST PROGRAM

The user equipment field tests for GPS con-

Captain Denaro is with USAF Space and Missiles System Organization. Messrs. Harvester and Harrington are with General Dynamics, Electronics Division, P.O. Box 85039, San Diego, CA 92138.

cept validation are separated into three test phases: field checkout, performance evaluation, and operational demonstrations.

The overall objectives of the field checkout phase are to integrate the user equipment with the instrumentation pallets and host vehicles, to insure that all hardware and software are operating properly, and to conduct initial verification of user equipment performance. Several user equipment sets are currently undergoing field checkout tests.

The performance evaluation phase will commence upon completion of the field checkout tests, operating with actual satellites as they become available. The purpose of this phase is to accumulate sufficient quantitative test data to support a decision on the validity of the GPS concept. Performance evaluation will consist of tests in a wide variety of environments and dynamics, including a statistical description of the basic system accuracy.

The operational demonstration phase consists of a series of demonstrations intended to show the military value of the GPS for representative operational applications. These demonstrations will be conducted throughout the performance evaluation phase.

DESCRIPTION OF THE INVERTED RANGE

The Inverted Range (Ref. 1) is a GPS user equipment test facility located at the Yuma Proving Ground. An RF environment closely simulating that of the GPS satellites is provided by four ground transmitters arranged in a triangular pattern (Fig. 1). The Inverted Range (IR) is controlled by the Inverted Range Control Center (IRCC), a complex which includes a GPS receiver and associated equipment which is used to synchronize the ground transmitters (GTs) to a central clock. The IRCC can also receive satellite signals and synchronize the GTs to the

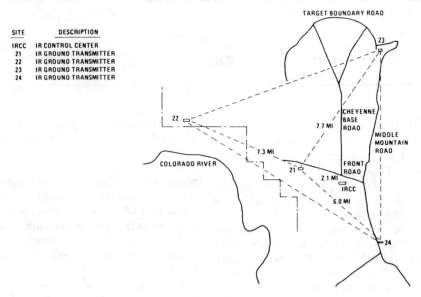

SITE	DESCRIPTION
IRCC	IR CONTROL CENTER
21	IR GROUND TRANSMITTER
22	IR GROUND TRANSMITTER
23	IR GROUND TRANSMITTER
24	IR GROUND TRANSMITTER

Fig. 1—Yuma Test Range, GPS Inverted Range.

satellite clocks; when operated this way, the IR is said to be in the hybrid mode.

Only the L1 (1575 mHz) GPS signal is provided by the Inverted Range, hence tests of ionospheric delay correction, which uses a dual-frequency correction scheme, cannot be made. The navigation message on the GT signal differs from that of the satellites in that fixed position coordinates are supplied in place of ephemeris data. Clock model coefficients are included, and the actual GT frequencies are controlled in a manner consistent with the transmitted coefficients. Other portions of the navigation message (special message and almanac) from the GTs are blank.

The Inverted Range is supported by YPG's Precision Automated Tracking System (PATS), a set of three laser trackers which track optical retroreflectors mounted on the GPS host vehicles. The PATS provides a reference trajectory against which the GPS solution is compared.

The Inverted Range was installed in March, 1977, and GPS receiver testing has been underway since that time. Operation with the first GPS satellite, the Navy Navigation Technology Satellite (NTS-2), was conducted from July, 1977, to February, 1978, when the navigation subsystem on NTS-2 ceased to operate. On February 22, 1978, the first Air Force satellite (NAV-STAR-1) was launched and is currently supporting tests.

RECEIVERS AND INSTRUMENTATION SYSTEMS

Receivers to be tested during the Phase I program are listed in Table 1. All testing up to the time of writing was with the Magnavox X Set, a high performance continuously tracking four-channel receiver. The X Set was the first receiver developed in Phase I, and it was developed for concept demonstration. The X Set is used in the IRCC on the Inverted Range and in the four Monitor Stations of the Phase I Control Segment.

Several test pallets and a test pod were built to support the Yuma tests. Four C-Pallets, shown in Fig. 2 installed in a C-141, were built for testing X, Y, HDUE, and AFAL/GDM receivers. Each C-Pallet is capable of carrying two receivers and contains an instrumentation computer, two tape transports, and operator control/display equipment. Two T-Pallets were also built. The T-Pallets, each of which is capable of testing one receiver, are used in truck helicopter and P-3B testing.

The test pod was built for testing user equipment in an F-4J (Fig. 3). The pod is a converted 600-gallon centerline fuel tank. It contains a

Table 1—User Receivers to be Tested

Set	Description	Contractor
XU	4 Channel, High Performance	Magnavox Advanced Products Div.
XA	4 Channel, Inertially Aided	Magnavox Advanced Products Div.
YU	1 Channel, Medium Performance	Magnavox Advanced Products Div.
YA	1 Channel, Inertially Aided	Magnavox Advanced Products Div.
HDUE	5 Channel, High Performance	Texas Instruments, Inc.
MVUE	1 Channel, Manpack, Ground Vehicle	Texas Instruments, Inc.
AFAL/GDM	5 Channel, High Anti-Jam Capability	Collins Radio Group, Rockwell Int'l
MP	1 Channel, Manpack, Ground Vehicle	Magnavox Advanced Products Div.
Z	1 Channel, Low Cost	Magnavox Advanced Products Div.

Fig. 2—C-Pallet Installed in C-141.

complete instrumentation package including an instrumentation computer and a 9-track tape transport. The pod always carries the XA Set which is aided by an inertial measurement unit (IMU).

Receiver testing to date has been conducted on an M-35 truck, UH-1H helicopter, C-141 transport, F-4J fighter, and P-3B patrol aircraft. Additional testing on a fast frigate and on a man's back (i.e., manpack) is planned.

Testing of the XU, XA, YU, YA and HDUE is supported by the User Field Test Instrumentation (UFTIN) computer program, which resides in the instrumentation computer. UFTIN produces the instrumentation tape for each flight, which includes all receiver outputs, navigation computer outputs, and operator commands. The recorded information thus includes navigation solutions (position and velocity), pseudoranges, delta ranges, IMU data, satellite

Fig. 3—GPS Test Pod on F-4J.

ephemerides, navigation filter states, GPS time and Inter Range Instrumentation Group (IRIG) time.

DATA REDUCTION

Flight tapes produced by UFTIN are processed at Yuma to produce "Quick-Look" plots of GPS-laser position and velocity differences. These results compare the GPS solution to a laser-based trajectory which is generated in real time (called real time estimate, or RTE). Yuma Proving Ground also produces a "Best Estimate of Trajectory," or BET, at a later date. The BET is a post flight optimum estimate of the trajectory from the laser data and IMU data when available.

Field test results are processed further by General Dynamics Electronics, the development contractor (currently Magnavox), and Aerospace Corp. During field checkout, this test data processing emphasizes diagnostic analysis of differences between the GPS navigation solution and the Yuma Proving Ground laser truth. During Performance Evaluation, the data processing will emphasize performance statistics and error isolation. A detailed description of the user equipment test data analysis procedures can be found in Ref. 2.

PRELIMINARY RESULTS

UH-1H Helicopter

The UH-1H helicopter was the first host vehicle used for tests at the Inverted Range. The IR equipment installation started on March 7, 1977. On March 15, a GPS test flight using a

UH-1H helicopter and three ground transmitters was made. The first continuous Precise (P)-code navigation mission occurred on 26 May with a UH-1H. Three ground transmitters provided the P-code signals.

IR readiness tests continued until June 26, 1977, when the first Phase I field checkout navigation mission was performed. Fig. 4 indicates the radial navigation position error time history for part of this mission. The host vehicle was a UH-1H helicopter. The GPS signal sources were three ground transmitters. Navigation occurred in a degraded mode (altitude hold). The flight profile was a racetrack pattern within the Inverted Range at approximately 5000 ft. altitude. The receiver was an X unaided Set. The average horizontal RSS position error for the complete mission was 7 meters. The average total radial position error including altitude errors was 10 meters.

C-141 Transport Aircraft

Almost all of the X unaided Set receiver field check-out missions conducted during 1977 were performed with the C-141. Initially, the signal sources were the four ground transmitters of the Inverted Range. These missions helped to identify X Set receiver design improvements as well as check out the laser tracking system and analysis routines.

The C-141 was the host vehicle for the first successful hybrid navigation mission on Septem-

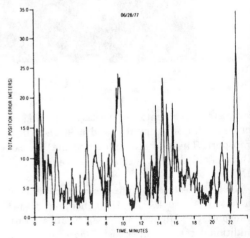

Fig. 4—Radial Error on First GPS Navigation Test, 28 June 1977.

ber 20, 1977. The signal sources were three ground transmitters and the NTS-2 space vehicle. Fig. 5 indicates part of the measured position error time histories for this mission. The flight profile on September 20 was a circular pattern centered at the IRCC at an altitude of 20,000 ft. The receiver was an X unaided Set. The average horizontal RSS position error for the complete mission was 4 meters. The average total radial position error was 6 meters.

M–35 Truck

The first GPS navigation mission with an M–35 truck occurred on January 18, 1978. The mission was land navigation using various Inverted Range truck profiles. Fig. 6 indicates the GPS navigation position errors as determined by the laser tracking system. Four ground transmitters provided the GPS signals. The receiver was an X unaided Set. The average horizontal RSS position error for the complete mission was less than 9 meters. The average total radial position error was 63 meters. This reflects the relatively large Vertical Dilution of Precision (VDOP) that occurs when the user is at approximately the same altitude as the four ground transmitters.

P–3B Long Range Patrol Aircraft

The P–3B is the host vehicle for medium dynamic flight profiles and environments typical of a large turbo–prop aircraft. It is the primary host vehicle that will be used to evaluate the effects of propeller modulation on user equipment performance.

The first P–3B GPS navigation mission occurred on November 30, 1977. The GPS signal sources were three ground transmitters and the NTS-2 space vehicle. Fig. 7 indicates position differences between the GPS navigation solution and the YPG laser tracking system for part of the mission. The flight profile on November 30 included both racetrack and circle patterns. The altitude was 20,000 feet. The receiver was an X unaided Set. The average radial position error for the total mission was less than 8 meters.

No noticeable degradation in GPS navigation performance due to propeller modulation was observed during the November–December P–3B test series. The P–3B has recently returned (March 1978) to the Yuma area for additional GPS field testing. This testing will include tests specifically designed to measure propeller modulation effects on GPS receiver performance.

F–4J Fighter/ Bomber

The Navy F–4J has been the primary host vehicle for the field check–out of the X aided Set GPS receiver. Aiding is provided by a Litton LP–36 Inertial Measurement Unit. The F–4J

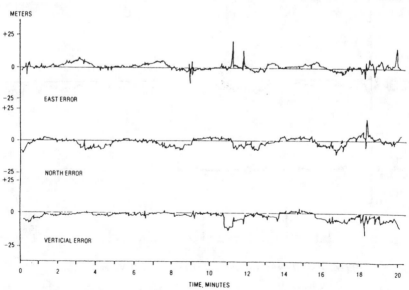

Fig. 5—Results from First GPS Hybrid Navigation Test, C–141, 20 September 1977.

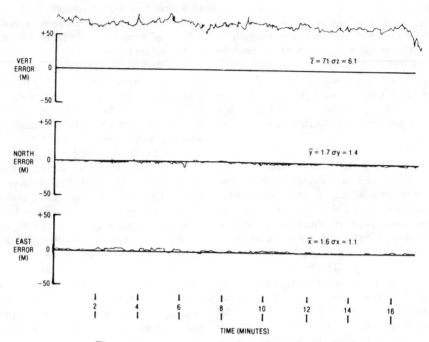

Fig. 6—*GPS Truck Test Results, 18 January 1978.*

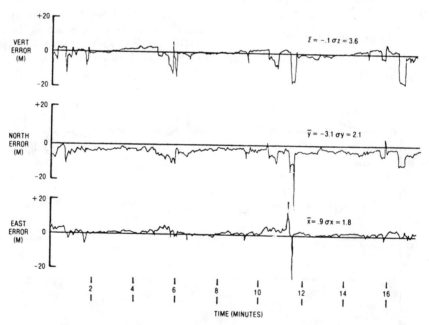

Fig. 7—*P-38 Hybrid Navigation Performance, 30 November 1977.*

has also been the host vehicle for the field check-out of the precision weapon delivery capabilities of GPS.

In its precision weapon delivery role, GPS performs the calculations required to predict bomb flight paths. The operator enters the latitude, longitude, and altitude of the target. For the Yuma field tests, this is a surveyed benchmark on the YPG bombing range. Then, the on-board GPS computer combines aircraft position and velocity with bomb characteristics to compute a release point. Steering commands are transmitted to the pilot via a pilot steering display. If the pilot steers to this release point within certain tolerances (the computer automatically compensates for some pilot errors such as off-nominal down-range velocity), an automatic discrete is sent to the bomb rack to release a bomb. Over 100 MK-82 low drag 500-pound bombs have been dropped from different delivery configurations in field tests to date.

Actual weapon delivery field test results are not releasable, but tests have demonstrated that a dramatic improvement in unguided bomb placement is possible using GPS.

SUMMARY

GPS Field Testing has completed initial checkout of the Inverted Range and the X Set receiver, tested aboard a UH-1H, C-141, P-3B, F-4J and M-35 truck. Although only a few environmental and dynamic conditions are represented in these tests, errors of less than 10 meters were obtained on all host vehicles. Recent tests of precision weapon delivery have further demonstrated the utility of GPS navigational accuracy.

The test program is currently in the field checkout phase. When performance evaluation begins, the emphasis will be on set performance in different environments, such as jamming, high dynamics, landing, rendezvous, etc. This categorized performance, as well as statistical measures of performance, will be stored in statistical analysis programs for later interpretation and reporting (Ref. 2). The performance evaluation tests will be performed primarily with satellites. The majority of this testing is planned to be complete by March, 1979, when the NAVSTAR GPS Program will be reviewed by the Defense System Acquisition Review Council (DSARC-II).

REFERENCES

1. Harrington, R. L. and J. T. Dolloff, "The Inverted Range: GPS User Test Facility," Proceedings of IEEE Position Location and Navigation Symposium, San Diego CA, November 1976.
2. Lorenzini, D. A. and J. L. Soulia, "GPS Field Testing," Proceedings of the Institute of Navigation 33rd Annual Meeting, Costa Mesa CA, June 1977.
3. Lorenzini, D. A. and R. P. Denaro, "NAVSTAR GPS Field Test Results," Proceedings of the National Aerospace and Electronics Conference, Dayton OH, May 1978.

Civil Marine Applications of the Global Positioning System

T. A. STANSELL, Jr.

INTRODUCTION

When considering what to write about civil marine applications of the Global Positioning System (GPS), my first thought was to review all of the diverse marine navigation requirements and show to what extent GPS could be used for each. The problem with this concept is that GPS will be nearly a universal navigation aid. Except for applications requiring underwater operation or sub-meter measurement precision, GPS will be able to do practically everything else!

Therefore, a different approach has been taken. First, GPS is defined for the marine operator. The intent is to show its inherent capabilities, partly by contrast with some of today's navigation systems. Following this is an attempt to express the natural desire of marine users for the system to be implemented and operated in a way to serve them best. It is suggested that civil users should be represented by a civil government agency during system development and as a point of contact for liaison after GPS becomes operational. The need for civil access to the best possible accuracy performance also is stressed.

Factors affecting the price of GPS civil user equipment are considered, followed by a discussion of whether proposed signal structure changes intended to reduce the cost of civil equipment should be considered at this time. Overall, the paper celebrates the potential offered by GPS and urges that the system evolve

Mr. Stansell is with Magnavox Government and Industrial Electronics Co., Advanced Products Division, 2829 Maricopa Street, Torrance, CA 90503.

so as to maximize benefits to a wide variety of civil users.

GPS SYSTEM DESCRIPTION AND STATUS

The U.S. Department of Defense is developing through a joint services program office (JPO) a satellite navigation system called NAVSTAR or GPS (Global Positioning System). Fig. 1 illustrates the planned GPS satellite coverage. There will be a maximum of 24 satellites, with 8 in each of 3 orbit planes. At about 10,900 nautical miles above the earth, the satellites will complete an orbit cycle every 12 hours. The objective is to provide direct, line-of-sight signals continuously from at least four satellites to all users on a worldwide basis.

A ground control network will track the satellite signals, determine the orbits precisely, and transmit an appropriate orbit definition to the memory system of each satellite. In this way, the satellites will be able to provide users with an accurate description of their position as a function of time.

To obtain a position fix, the user must be equipped with a receiver capable of tracking four satellite signals, either simultaneously or sequentially depending on the user's dynamics. Part of the task will be to select which four satellites to track at any time in order to optimize accuracy as the satellites slowly pass by.

The navigation solution requires making time-of-arrival (TOA) measurements on signals transmitted from discrete positions defined by the satellite orbit message. Each set of four TOA measurements permits determination of four independent variables, usually: clock time offset, latitude, longitude, and altitude. (The fourth measurement can be deleted if altitude above the reference spheroid is known with sufficient accuracy.)

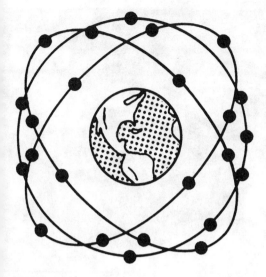

1177-6595

Fig. 1—GPS Satellite Coverage (8 satellites in each of 3 orbit planes).

In order to provide the precise time marks, to separate the various satellite signals, and to obtain processing advantages against multipath and jamming signals, GPS employs a pseudo-noise (PN) signal modulation structure. The PN modulation is transmitted continuously, and TOA measurements are made by precise alignment of a PN code generator in the receiver with the PN signal being received. This process is easier to understand with reference to the PN autocorrelation function of Fig. 2. The curve shows that the receiver detects maximum signal strength when its internal PN code generator is perfectly aligned with the received PN code, i.e., the autocorrelation function is at its peak. Misalignment of the codes causes the detected signal to decrease to a very small, essentially negligible value. The two important characteristics of the autocorrelation function are: (1) the sharpness of the autocorrelation pulse, which determines how precisely TOA can be measured, and (2) the length of the PN code, i.e., how often it repeats.

As presently planned, two types of PN code will be used. The "P" code (for precise code) has an autocorrelation pulse width of ±97.8 nanoseconds, which is equivalent to ±29.3 meters when measuring distance to the satellite. The P code is so long that it does not repeat for days,

so assistance is needed when first trying to achieve synchronization. This is one of the purposes of the second PN code, which is called C/A for coarse/acquisition. The C/A code has an autocorrelation pulse width of ±978 nanoseconds, which is equivalent to ±293 meters, and the code repeats every millisecond, which is equivalent to repeating every 300 kilometers between the user and the satellite. TOA measurements to an accuracy of about 10 percent of the autocorrelation pulse width can be made fairly easily, and with extreme care the accuracy can approach one percent of the pulse width.

GPS satellites will transmit on two frequencies, one at 1575.42 MHz called L_1 and the other at 1227.6 MHz called L_2. The C/A PN code will be transmitted only on L_1, but the P code will be transmitted on both L_1 and L_2. By using the P codes and both frequencies, the expected navigational accuracy is as shown in Fig. 3, although the U.S. Government has not decided whether to release this level of accuracy performance for general civil use. It has been announced that the single–frequency C/A signal will be made available, and Refs. 1 and 2 indicate that the C/A signal offers an accuracy potential of 30 to 75 meters.

Civil marine navigation equipment using the C/A signal could look very much like the instruments shown in Fig. 4. On the left is the Magnavox MX 1102 Satellite Navigator, now in wide

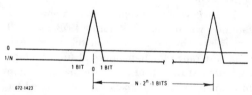

672-1423

Fig. 2—Autocorrelation Function of Maximal Linear PN Code.

ACCURACY (METERS)		PERCENT OF THE TIME
HORIZONTAL	VERTICAL	
5	7	50
9	10	90

1177-6594

Fig. 3—Expected GPS Accuracy Performance With the Best Military User Equipment (Dual-Frequency P-Code System).

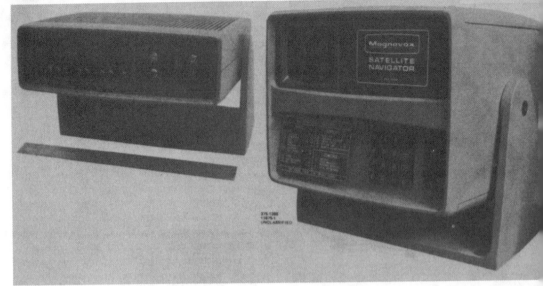

Fig. 4—Civil Marine Navigation Sets Could Look Like These. Magnavox plans to Offer a GPS Modification Kit for the MX 1102 Transit Satellite Navigator on the Left. On the Right is a Conceptual Model of the Magnavox GPS Spartan Navigator.

use obtaining position fixes from Transit, the Navy Navigation Satellite System. Magnavox plans to offer a modification kit so the MX 1102 can be converted to GPS when it becomes operational. On the right of Fig. 4 is the conceptual model of the Magnavox "Spartan" Navigator, which illustrates the size reductions which can be made with a different type of display and by application of special purpose integrated circuits.

GPS is now in a concept validation phase. Six satellites will be launched during 1978 and 1979 into orbits which converge over the Yuma, Arizona test range for four hours of full coverage each day. At the left of Fig. 5 are the navigation instruments which Magnavox has developed for the Phase I concept validation test program.

Phase II of the program will see development of military user equipment suitable for full scale production, and Fig. 5 shows how the Phase I test instruments are expected to evolve during the next few years of this development. Phase II is expected to end in 1982 when the Defense Systems Acquisition Review Council (DSARC) has scheduled a program review. At that time, approval will be sought to proceed with operational implementation. If approval is granted, development and production of the operational satellites will begin, with the first launches ex-

pected by late 1984 and continuing perhaps into 1987. Full operational status would be achieved somewhere in this time frame.

MEANING OF ACCURACY

The next section of this paper will compare the navigational accuracy potential of GPS with the performance of several existing systems. To do this, we must agree on the meaning of "accuracy".

All marine operations require some form of nagivation or positioning. The objective is to reach or identify a location or to avoid obstacles. Thus, navigation is performed with respect to the physical world; it is most directly done by visual observation or by means of a radar picture. In contrast, electronic navigation systems, including satellite systems, provide positioning information in terms of numbers which must be related to geographic location by means of charts, maps, tables, etc. Accuracy, therefore, should be defined in terms of the ability to find or to identify a physical location, and three separate areas of performance are involved.

The first is repeatability of the position fix information. For example, Loran–C readings in good signal areas are repeatable to within 15 to 30 meters. It is expected that the best military GPS equipment will demonstrate a repeatability

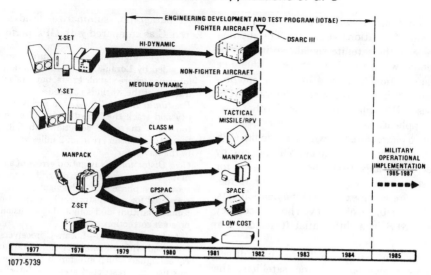

Fig. 5—*GPS User Equipment Plan and Schedule.*

of about 10 meters. Although repeatability is an important characteristic, it does not fully define accuracy.

The second major concern is grid warp, which is distortion of the navigation grid over some area. For example, the propagation velocity of Loran-C signals is affected by ground conductivity. Therefore, a grid warp called secondary phase error is caused whenever the signal passes over the land to the sea. Warps of up to 0.6 mile have been measured off the U.S. east coast, and warps greater than a mile have been reported off the west coast. In contrast, satellite navigation systems have much less grid warp. That which does exist is due to error in the model of the earth's gravity field used to predict the satellite positions, and such warp is believed to be less than 10 meters typical.

The third concern is the conversion of instrument readings to geographic position. In the case of Loran-C, for example, this may be done with a chart on which Loran-C time-difference grid lines are superimposed on a map of geographic features. In this case, chart accuracy may have more to do with Loran-C navigation performance than any other factor, partly because it also is customary to compensate for known grid warp when preparing these charts.

We must realize that even satellite navigation systems require charts to convert instrument readings into geographic position. The instru-

ment may read out latitude and longitude, but the navigator is interested in his position relative to physical features such as the harbor, the reef, or the mineral deposit on the bottom. Only maps can convert from the grid lines of latitude and longitude to physical features of the earth.

It also is important to realize that maps are drawn in accordance with a local reference datum. In the United States we use the North American Datum, in Japan the Tokyo Datum, in Europe the European Datum, etc. The satellite system datum is called the World Geodetic System (WGS), such as WGS–72 now employed for Transit Satellite Navigation. The difference between coordinates in WGS–72 and in the Tokyo datum can be 1/2 kilometer. In Europe and the United States the differences typically range from 100 to 200 meters.

Radionavigation accuracy is difficult to define. The navigator wants to know where he is with respect to physical features of the earth. The ability of a radionavigation aid to provide this information depends on its repeatability, the amount of grid warp, and the adequacy of local charts and maps to convert the instrument readings into meaningful geographic positions.

GPS IMPORTANCE TO CIVIL MARITIME USERS

As stated in the introduction, GPS will be nearly the universal navigation aid. There are some limitations. It will not provide relative navigation information like a radar. The antenna must receive the satellite signals, so it will not work under water or when otherwise shielded. Some applications require a measurement precision not attainable even with differential GPS. Otherwise, GPS will be useful for all other navigation applications.

The two characteristics which will make GPS so useful are accuracy and availability. Accuracy is expected to range from about 100 meters for the least expensive equipment to about 10 meters for more complex military navigation sets. It may be possible to obtain even better accuracy by using GPS in a differential (translocation) mode.

Because the user will receive direct, line-of-sight signals from the satellites, the usual tradeoff between accuracy and coverage forced upon terrestrial systems does not apply. Therefore, GPS promises both outstanding accuracy and total availability. Navigation coverage will be: continuous, worldwide, and all-weather.

One other important characteristic of GPS navigation is that a computer is required, thus permitting other useful tasks to be performed. For example, the set can display the great circle range and bearing to any way point, execute a thorough self-test and diagnose system faults, or automatically adjust to the local map datum. Because the computer must be there anyway, these features will cost very little extra, but they increase system value considerably.

Descriptive terms such as automatic, continuous, worldwide, all-weather, etc., sound like advertising copy. We are so used to superlatives that they do not carry the intended meaning. To illustrate the full potential of GPS, the next few paragraphs will contrast it with other navigation systems, emphasizing limitations which GPS does not have. The intent is not to downgrade any other system; it is to highlight the future power of GPS when contrasted with system limitations we may have grown accustomed to.

Loran-C

In good signal areas, the inherent Loran-C system resolution and repeatability is in the range of 15 to 30 meters, which is better than expected with a low-cost GPS set. The following brief paragraphs summarize disadvantages of Loran-C as compared with GPS performance.

Coverage—Fig. 6 shows the approximate coverage provided by Loran-C. A user can obtain good performance where signals exists, but a relatively small fraction of the world is covered.

Positional Reliability—Loran receivers must identify and track the "third cycle" of each pulse. All too often the cycle selection can fail, producing typical navigation errors of 2 miles with no warning to the navigator.

Grid Distortion—Navigation errors of a half mile or more can occur because of grid distortion called secondary phase error. Navigation charts can be corrected for grid distortion by calibration, but automatic latitude and longitude sets usually provide no such correction.

Interfering Signals—Loran-C receivers must be equipped with adjustable notch filters in order to cancel signals which interfere with proper operation. For use in a restricted area, the filters can be set and thereafter neglected. For widespread use, the navigator must be trained to adjust these filters often or else improper operation will result.

Weather Problems—Loran-C suffers from weather-related problems, e.g., precipitation static carried by a light rain or mist which can drown out the desired signals.

Omega

Omega is intended to provide worldwide navigation coverage with only eight transmitting stations. System difficulties with Omega which contrast with GPS capabilities are as follows:

Repeatability—At a fixed location, the indicated Omega position wanders with a non-Gaussian distribution. A 0.5 mile repeatability exists about half the time with peaks of 2 or 3 miles occurring about 10% of the time.

Positional Reliability—Due to a number of problems, Omega position error can increase dramatically at times depending on specific user equipment characteristics. Errors of 10, 30, or even 100 miles have been noted in some trials. The reasons for these problems include lane count slips, polar cap anomalies (PCA's), sudden ionospheric disturbances (SID's), modal interference, and long path (wrong way around the world) reception. Some of these problems can be anticipated, but others can not.

Skywave Corrections—Successful Omega navigation requires the application of "skywave correction values". Large scale as well as local distortions exist. The U.S. Coast Guard is conducting a calibration program to improve these predictions.

Weather Limitations—Precipitation static affects Omega as well as Loran-C.

Coverage Limitations—Omega was intended to be a worldwide navigation system. Unfortunately, the

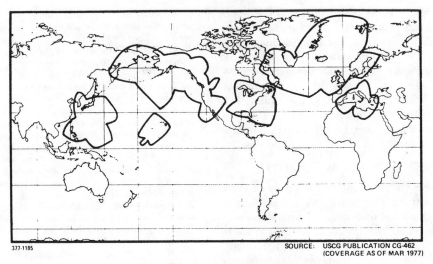

SOURCE: USCG PUBLICATION CG-462
(COVERAGE AS OF MAR 1977)

377-1185

Fig. 6—Approximate Loran-C Coverage Chart.

combination of modal interference and long path reception severely limit the number of stations which can be used in certain areas, compounded by PCA's, SID's, and by occasional down time for maintenance of the transmitters. As a result, Omega will not provide 24-hour, worldwide coverage.

Transit Satellites

Transit, the Navy Navigation Satellite System, currently consists of 5 satellites orbiting about 600 miles above the earth. In comparison, it is planned that GPS will have 24 satellites orbiting 10,900 miles above the earth. Transit provides accurate position fixes on a worldwide basis, as will GPS, so our experience with Transit is quite valuable in anticipating GPS applications. The areas where Transit is less competent than GPS are:

Update Interval—The Transit system provides a single position fix each time one of the satellites is in electronic view of the user. The interval between fixes is about 90 minutes on the average, but longer gaps of several hours often occur, especially at low latitudes. In contrast, GPS signals will be available continuously.

Repeatability—Although the accuracy of a Transit position fix is competitive with GPS, this accuracy is degraded by unknown ship's velocity. As a result, individual merchant ship Transit fixes have an accuracy of about 0.1 nautical mile. In contrast, low cost GPS equipment should provide twice this accuracy on a continuous basis.

Short Range Systems

There are a number of short range systems such as Raydist, Hi-fix, etc., which provide very high resolution but over extremely short distances. Although some of these systems provide better repeatability than GPS is likely to give, many of their applications can be satisfactorily met by GPS or differential (translocation) GPS. Using GPS would eliminate the logistics of moving, establishing, and maintaining shore stations during a local survey.

GPS Value

By examining the comparative limitations of several typical radionavigation systems, the functional advantages of GPS become more obvious. The true meaning of "worldwide coverage" is emphasized when contrasted with the Loran-C coverage illustrated in Fig. 6. All-weather operation means just that; there are no weather conditions that will deny navigation information as with low frequency systems like Loran-C and Omega. The number of Transit satellite navigation users is growing rapidly because it too provides worldwide, all-weather, accurate position information. However, there is a vast difference between position updates every hour or so and the continuous coverage planned for GPS.

Although the promise of GPS is very tantalizing, it must be tempered with realism. Today's navigation problems must be solved with systems and with equipment which are proven and available now. In contrast, the GPS system is under development at this time, and before implementation a major funding commitment must be made by Congress and the Administration. Based on the current schedule, civil use would not be feasible until 1985 or possibly later. Nevertheless, in contrast with all other navigation aids GPS promises outstanding value. It is clear that it will have a major impact on safety, economy of operation, and effectiveness of mission for a vast array of marine applications.

CIVIL ACCURACY AND AVAILABILITY

Because GPS is being developed by the U.S. Military, there is concern about civil availability of the signals and what accuracy limitations may be imposed on civil users. Current plans are to release the single–frequency C/A signal for civil use, but a decision regarding the dual–frequency P signals, which give higher accuracy, has not been made. It might be assumed that high accuracy signals are not required for civil applications. On the contrary, many civil applications will need the best possible accuracy. The economic benefit of having truly precise navigation available on a global basis can be enormous. The following paragraphs summarize some of today's needs for precise navigation, and other applications are bound to develop when the capability exists.

Hydrographic Survey—Quoting from Reference 3, "Hydrographic charting activities of the National Oceanic Survey presently require an accuracy of 5 meters (0.0049 mile) in the immediate coastal area, and 8 meters (0.007 mile) in the areas out to approximately 100 miles." From this reference it can be seen that hydrographic survey activities demand slightly better accuracy than GPS is planned to provide. Differential GPS should be able to meet the requirements, although the standard accuracy may prove to be acceptable.

Setting Buoys—Also according to Ref. 3, the tolerance for setting navigational buoys ranges from 10 to 30 meters.

Geophysical Surveys—Navigational requirements for marine geophysical surveys always have presented a challenge. The seismic, gravity, or magnetic data being recorded have no meaning without precise knowledge of the position where these data were obtained. Collecting gravity data also requires accurate knowledge of ship's motion to compensate for motion–induced accelerations. Until recently, a positioning accuracy of 50 to 100 meters was considered adequate if the relative positions of seismic data points along the ship's path were known to within 2 to 5 meters. Recently, however, three-

dimensional marine seismic surveys are being attempted in which the relative position of data points between lines is as critical as along a single line. Thus, there is a requirement for continuous navigational accuracy to about 5 meters.

Offshore Pipe Laying—For a variety of reasons, offshore pipes must be laid along precisely surveyed corridors. The only radiolocation systems with sufficient precision have very limited range and require installation and maintenance of shore stations. An increasing number of pipes are being laid beyond the range of these shore–based transmitters, so that very sophisticated and costly systems are being developed. GPS could solve a most serious problem, which is becoming worse as the search for offshore oil continues to expand.

River and Harbor Navigation—Finally, even large, ocean-going ships navigate in rivers and harbors. Here, navigational requirements can be extremely severe. For example, the U.S. Coast Guard is conducting experiments in the St. Marys River to see if Loran–C can permit winter navigation through narrow channels after ice has removed all buoys and other visible markers. The requirement is for continuous 3 to 5 meter accuracy relative to the center of the channel!

It should be clear that there are many important civil navigation applications requiring extreme accuracy. Therefore, an early indication of system availability and of the accuracy attainable would be desirable. The best information we have so far is from Ref. 4, Page 76, which includes a letter from the Department of Defense stating that:

"Our current thinking is that we will make navigation information of 100–200 meters available for civil use under all conditions. We expect to maintain control of the system so that we can deny the precision information to unauthorized users under certain conditions."

Civil users who need extreme accuracy will be very pleased if they can have this capability most of the time. It would be extremely helpful, however, for the GPS Navigation message itself to warn such users whenever the available accuracy was degraded.

CIVIL AGENCY INVOLVEMENT

A number of interested groups within the U.S. Government are looking at the overlap of different navigation systems and calling for cost savings through consolidation and better interagency coordination. Development of GPS has sparked this interest because it is the one system capable of replacing so many others, including perhaps VOR, TACAN, Loran-C, Loran-D, Transit, and other systems as recommended by Refs. 3 and 4. These initiatives are being promoted by:

- The Office of Telecommunications Policy (OTP), (Ref. 3)
- The General Accounting Office (Ref. 4)
- Various Congressional Committees, e.g., the Subcommittee on Transportation, Aviation, and Weather.

From Ref. 4 it appears that the Office of Management and Budget (OMB) has taken an active interest in this subject and that the President has authorized OMB to develop a Federal Radio Navigation System Plan, presumably along the lines of the OTP recommendations. The important aspects of these plans are:

1. Redundant systems would be phased out, leaving a smaller number of more cost effective, complementary systems to cover all navigation requirements. GPS would be the cornerstone of the remaining navigation capability.
2. The President would assign a single manager the responsibility and authority to develop and then implement a Federal Navigation Plan. This would promote better coordination of navigation activities within the Departments of Defense, Transportation, and Commerce.
3. A definite schedule would be established for the phase out of unnecessary systems, thus giving users sufficient time to amortize existing equipment investment and to evaluate and obtain equipment compatible with the final system mix.

In light of these initiatives it would seem that one or more civil government agencies should begin to take an extremely active role in the GPS system, as suggested by Ref. 4. The time for such involvement, if it is to be effective, is now. Unfortunately, participation by civil agencies so far has largely been to evaluate progress from the sidelines, although there are signs of change.

My strong desire to encourage civil agency involvement springs from experience with the Transit Satellite Navigation System, as detailed in Refs. 5 and 6. Transit became operational in 1964 as a military navigation system designed to

provide precise position updates for the Polaris submarine fleet. Thus, the system was developed by the military for military applications. However, in 1967 the government released details of the Transit system and encouraged civil use.

At first, the user equipment was complex and expensive, so the number of civil applications was rather limited. Over the years, however, the user population has grown steadily. The growth has been fueled by an increasing awareness of the benefits provided by global, all-weather, accurate position fixes and the decreasing cost of satellite navigation obtained by technology improvements and by increasing production volume. As a result there are now several thousand civil users of Transit, and the number is growing at about 50% annually (Ref. 5). Furthermore, civil users far outnumber the military users for which the system was developed.

A more dramatic growth in civil use of GPS is expected to occur after its release. The total number of users will be much greater than with Transit because GPS will provide continuous rather than intermittent position fixes. As with Transit, however, the GPS civil community quickly will outnumber the military users.

Even though the number of Transit civil users has grown dramatically, the Transit system continues to be operated exclusively for and by the U.S. military. Civil users of Transit receive the signals at no charge and have obtained exceptionally reliable performance, but there are problems. These have been detailed in Refs. 5 and 6, but briefly they are:

1. The orbit spacing now permits long gaps to occur between some fixes. Another satellite should be launched to fill the gap.
2. Occasionally the Navy knowingly conducts tests in which a satellite can give a position fix significantly worse than normal. There is no need to permit such a risk or even the inconvenience caused to those doing precise survey work.
3. There is no one to whom a civil user officially can complain about service or even ask questions about the system, although the Navy Astronautics Group attempts to be helpful to the extent possible within their charter.

When it has been suggested to civil government agencies that it would be good to have their involvement in Transit, the response has been quite negative. The reasons given are: (1) they do not want to risk diversion of funds from other efforts, (2) they are fighting hard to defend their own navigation systems, and (3) they fear Congressional criticism about support of multiple, redundant navigation systems. The net result is that the needs of civil users have no influence on operation of the Transit system. Without the involvement of government agencies representing civil users, this same situation could well develop with GPS.

Potential civil users of GPS are raising a number of questions and looking for a civil government agency to represent their interest in the answers. Some of the questions are:

1. When will GPS be released for civil use?
2. Will the ultimate accuracy potential be available to the civil user?
3. Will periods of reduced accuracy performance occur, and if so how will the civil user be warned?
4. Shouldn't civil government agencies participate in the system development, the development of appropriate civil user equipment, and perhaps in eventual system operation?
5. Is the GPS signal structure, which now is oriented toward military objectives of fast acquisition and jamming immunity, most appropriate for low cost civil use?
6. Should there be a separate signal transmitted specifically for civil use?

While it is true that only the military has the pressing operational requirements to justify the expense of developing the GPS, it also is true that there are potentially many more civil users than military users. I hope that U.S. civil government agencies will consider the enormous future impact of GPS and begin to participate fully rather than leave the job solely to the military.

PRICE OF CIVIL USER EQUIPMENT

There has been more speculation and wishful thinking about the price of GPS civil user equipment than hard data. The only published studies of low cost "Spartan" equipment are Refs. 7 and 8, which were completed in mid-1975. Since these limited studies, all other cost data has come from guesses and extrapolation based on

the military equipment now being built.

This situation was emphasized in a recent letter by the Honorable Dale Milford, chairman of the House Subcommittee on Transportation, Aviation and Weather, after extensive hearings on GPS application to civil navigation requirements. He opened the letter by saying:

"Enclosed is a partial listing of the wide variety of GPS cost and accuracy data submitted to the Committee and given in testimony. It becomes immediately apparent that there will be considerable difficulty in our effort to assess GPS civil application because of the variety of criteria addressed. It also appears that the requirements of the civil fleet, if it is to attain substantial gain from GPS, have not been thoroughly thought out."

The uncertainty and confusion is compounded by many factors which will be reviewed here. However, the eventual price of GPS civil user equipment is an extremely important parameter in a most important equation.

Price will be the primary factor in determining the eventual number of civil users. Although a very strong case can be made for the value of GPS performance, equipment will be purchased only if an adequate return on the purchase investment can be foreseen, e.g., lower operating costs, increased safety, or even pride of ownership. The fact that equipment price so stongly affects the number of users also causes it to be an important factor in the following three considerations:

1. *Implementation Decision*—Although the system is being developed and justified for military applications, it appears that government approval to finally implement an operational system may be influenced by its potential for widespread civil use.
2. *Support of Redundant Systems*—If GPS civil user equipment could be purchased at a sufficiently low price, then most other radio navigation aids, including Loran-C, VOR, Transit, etc., could be phased out over perhaps a 10-year interval as suggested by Refs. 3 and 4. Long-term government support for these systems depends heavily on the eventual price of GPS civil user equipment.
3. *GPS Design*—As indicated in Refs. 4, 7, and 8, recommendations have been made

to change the GPS signal structure so as to minimize the cost of civil user equipment. If truly meaningful cost reductions can be made, then appropriate modifications should be considered immediately. Otherwise, such considerations will only delay system implementation and increase the development cost.

As important as price is to these considerations, there seems to be very little agreement about what it will be. Unfortunately, this uncertainty may well continue, perhaps until the system becomes operational and competitive market pressures begin to operate. It may be instructive, however, to examine the price structure of marine navigation equipment available today, keeping in mind the relative complexity of a GPS set. Loran-C receivers range in price from about $2,000 for a set with two internal notch filters and a sequential display of time difference coordinates to about $7,000 for sets with four externally adjustable notch filters and a latitude and longitude display. Omega receivers range in price from a few thousand dollars for the least expensive manual units to about $12,000 for automatic sets giving latitude and longitude. Depending on features, Transit satellite navigation sets, all of which provide latitude and longitude, can be purchased for between $18,000 and $25,000.

It is clear that GPS user equipment will be more complex than that for Loran–C, Omega, or Transit. Thus, if all else were equal and if GPS sets were being manufactured today, we would expect them to sell at or above the price for Transit equipment. However, the Spartan reports envisioned substantial technological progress between now and 1985, enabling price reductions for all types of electronic navigation equipment. Furthermore, the number of sets produced per year should be much greater for GPS than for Transit. Therefore, much lower prices can be envisioned in the 1985 to 1990 time frame. Some of the factors which will influence eventual price are:

Production Quantity—The most important cost factor probably is production quantity, i.e., the number of items released for production at one time. That an automobile can be bought for a few thousand dollars or that a color television set can be bought for a few hundred attest to the power of mass production in reducing costs.

High volume production lowers costs in a number of ways. Parts can be bought for less and production personnel can be trained and organized to build equipment in less time when large quantities are involved. Investment in extensive use of automatic assembly and test equipment becomes more feasible, and the incentive for making cost saving engineering changes is increased.

The cost reduction trend for increasing production quantity is called the "learning curve". For example, when building 10,000 instruments one can expect the unit cost to be between 58% and 84% of the cost for lots of 1,000, depending on steepness of the particular learning curve in effect.

Because the military intends to procure from 25,000 to 40,000 GPS navigation sets, the opportunity for minimizing the cost of civil equipment exists to the extent that standard modules and parts are applicable to both designs. Two factors may work to reduce this opportunity, however: 1) any tendency for the military to purchase smaller quantities of many specialized types of sets, and 2) substantial difference between military and civil designs. In addition, it is very unlikely that a manufacturer would be willing to risk building more than a few thousand commercial navigation sets at one time, perhaps 10,000 being the upper limit.

Technology—GPS is expected to become fully operational between 1985 and 1987. Because the pace of electronic technology development has been steadily accelerating, we can reasonably expect this progress to permit significant cost reductions in all types of navigation equipment, including that for GPS. The most rapid technology advance has been in the area of digital electronics, including computers. By 1985 the digital and computer portions of a GPS set will have become a minor fraction of the total cost. Therefore, as much of the signal processing will be done digitally as possible. The major cost challenges will be the power supply, the control and display components, and the radio frequency amplifiers, filters, mixers, etc.

Cost Versus Price—Cost and price often are confused. An instrument which can be manufactured at a material, labor and overhead cost of $1,000 probably will sell commercially at a price of $2,000 to $4,000. The higher price is because of the many additional costs associated with commercial business, such as: advertising, trade shows, warranty reserves, dealer commissions, distribution costs, training, marketing support, and research and development. Often those familiar only with government procurements assume that price will be very nearly the same as manufacturing cost. The distinction was made clear in Reference 7.

Performance—Price is influenced by the required performance. Some of the parameters will be: navigational accuracy, signal holding sensitivity, time to first fix, update interval, and how easy the system will be to use in terms of its keyboard, display, initialization process, and position readout.

Options—Some of these might include: battery backup for emergency position display, range and bearing to multiple way points, a printer output, or interface with a gyrocompass to determine the heading offset to follow a desired course. Such options will add value but increase price.

Reliability—Perhaps the reliability of equipment used on pleasure craft and on general aviation aircraft can be relatively low. For example, Ref. 8 determined that a low cost GPS set with commercial grade components would have a mean time between failure (MTBF) of 1,034 hours, i.e., 1.4 months. This seemed adequate on the assumption that the equipment would operate an average of 30 hours per month for five years. In contrast, electronic navigation equipment for ocean-going vessels which make infrequent port calls must be far more reliable. The MX 1102 Transit Satellite Navigator shown in Fig. 4 was designed to have an MTBF of at least six months, and field experience shows that the MTBF actually exceeds one year. Navigation equipment for ocean-going ships must be reliable, and reliability costs money.

SIGNAL STRUCTURE CONSIDERATIONS

Questions have been raised as to whether the planned GPS signal structure is optimum for low cost civil applications. Ref. 4 touches on the issue, and the Department of Transportation has begun a small study of the question. Suggestions range from modification of the present signal structure to adding a separate signal just for civil applications.

For example, Ref. 8 suggested that only by having a radically different signal could truly low cost civil equipment be produced. This report recommended that the carrier frequency be reduced from L–band to near 400 MHz and that each of the 24 satellites transmit a 4.5 millisecond signal burst at a designated slot within a one–second time frame. The spacing of these signals would assure that only one could be received at a time, similar to the Loran–C signal concept. Each signal burst would provide a time measurement signal at 32 KHz plus four data bits. Expected navigational accuracy would be 853 meters or 0.46 nautical mile.

In contrast to a radically new signal, this author in Ref. 7 suggested a modification of the present signal structure. The key elements of the suggested modification were:
· Provide a stronger signal for more system margin.
· Trade 3 dB of data modulation power for 3 dB better threshold performance and sim-

pler tracking circuits.
· Extend the C/A PN code length to 20 milliseconds to eliminate range ambiguities and the need for bit synchronization.
· Reduce the number of C/A PN codes to at most three and preferably to one to simplify circuitry and initial signal acquisition.
· Provide a Doppler acquisition aid to speed initial acquisition from a cold start.

The first approach is attractive in several ways, but the major fault is its limited accuracy. Most marine users will be operating in the coastal confluence zone where accuracy requirements today are 0.25 mile and are likely to be 0.1 mile or better in the future. Investment in a magnificent system like GPS should not produce worse results than we have now with Loran–C. On the contrary, it would be wise to provide somewhat better accuracy than is projected to be necessary. Another problem with the separate signal concept is that commonality between military and civil equipment would be lost along with the opportunity for cost savings through larger production runs.

Simply modifying the present signal structure as suggested by Ref. 7 would not degrade accuracy and presumably both military and civil equipment would be able to employ the same signal. However, the suggestions would increase the time to first fix, and Ref. 7 suggests that receiver cost savings would only amount to 10 to 15 percent.

Therefore, the fundamental question is whether enough benefit could be obtained from a signal modification to justify the probable delay which would occur in deploying this important national asset. The present signals have been proved to work and to work well. Though I have suggested changes in the past, I am convinced that further consideration would lead to unacceptable program delay. If civil agencies wish to pursue this question, I hope that it can be done in close cooperation with the GPS Joint Program Office so as to minimize impact on the program schedule.

SUMMARY

I have attempted to communicate the true breakthrough in navigation capability offered by development of the GPS. If implemented, it will serve a vast range of marine applications from pleasure cruising to oil exploration and retrieval. Because of this potential, and based on experience with the Transit Satellite Navigation System, the paper also has called for meaningful involvement of a civil government agency in this development phase and for liaison during operation of GPS, thus representing the interests of civil users who will far outnumber military users after a short time. The need for maximum accuracy to support a number of important civil applications also was stressed.

A note of caution was sounded regarding the developmental status of GPS. The basic concept has been proved, but funding commitments must be made before the system finally will be implemented, and civil use will not be possible before 1985 or later.

Price of user equipment eventually will determine the number of civil users. No agreement exists as to the likely minimum price of user equipment, but limits can be set based on present-day equipment, and the pace of technology will aid in achieving truly affordable equipment.

A brief review was given of possible signal structure changes which could reduce the cost of civil user equipment. Because the present signal structure has been shown to work well, it was argued that further consideration of change probably was not worth the likely delay in system implementation which would result.

As stated in the introduction, this paper celebrates the potential offered by the GPS. A development with so much potential for improving safety, reducing costs, and aiding access to important natural resources should evolve quickly so as to maximize the benefits to a wide variety of civil users.

REFERENCES

1. C. R. Cahn and E. H. Martin, *Design Considerations for a Spread Spectrum Navigation Receiver (NAVSTAR)*, Magnavox Report MX–TM–3259-77, International Conference on Electronic Systems and Navigation Aids, Paris, France, 14–18 November 1977.
2. B. G. Glazer, "GPS Receiver Operation", *Navigation,* Volume 25, No. 2, Summer 1978.
3. *Radio Navigation Systems Economic and Planning Analysis, Final Report,* Volumes 1, 2 and 3, Prepared for Office of Telecommunications Policy by Computer Sciences Corporation, July 1977.
4. *Navigation Planning—Need for a New Direction,* Report LCD–77–109 of the U.S. General Accounting Office, March 21, 1978.
5. T. A. Stansell, "The Many Faces of Transit", *Navigation,* Volume 25, No. 1, Spring 1978.
6. T. A. Stansell, *Positioning and Navigation by Satellite,* Magnavox Report MX–TM–3261-77, Joint Conference on Satellite Applications to Marine Operations, New Orleans, Louisiana, 15–17 November 1977.
7. S. Fascher et. al., *Design Development Study for the Global Positioning System Spartan Set,* Magnavox Reference No. 85001042/R–5321, 4 September 1975.
8. *Global Positioning System Spartan Reciver/Processor,* Rockwell Space Division Reference No. SD 75–GP–006, April 11, 1975.

Integration of GPS with Inertial Navigation Systems

D. B. COX, JR.

1. INTRODUCTION

The state of the art in inertial navigation has been under development for over two decades, is widely utilized in military and civilian applications, and is well documented in the technical literature. On the other hand, the NAVSTAR Global Positioning System (GPS) has been under development for a much shorter period and has not yet been utilized to a significant extent in practical applications. With the publication of this special issue of *Navigation,* a forthcoming special AGARDOGRAPH[1] and with reference to a host of government reports, conference papers, and journal articles, the state of current GPS technology will be quite well documented. Because of the many desirable features of GPS, it is very likely to be utilized world–wide in a very large number of practical applications[2].

In some applications, e.g., for tactical aircraft, the combination of an inertial navigation system (INS) and the GPS offers particular advantages, and integrated GPS–INS systems are being developed to capitalize on these advantages. Early integrated systems will be achieved by integrating GPS navigators with existing INSs. These integrated systems will exploit the synergism between the GPS and inertial subsystems, but because these INSs have not been designed for integration with GPS hardware, exploitation may be only partial.

Integration of GPS and INS subsystems with other subsystems such as JTIDS[3], will also occur in the future. Although more and more complex

Dr. Cox is with The Charles Stark Draper Laboratory, Inc., 555 Technology Square, Cambridge, MA 02139.

functions will be able to be optimized via future digital computing power, it is likely that the major hardware and software subsystems on tactical aircraft will remain substantially autonomous. Maintaining subsystem autonomy will take advantage of the enhanced reliability and maintainability associated with such architectures and the steady reductions in costs of local processors and multiplexors[4].

2. BENEFITS OF INTEGRATION

GPS is expected to operate in a stand-alone configuration in a benign environment. However, GPS and inertial navigation systems have complimentary features which can be exploited in an integrated system to create synergistic improvements in navigation performance. The improvements are most pronounced when the GPS signal–to–noise ratios are low and the vehicle is undergoing high-dynamic maneuvers.

As long as vehicle dynamics or noise–to–signal ratios are not excessive, the GPS receiver can provide pseudorange and pseudorange-difference data which can be used for estimating errors in position and velocity, and certain other error parameters of the INS and of the GPS receiver clock. The estimates of INS error parameters allow GPS-INS navigation with substantially smaller errors than could be achieved with either a GPS navigator or an INS alone. On the other hand, the INS is able to provide accurate "aiding" data on short–term vehicle dynamics to the GPS receiver. By utilizing those aiding signals to effectively reduce the dynamics of the signals to be tracked, the GPS receiver can maintain relatively low tracking bandwidths and can withstand relatively high noise–to–signal ratios, perhaps due to high levels of jamming. The INS signals can also be used as a basis for pointing narrow-beam antenna patterns at the GPS satellites, thereby also reducing the effects of jamming. When noise–to–signal ratios become so high that tracking of GPS signals is impossible, the INS is capable of navigating independently. When GPS signal conditions improve sufficiently to allow tracking, the INS provides data on initial position, velocity, and acceleration for use in reacquiring the GPS codes and carriers quickly. The INS also provides data for use in adapting the tracking-loop parameters to varying conditions of signal dynamics and signal-to-noise ratios, thereby improving the ability of the tracking loops to acquire and maintain lock on the GPS signals.

3. DESCRIPTION OF STAND-ALONE GPS AND INERTIAL SYSTEMS

Because a variety of stand-alone INSs are currently in use and some GPS receivers are being configured for stand-alone operation, it is instructive to examine briefly these stand-alone systems in preparation for showing how systems with varying degrees of integration might logically evolve from them.

Fig. 1 shows several important functional elements of stand-alone GPS and inertial navigation systems, and of some ancillary systems typically appearing on tactical fighter aircraft.

The inertial measurement unit (IMU) provides from its accelerometers three axes of time-integrated acceleration (specific-force) information in a reference (usually local-level, wander-azimuth) coordinate frame which is stabilized by its gyroscopes (gyros). Current tactical aircraft utilize gimballed platforms wherein the accelerometers and gyros are mounted on a stable platform, oriented accurately by gimbal-control loops on the basis of information supplied by the gyros.

An alternative, "strapdown", mechanization is also possible, wherein the accelerometers and gyros are mounted on a nonstabilized structure attached to the frame of the aircraft. Data from the strapdown gyros are used for determining the orientations of the accelerometers as they vary with aircraft attitude. The IMU transformation processor shown in Fig. 1 resolves at high speed the strapdown accelerometer data into the gryo-stabilized coordinate system, and is not present in a stabilized-platform mechani-

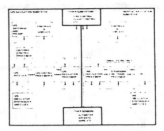

Fig. 1—Stand-alone GPS and inertial navigation systems.

zation. As inertial components are developed that can provide accurate long-term navigation in the face of the dynamics of the aircraft's attitude, strapdown IMUs are likely to see increasing utilization, and they are candidates for future integration with GPS equipment.

The stabilized accelerometer data are supplied to the navigation processor. Data from an altimeter and from other auxiliary sensors are also supplied. INS mechanization algorithms in the navigation processor propagate the standard inertial navigation equations at a high rate (10–50 Hz) and supply torquing commands to the gyros (in the stable–platform mechanization). The INS mechanization algorithms also accomplish gyrocompassing for preflight alignment of the inertially stabilized frame[5–15, 17].

The INS navigation processor may also incorporate Kalman (or less optimal) filter algorithms for improved in-flight estimation of such variables as position, velocity, baroaltimeter bias, misalignments of stabilized axes, and gyro drift-rate biases, on the basis of data from external sources. Examples of such external data are visual position fixes by the pilot, radar fixes, Loran fixes, Doppler radar data, etc. The Kalman filter algorithms require substantial execution time, but because the errors of the unaided INS grow slowly in comparison to the vehicle dynamics the Kalman filter corrections need be incorporated only infrequently. The design of the navigation filter algorithms and the performance of INSs that are aided by auxiliary sensor data have been reported extensively in the literature[11–32]. Ths INS mechanization and filter algorithms may be incorporated in a single navigation processor as suggested by Fig. 1, or in separate processors.

The main functional elements of a possible

stand-alone GPS navigation subsystem are shown on the left-hand side of Fig. 1. The heart of the subsystem is the GPS receiver which amplifies and filters the GPS radio signals, correlation-detects and tracks the carriers and codes, and correlation-detects the GPS satellite data modulations. The GPS control processor controls the moding of the receiver so as to accomplish acquisition, tracking, etc., and generates estimates of certain signal-processing parameters. The antennas feeding the receiver can be simple ones with broad beam patterns covering the different regions of the space around the aircraft, or they can be capable of beam steering or null steering, in which case an antenna control processor is needed.

The GPS control processor assembles the pseudorange and deltapseudorange data from the receiver and passes it on to the GPS navigation processor. The navigation processor receives the GPS data and auxiliary sensor data and provides extended Kalman filter estimates of, e.g., position, velocity, and acceleration of the aircraft, time offset and frequency offset of the GPS user clock, and altimeter bias. The unaided (stand-alone) GPS navigation filter must incorporate new GPS data somewhat more frequently than the aforementioned INS Kalman filter incorporates INS data because the aircraft dynamics, rather than the relatively mild INS-error dynamics, must be modeled in the unaided GPS navigation filter. All measurements must be accurately time tagged, particularly if measurements to different satellites are made sequentially, rather than simultaneously. The navigation solution is delivered to pilot displays as well as to other subsystems such as fire control and flight control.

A new GPS navigation solution may be desired as often as every 100 ms, but the complete solution of one cycle of an 11-state extended Kalman filter by the GPS navigation processor generally requires substantially more time, on the order of 5 seconds for one existing design. In that design the covariance matrix and the gain matrix are computed every several seconds and the last gain matrix is used for incorporation of new data more rapidly, about every 300 ms, until a new gain matrix is computed[33, 34]. The result is a reasonable compromise between processor cost and navigation performance.

A prime function of the unaided GPS Kalman filter is to incorporate more than the minimum GPS data required for a navigation fix and thereby to minimize the effects of random measurement errors. But many of the measurement errors are correlated in time, and the effects of severe aircraft dynamics tend to dwarf the effects of the random error components. It is possible that simpler deterministic solutions for position and time and for velocity and frequency from the pseudorange and pseudorange-difference data may prove to be advantageous in some applications where speed of response or computational simplicity are prime considerations[35, 36]. But algorithms for propagating the navigation solution through occasional lapses in GPS data must still be provided. Regardless of the computational techniques employed, the unaided GPS navigation solution under high-dynamic conditions will always exhibit very large velocity errors in comparison to what can be achieved with an integrated GPS-inertial system.

In the remainder of this paper, various means of integrating the GPS and inertial subsystems in order to obtain improved performance will be discussed. Integration of the navigation filters will be discussed first. Then the discussion will cover aided acquisition, aided tracking, and adaptive tracking. Finally, antenna control will be described briefly. Each of these functional integrations requires implementation of data transfer and/or data processing functions. These additional functions and the structure of an integrated system are illustrated in Fig. 2. This figure gives an indication of the degree of increase in complexity associated with the integration functions that are designed to provide increased performance. The increase in complexity is offset to a degree by the opportunity to consolidate navigation filters, and common functions such as controls and displays. It should be stressed that the system should be capable of reconfiguration to stand-alone GPS or inertial navigation systems in the event of failure of key GPS or INS components.

4. INTEGRATED GPS-INERTIAL NAVIGATION FILTERS

The simplest way to integrate the stand-alone GPS and inertial subsystems is to provide a

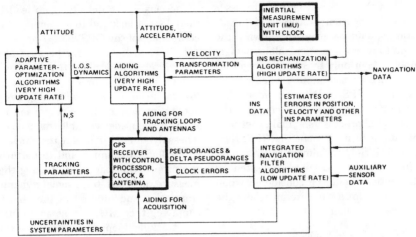

Fig. 2—Structure for integrated GPS inertial navigation system.

channel for delivering the position and velocity data from the GPS navigation solution to the INS navigation processor. The INS software could simply reset its mechanization algorithms to the positions and velocities specified by the GPS navigation processor. However, this procedure suffers from the relatively large errors made by the unaided GPS navigation filter in the presence of severe aircraft dynamics, from the failure to estimate several observable IMU error parameters, and from the lack of resolution of the typical INS mechanization algorithms.

Substantially better navigation accuracy can be obtained by supplying, with proper GPS–INS time tags, raw GPS data and data from the INS mechanization algorithms (together with auxiliary sensor data) to an integrated GPS–inertial navigation filter as illustrated in Fig. 2. The integrated navigation filter supplies Kalman estimates of a combined set of GPS–INS error parameters, e.g., 3 positions, 3 velocities, 3 misalignments of the inertially stabilized frame, 3 gyro drift rates, 1 time, 1 frequency, 1 altimeter bias, and 1 altimeter scale factor. These estimates of error parameters are used as infrequent updates to the INS mechanization algorithms, which in turn provide frequent estimates of position, velocity, and acceleration of the vehicle on the basis of data from the IMU. The number of error states to be mechanized is dependent upon the desired error–update rate, the processing power available, and the number of significant error sources to be encountered. Because the INS system errors grow so slowly, in com-

parison with the rate of growth of uncertainties in vehicle dynamics without the benefit of IMU measurements, the update rate of the GPS–INS navigation Kalman filter can be much slower than that for the unaided GPS navigation filter while still obtaining substantially superior results (particularly in estimation of velocity). However, there is still the problem associated with execution of the high–order Kalman algorithms at the desired rate. A variety of approximation techniques are employed to ease the computation burden.

The INS mechanization equations, updated by the GPS–INS navigation filter, can be used for accurate INS navigation during periods when GPS is unavailable. The in–flight estimation of IMU alignment and other INS error parameters made possible by the earlier availability of GPS improves the accuracy of INS navigation when GPS is not available. The quality of the IMU must be sufficient to meet the requirements of stand–alone INS navigation under these circumstances.

For best performance, the integrated GPS–inertial system should utilize INS data with resolutions consistent with GPS accuracies, i.e., finer than the resolutions of data from typical stand–alone INSs. The needed increase in resolution can be achieved through modification of the INS mechanization algorithms or by utilizing raw IMU data in separate high–resolution algorithms for inertial extrapolation between GPS updates.

The integrated system navigation filter can be

implemented in the GPS navigation processor or in the INS navigation processor of Fig. 1. Consideration should be given to allowing the configuration to revert to a stand-alone navigator with only GPS or only INS inputs (together with other auxiliary sensor inputs), in case there is a failure in the GPS or INS equipment. Because of continued progress in increasing the reliability of digital processors, it makes sense in some applications to implement the GPS, INS, and integrated GPS-INS Kalman navigation algorithms in a single processor as suggested by Fig. 2. This option should be considered when designing a system for a new aircraft where the INS is not already resident.

5. AIDED GPS ACQUISITION

When the GPS subsystem is jammed, or otherwise inactive, navigation can proceed on the basis of the INS (and auxiliary aids) only. The INS will perform well because its error parameters will have been previously calibrated in flight when the GPS subsystem was operating. Nonetheless, the unaided INS errors will gradually grow, and GPS updates should be used as soon as they are available. When the GPS signals again become usable the INS navigation solution can act as an aid to direct reacquisition of the GPS codes and carriers. The time-tagged INS navigation solution and covariance estimates, together with estimates of clock errors and covariances, are used to generate estimates of pseudorange, pseudorange rate, and search regions in time and frequency. In this way the INS not only provides navigation during outages but also greatly shortens the time required for reacquiring the GPS signals after they again become usable. The improved calibration of the GPS clock made possible by inertially aiding the GPS navigation solution also supports the reacquisition process.

6. AIDED TRACKING

Useful GPS data is obtained only while the carrier-tracking and/or code-tracking loops are locked onto the desired signals. When any tracking error becomes too large, the correlation detector becomes excessively nonlinear and its effective gain is accordingly lowered. Progressive increases in the tracking error and attendent

reductions in the detector gain lead to a complete loss of lock and to a complete loss of that component of the GPS data.

Loss of lock can occur because of excessive tracking error in response to radio noise, perhaps due to jamming. Lowering the loop bandwidth lowers the noise-induced tracking error, but also acts to increase errors in response to dynamics in the pseudorange variable that is to be tracked. These dynamics can be due to vehicle dynamics, to oscillator dynamics, and to perturbations in the propagation path. By utilizing the IMU to measure the short-term signal dynamics due to translation and rotation of the vehicle and by supplying the IMU data as an aiding signal to the tracking loop, the tracking-error components due to vehicle dynamics can be substantially reduced. With reduced errors due to vehicle dynamics, the bandwidth of the loop may be reduced to further attenuate jamming. Hence, IMU aiding of the tracking loops increases the antijamming margins of the tracking loops in dynamic environments[41-45].

Generally, aiding signals are introduced as shown in Fig. 3, where τ is the time delay to be tracked, $\hat{\tau}$ is the estimated value of τ, and $\dot{\tau}_{aid}/K_{FC}$ is an aiding signal. Alternatively, with exactly the same effect on the detected error signal $D(\tau - \hat{\tau})$, the aiding signal τ_{aid} could be added to the feedback signal as shown by the dotted line in the figure. If τ_{aid} were subtracted from the input τ instead of being added to the feedback signal $\hat{\tau}$, its effect on the output of the detector would be the same. Hence the effect of aiding is to make the loop track an effective pseudorange signal $\tau_e \equiv (\tau - \tau_{aid})$. The IMU can supply an aiding signal τ_{aid} that matches the high-frequency components of τ quite well so that $\tau - \tau_{aid}$ contains smaller high-frequency components than τ. Then, with aiding, the band-

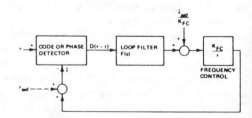

Fig. 3—The use of an aiding signal in a tracking loop.

width of the loop can be lowered in order to attenuate jamming noise while still maintaining linear operation of the detector.

In order to avoid loss of lock, the tracking error of each carrier-tracking loop should be kept well within the small value of 0.1 ft (phase-locked) or 0.05 ft (Costas). In order to provide this accuracy with narrow tracking-loop bandwidths during high-dynamic maneuvers of tactical aircraft, aiding velocity signals must be delivered from the IMU to the carrier loops very frequently, on the order of every 10 ms, and transport delays must be accounted for. Because data are generally not available from the INS mechanization algorithms this frequently, the aiding data should be obtained directly from the IMU, or from its strapdown processor, as shown in Fig. 2.

Transport delays can occur in the implementation of the tracking loop as well as in the implementation of the aiding algorithms. The aiding signal for each loop is generally a series of increments $\Delta\tau_{aid}$ each of which, when implemented at some accurately specified time in the future as the frequency command to the loop over an interval Δt, represents the predicted change $\widehat{\Delta\tau}$ in the signal to be tracked over that interval. Past values of acceleration and attitude data from the IMU are used as inputs to an extrapolation algorithm. The output of the extrapolation algorithm is the predicted $\widehat{\Delta\tau}$, which is delivered to the tracking loop. The extrapolation algorithm can be very simple, but should be repeated very frequently, every 10 ms, or so for each carrier loop. The code-loop tracking errors can be on the order of tens of feet, much larger than the allowable carrier-loop errors. Velocity information from the INS mechanization algorithms may be used for aiding the code loops.

The parameters for the coordinate transformation and scaling of the translational aiding data can be obtained from the integrated navigation filter, as shown in Fig. 2. These parameters, relating to the bearings of lines of sight to the GPS satellites, and relating to the orientation of the gyro-stabilized accelerometer frame, change slowly and need to be updated only infrequently. With these parameters being known, the incremental, gryo-stabilized, accel-

erometer data are scaled and transformed into changes in velocities along the lines of sight. The transformation parameters for attitude data must be obtained from the IMU. Then incremental attitude data from the IMU are transformed into changes in ranges from the antenna(s) to the satellites. The transformations of data on translations and rotations are simple, but must be performed rapidly with proper time-tagging.

The transformation, scaling and extrapolation functions for inertially-aided GPS tracking require special software not needed for the unintegrated systems. These will be warranted in some applications because of the resulting improvement in antijam performance.

In high-dynamic maneuvers of tactical aircraft, the effects of acceleration on the frequency of the GPS crystal oscillator can be a significant cause of residual tracking error in inertially aided code or carrier tracking loops[42,47]. The frequency shifts appear as pseudorange-rate inputs to all the tracking loops and are not directly detectable by the IMU. Specifications for currently available crystal oscillators are not lower than $10^{-9}/g$, which is equivalent to a pseudorange rate input of $1(ft/s)/g$. For a code loop operating with a time constant of 30 seconds, a 2-g input to such an oscillator would lead to 60-ft tracking error in addition to other dynamic error components. Hence the oscillator sensitivity limits antijamming performance of the code loops. It affects the antijamming performance of IMU-aided carrier loops too, especially during high-jerk maneuvers. Fortunately, it appears that crystal oscillator assemblies with sensitivities below $10^{-10}/g$ are on the horizon[48].

IMU errors also limit the antijam performance of aided code and carrier tracking loops. For the carrier loops, care must be taken to keep tracking errors due to attitude errors, bending modes, etc., to less than about 0.1 ft, with loop response times of about 0.5 s, or less, during severe attitude maneuvers. With one milliradian attitude errors, a lever arm length of much less than 100 ft would not be a problem, but structural flexure between the antenna and the IMU could be a problem. Either gimballed or strapdown IMUs are capable of supplying sufficiently accurate attitude data in most applications. For the gimballed IMUs the pacing requirement is on the accuracies and update rates of the gimbal angle encoders. References (44-45) provide quantitative data on the effects of a variety of error sources on the performance of IMU–aided carrier loops under jamming and with high dynamic maneuvers.

For aiding the code loops, the ability of the INS to measure dynamic translational motions sufficiently accurately so that tracking errors are much less than 100 ft with loop response times on the order of 1-100 s is the dominant requirement. Only high–quality stable-platform IMUs are currently capable of successfully aiding code loops with time constants on the order of 100 s during high–dynamic tactical aircraft maneuvers. The code–loop time constant determines the ultimate antijam margin.

Aided tracking loops provide GPS data that are corrupted to some extent by the aiding signals. This corruption has been reported in the literature[49] as sometimes leading to problems of instabilities in navigation algorithms designed to receive pure GPS data, and some solutions have been proposed. Because the aiding signal τ is effectively high–pass filtered by the tracking loop, subtracting a similarly high–pass filtered version of the aiding signal from the output of the aided tracking loop is an alternative approach to this problem which requires extra hardware or software.

Aided code loops will have very long time constants in order to maximize anti–jamming performance. When the time constants are longer than the sampling period of the navigation filter, the data samples will be correlated. Prewhitening filters have been implemented in some designs to reduce the correlations and thereby to improve the performance of the Kalman navigation filter.

7. ADAPTIVE TRACKING

When the conditions of signal dynamics and jamming noise are such that maintaining lock is difficult, choosing the tracking–loop parameters to optimize performance is important. Because the conditions usually cannot be predicted in advance, the parameter adjustment is best done adaptively. The availability of data from an IMU greatly facilitates the adaptation process, as indicated in Fig. 2.

The best values for the parameters of each loop are dependent upon the dynamic model for the effective pseudorange $\tau_e \equiv (\tau - \tau_{aid})$ being estimated (tracked) by the loop, the signal–to–noise ratio, and the covariances of the tracking loop's estimates of the model states. In an integrated GPS–inertial system, data from the INS can be used directly to determine the time-variable parameters in a model of the effective pseudorange dynamics. Data from the INS can also be used, together with data from the receiver to determine the signal–to–noise ratio. From this information, together with initial values for covariances of the tracking error states, the succeeding tracking-error covariances and optimum tracking loop parameters can be calculated.

Each optimally adaptive, n^{th} order, tracking loop can be considered as a Kalman filter operating on noisy measurements of τ_e, which is generated by an nth order dynamic process model with white noise sources. Once the model is characterized adaptively, the optimal tracking loop parameters can be obtained from the standard Kalman algorithms. For example, for a third-order carrier tracking loop, an adequate process model might be $\dot{\tau}_e = v_e$, $\dot{v}_e = a_e$, $\dot{a}_e = -a_e/T + n_j$, where n_j is a white noise source with power spectral density N_j, and T is the correlation time of the acceleration state. The variations in effective pseudorange dynamics could be represented by variations in N_j.

If the loop is unaided, this process represents the full pseudorange dynamics. Then accelerometer and attitude outputs from the IMU can be used to designate appropriate values of N_j. If the loop is aided by the INS the process represents the dynamics of aiding error. Then the accelerometer and attitude outputs are used with the INS and oscillator error models to obtain appropriate values of N_j. For example, if the uncertainties in alignments of the stabilized axes are 10 milliradians rms, 1 percent of the acceleration indicated by the IMU could be allocated to the effective pseudorange dynamics. The uncertainties of the INS parameters will vary only slowly (as solutions of the navigation filter), but the accelerometer and attitude data can vary rapidly, and must be converted into selections of values for N_j very rapidly so that the loop will be able to adapt itself in time to llow high-jerk dynamics. The algorithms for lecting values for N_j must be very simple to be actical. The values of N_j should be appropriately bounded to prevent selection of excessively rge or small tracking-loop bandwidths, but ed to be only approximate indications of levels dynamics within these bounds.

The measurement of the effective pseudonge τ_e by the code or carrier detector is corpted by noise n_r. The power spectral density , of n also is needed for deriving the optimum acking-loop parameters. The value of N_r is oportional to the spectral density of the radio ise (perhaps due to jamming) divided by the gnal power. The radio noise density can be easured directly and rapidly by the receiver. he signal power is a weak function of the angle the satellite above the horizon and a strong nction of the attitude of the aircraft. By utilizg attitude data from the IMU and the known tenna patterns of the vehicle, the signal power n be predicted. Since the signals will usually at full power, it may be sufficient to characrize each of them merely as present or absent. ecause malfunctions or interveining fixed ructures, such as mountains, can cause unprected blackouts of some signals, the receiver ust also estimate the signal power that is acally received from each satellite. But this esnate requires code demodulation and, hence, not valid when the code detector range is ceeded. It also depends upon the parameters the measurement filter, which should themlves be optimized adaptively. Although the sponse time may be slow, provision should be ade for the signal power measurement by the ceiver to provide a "signal-absent" override to e adaptive algorithm, and to satellite-selection d navigation algorithms.

With the parameters N_j (representing effecve pseudorange dynamics) and N (representing easurement noise) determined, Kalman soluons for the gains in the tracking loops can be tained. The solutions are straightforward, but e time consuming when performed rapidly ough to be accurate for a loop with wide ndwidth. Time-scales approximation techques have been applied to the simplification of numerical solution of the Kalman equations r a second-order tracking loop[50], thereby proding a practical approach to that part of the real-time adaptive tracking task.

The solution for optimum tracking loop parameters has been extended to cover the effects of code-detector nonlinearity and to cover the possibility of also varying the code-detection range optimally so that tracking and acquisition can be handled with improved performance by a single adaptive tracking process.[51]

Improvements in antijam performance can also be obtained by adaptively varying the pre-detection bandwidth. The predetection bandwidth of each Costas carrier-tracking and incoherent code-tracking loop can be varied in proportion to the uncertainty in the effective pseudorange rate. Each bandwidth should be large enough to pass the carrier and data (if present), but otherwise should be as small as possible in order to minimize signal suppression when the predetection signal-to-noise ratio is less than unity. The improvement in performance through adaptation is most pronounced during acquisition, or when the code loop is data-aided so that its predetection bandwidth can be small[42]. If the carrier loop is in lock, the predetection bandwidths of the carrier loop and its associated code loop should be proportional to the frequency uncertainty of carrier-loop tracking, as indicated by the Kalman adaptive tracking equations for the carrier loop. When the carrier loop is not in lock, and both the carrier and code loops are IMU-aided, the much slower navigation filter solutions for uncertainties in clock frequency and vehicle velocity can be utilized.

7. ANTENNA CONTROL

In order to enhance the antijam performance of the integrated GPS inertial system, beam-pointing antennas can be employed[38]. The beams must be pointed at the GPS satellites throughout aircraft maneuvers. Control for the beam pointing is generated on the basis of data from the IMU on the attitude of the vehicle and data from the GPS navigation processor on the position of the vehicle with respect to the satellites. The attitude data must be updated rapidly enough to allow predictions by the antenna control processor of the attitude of the vehicle with errors substantially less than the beamwidth during all attitude maneuvers. The position data, used to calculate the bearings to the satellites, need be updated only rarely.

8. CONCLUSION

Benefits and means of integrating GPS and inertial systems have been described. Emphasis has been on the data to be transferred and the operations to be performed in attaining varying degrees of integration. The intent has been to provide an understanding of the mechanisms and degrees of complexities involved.

It is clear from the discussion that very substantial performance improvements can be obtained through integration of GPS and inertial systems in comparison to what can be achieved by either system alone.

9. ACKNOWLEDGEMENT

The author is grateful for the advice and consultation of Dr. Bernard Kriegsman, Dr. James Negro, Mr. W. Michael Bowles, and Mr. William Stonestreet during the preparation of this paper.

REFERENCES

1. C. T. Leondes, ed., *Principles and Operational Aspects of Position Determination Systems*, NATO Agardograph to be published in 1978.
2. *Federal Radio Navigation System Plan*, Preliminary Draft, Office of Telecommunications Policy, Fall 1977; to be published after coordination.
3. "GPS-JTIDS-INS Integration Study" Final Report, Charles Stark Draper Laboratory Report R-1151, June 1978.
4. R. Q. Lee and G. R. England, "The Digital Airplane", *Astronautics & Aeronautics*, January 1978, pp 58–64.
5. C. S. Draper, W. Wrigley, J. Hovorke, *Inertial Guidance*, Pergamon Press, N.Y., 1962.
6. G. R. Pitman, ed., *Inertial Guidance*, John Wiley & Sons, Inc., N.Y., 1962.
7. C. F. O'Donnell, ed., *Inertial Navigation Analysis and Design*, McGraw Hill Book Co., 1964.
8. C. Broxmeyer, *Inertial Navigation Systems*, McGraw Hill Book Co., N.Y., 1962.
9. M. Kayton, W. Fried, *Avionics Navigation Systems*, John Wiley & Sons, Inc., N.Y., 1969.
10. W. Wrigley, W. M. Hollister, W. G. Denhard, *Gyroscopic Theory, Design, and Instrumentation*, MIT Press, Cambridge, MA, 1969.
11. J. Sciegienny, R. Nurse, J. Wexler, P. Kampion, "Inertial Navigation System Standardized Software Development", Final Technical Report, C. S. Draper Laboratory Report R-977, Vols. 1-4, June 1976.
12. K. Britting, *Inertial Navigation Systems Analysis*, Wiley-Interscience, 1971.
13. J. L. Farrell, *Integrated Aircraft Navigation*, Academic Press, N.Y., 1976.
14. G. T. Schmidt, ed., AGARD Lecture Series #95, *Strapdown Inertial Systems, Theory and Application*, NATO AGARD Report LS-95, June 1978.
15. C. T. Leondes, ed., *Theory and Applications of Kalman Filters*, AGARDOGRAPH No. 139, NATO AGARD, Feb. 1970, AD704306.
16. Bryson, A. E., and Ho, Yu-Chi, "Applied Optimal Control", Blaisdell Publishing Co., Waltham, MA, 1969.
17. G. T. Schmidt, ed., AGARD Lecture Series #82 on *Practical Aspects of Kalman Filtering Implementation*, North Atlantic Treaty Organization, Advisory Group for Aerospace Research and Development, Report AGARD-LS-82, March 1976.
18. A. Gelb, ed., *Applied Optimal Estimation*, MIT Press, Cambridge, MA, 1974.
19. C. T. Leondes, ed., *Filtering and Stochastic Control in Dynamic Systems*, Vol. 12 of *Control and Dynamic Systems*, Academic Press, N.Y., 1976.
20. Kaminski, P. G. and Bryson, A. E., "Discrete Square Root Filtering", IEEE Transactions on Automatic Control, Vol. AC-16, No. 6, 1971.
21. Carlson, N. A., "Fast Triangular Formulation of the Square Root Filter", AIAA Journal, Vol. 14, No. 9, 1973.
22. Bierman, G. J., "Factorization Methods for Discrete Sequential Estimation", Academic Press, N.Y., 1977.
23. *Hybrid Navigation Systems*, AGARD Conference Proceedings, No. 54, Jan. 1970, US Government Report No AD-701775, pp. 14-1 thru 14-20.
24. D. E. Gustafson and B. A. Kriegsman, "A Guidance and Navigation System for Automatic Station Keeping in an Earth Orbit" *Journal of Spacecraft and Rockets*, Vol. 10, No. 6, June 1973, pp 369-376, Draper Laboratory Report E-2534, August 1970.
25. B. A. Kriegsman and Yee, "Shuttle Navigation System for Entry and Landing Mission Phases", *Journal of Spacecraft and Rockets*, Vol. 12, No. 4, April 1975, pp 213-219.
26. B. A. Kriegsman, "NAVSTAR-Aided Inertial Navigation Studies", Draper Laboratory Report R-1115, Sept. 1977.
27. C. A. Wolfe, "NAVSTAR/GPS Navigation Analysis and Algorithm Development Study", Final Report OC-R-76-0564-1, ORINCON Corp. AD-A-034 873 30 November 1976.
28. R. A. Clark, M. A. Needler, "Performance and Adjoint Sensitivity Analysis of the NAVSTAR Global Positioning System", *NAECON '76 Record*, pp 834-840.
29. K. A. Myers, R. R. Butler, "Simulation Results for an Integrated GPS/Inertial Aircraft Navigation System", *NAECON '76 Record*, pp 841-848.
30. A. J. Brockstein, "GPS Kalman Augmented Inertial Navigation System Performance", *NAECON '76 Record*, pp 864-871.
31. D. W. Candy, "A NAVSTAR/GPS Simulator"

NAECON '77 Record, pp 323-329.

32. B. A. Kriegsman, K. B. Maher, G. Prado, and G. W. Hurlbut, *Deep Ocean Mining Site Navigation System Evaluation*, C. S. Draper Laboratory Report R-1049, January 1975, presented at 10N National Marine Meeting, Nov. 1977.

33. Damoulakis, J. N. and Hinderer, J., "A GPS-HDUE System Configuration with Increased Processing Power on Range and Range-Rate Measurements", Position Location and Navigation Symposium, Institute of Electrical and Electronics Engineers (IEEE), 1-3 November 1976, San Diego, CA.

34. Dressler, R. M. and Ross, D. W., "A Simplified Algorithm for Suboptimal Non-Linear State Estimation", *Automatica*, Vol. 6, pp 477-480, 1970.

35. P. S. Noe, K. A. Myers, "A Position Fixing Algorithm for the Low-Cost GPS Receiver", *IEEE Transactions on Aerospace and Electronic Systems*, Correspondence, March 1976, pp 295-297.

36. W. H. Foy, "Position Location Solutions by Taylor Series Estimation, *IEEE Transactions on Aerospace and Electronic Systems*, Vol. AES-12, #2, March 1976, pp 187-194.

37. *Spread Spectrum Communications*, AGARD Lecture Series No. 58, NATO AGARD July 1973.

38. G. L. Bjornsen, W. M. Hutchinson, "GDM/GPS Receiver Hardware Implementation", *NAECON '77 Record*, pp 303-309.

39. W. M. Stonestreet, *A Functional Description of the NAVSTAR GPS Receiver Model-X*, C. S. Draper Laboratory Report #R-981, Vol. I, Rev. 1, Feb. 1977.

40. *GPS User Equipment (UE) Orientation Course*, Magnavox Report MX-125-C-US-7701, Magnavox Government & Industrial Electronics Co., Advanced Products Div., Torrance, CA, 1977.

41. P. P. Yeh, "A Treatise on the Antijamming Margin of an IMU/Computer-Aided Global Positioning Navigation System", Aerospace Corporation Report TOR-0076(6473-01)-1, 15 Oct. 1975.

42. L. L. Horowitz, J. R. Sklar, "ECM Vulnerability of the GPS User Receiver in a Tactical Environment", Lincoln Laboratory Report XR-1, 7 May 1976.

43. E. H. Martin, "Aiding GPS Navigation Functions", *NAECON '76 Record*, pp 849-856.

44. B. A. Kriegsman, D. B. Cox, Jr., W. M. Stonestreet, "An IMU Aided GPS Receiver", CSDL Report P-490, June 1977, Presented at the 33rd Annual Meeting of the Institute of Navigation, Costa Mesa, CA., 22-24 June 1977.

45. B. A. Kriegsman, W. M. Stonestreet, and D. B. Cox, Jr., "Functional Requirements of the Interface Between the NAVSTAR GPS Receiver Model X and the Advanced Inertial Reference Sphere", Draper Laboratory Report R-981 (Air Force Report SAMSO TR 77-120), Volume II, December 1977.

46. R. Maher, "Oscillator and Frequency Management Requirements for GPS User Equipment", *Proceedings of 1976 Frequency Control Symposium*, June 1976, pp 384-389.

47. J. M. Przyjemski, P. L. Konop, "Limitations on GPS Receiver Performance Imposed by Crystal Oscillator G-Sensitivity", C. S. Draper Laboratory Report P-432, March 1977, *NAECON '77 Record*, pp 319-322.

48. J. M. Przyjemski, "A Compensation Technique for Acceleration-Induced Frequency Changes in Crystal Oscillators", Draper Laboratory Report P-606, *NAECON '78 Record*, May 1978.

49. R. W. Carrol, W. A. Mickelson, "Velocity Aiding of Non-Coherent GPS Receiver", *NAECON '77 Record*, pp 311-318.

50. R. V. Ramnath, W. M. Bowles, "Asymptotic Analysis of a Class of Time-Varying Linear Filters", C. S. Draper Laboratory Report R-994, 25 Aug. 1976.

51. W. M. Bowles, "Optimal Acquisition and Tracking of a Pseudo-Random Code", Draper Laboratory Internal Memo 15L-76-005, 8 Jan 1976.

Aircraft Navigation with the Limited Operational Phase of the NAVSTAR Global Positioning System

L. R. KRUCZYNSKI

ABSTRACT

THE NAVSTAR Global Positioning System (GPS) will soon be in the limited operational phase. During this phase, a GPS user will not generally be able to determine his position using satellite measurements only. This paper describes the simulation of an aircraft navigation technique which uses the limited operational phase GPS and barometric altimeter measurements.

For this research effort, the GPS user was assumed to be a cargo-type aircraft equipped with a single-frequency, sequentially-tracking GPS receiver and a barometric altimeter. The flight profile consisted of a New York to Chicago flight and included takeoff and landing maneuvers. A small amount of wind gusts were simulated. To make the simulation more realistic, random effects were included in the user and satellite clocks, in the atmospheric radio delays, and in the measurement process itself.

The tested navigation algorithm is based on the well-known Kalman filter equations. Three different models of aircraft acceleration were evaluated. Results indicate that, for a wide range of filter parameters, navigation errors are generally less than 100 meters. Poor geometry, however, results in kilometer-sized position errors.

INTRODUCTION

The NAVSTAR Global Positioning System

Major Kruczynski is with the Department of Astronautics and Computer Science, United States Air Force, CO 80840. He presented this paper at the National Aerospace Meeting in Denver, CO, on April 14, 1977.

(GPS) will be the navigation system of the 1980's. When fully operational, it will consist of 24 satellites in 12-hour, circular orbits and the ground equipment necessary to maintain the system. The GPS will use a passive ranging technique to provide real-time, continuous navigation information to an unlimited number of users.

Much analysis has been done for the fully operational system. Little analysis, however, has been performed for the limited operational capability phase, Phase II, even though this phase is expected to last from 1980 to 1984. This paper describes an analysis of the performance of three navigation algorithms during Phase II GPS. The user is a simulated airplane on a New York to Chicago flight with inexpensive GPS equipment and a barometric altimeter. Because only one flight profile was examined, the results are not conclusive. The simulation is, however, realistic and the performance achieved is a reasonable expectation of what could actually occur.

THE GEOMETRY OF GPS AND LORAN

The GPS navigation technique is similar to the hyperbolic ranging technique used in LORAN. A LORAN user measures the difference between time of reception of signals from two LORAN transmitters. After accounting for fixed delays in the transmission of the LORAN pulses, the user can multiply the time difference by the speed of light to obtain a range difference measurement. This range-difference measurement defines a hyperbolic line-of-position (LOP) in the plane defined by the location of the two LORAN transmitters and the user. Recall that a hyperbola is the locus of points for which the difference of the distance of any point from two fixed points, the foci, is constant. In LORAN, the transmitters are at the foci of the hyperbola.

If the LORAN user has a third transmitter available, he can form a second independent range–difference measurement. In the plane defined by the three transmitters, the LORAN user now has two hyperbolic LOPs and he can calculate his position at the intersection of the two hyperbolas.

To understand the GPS pseudo-ranging technique, we recall that a single LORAN range–difference measurement defines a hyperbola. In three–dimensional space, this single range–difference measurement actually defines a hyperboloid of revolution or one part of a two–sheeted hyperboloid. To visualize this hyperboloid, rotate a hyperbola about the line connecting the two foci (the two transmitters). The second independent range–difference measurement defines a second hyperboloid and the intersection of the two hyperboloids forms a line–of–position. Knowledge of his altitude provides the user with a third surface whose intersection with the two hyperboloids defines a navigation fix (assuming any ambiguities can be resolved).

GPS MEASUREMENT MODEL

The preceding discussion must be considered as strictly philosophical, that is, the basic performance of the GPS can be considered in light of a hyperbolic ranging technique but the actual mechanization may differ significantly. For example, if the user has a very stable clock which is synchronized to GPS time and if he has equipment capable of receiving three satellite signals simultaneously, then each satellite signal will place him on a sphere whose center is located at the satellite position and whose radius is equal to the speed of light times the time difference between signal transmission and signal reception. This is a range measurement. Of course, equipment delays and atmospheric delays must be accounted for. Use of range measurements is a departure from the hyperbolic ranging philosophy and error behavior is quite different [1:pp 365–369]. If the user's clock is not synchronized to GPS time, then a user with a simultaneously tracking receiver can, if he so desires, form range–difference

measurements nearly identical to LORAN range–difference measurements. In this case, however, he needs four satellites in order to form three independent range–differences. Such measurements are called pseudo–range measurements because they include an unknown time bias in user's clock. A single pseudo–range measurement thus takes the form

$$Y = c(t_r + b - t_s + \delta) \tag{1}$$

where

c is the speed of light,

t_r is the best estimate of the time of signal reception,

b is an unknown bias in the user's clock,

t_s is the best estimate of the time of signal transmission, and

δ is a term to account for all other signal delays.

Equation 1 assumes that the user has removed all known clock errors, all known equipment delays, and all known atmospheric delays. This measurement should be equal to the actual range between the position of the user at the time he received the signal and the position of the satellite at the time the signal was transmitted. By differencing the pseudo–range measurement with the best estimate of the range difference, the user with a simultaneously tracking receiver has a set of four equations as follows

$$y_i = c(t_r + b - t_{s_i} + \delta_i) - |R_i(t_{s_i}) - r(t_r)| \tag{2}$$

where

y_i are the pseudo–range residuals,

$R_i(t_s)$ is the vector position of the i–th satellite at the time of transmission of the signal, and

$r(t_r)$ is the best estimate of the vector position of the user at the time he received signals from the four satellites.

DETERMINISTIC SOLUTION

In an error free system, the user can solve for his clock bias and his position by solving Eq. 2 such that

$$y_i = 0, \quad \text{for} \quad i = 1,2,3,4$$

Various techniques have been suggested to do this. Many of these techniques are oriented to the solution of a linear matrix equation

$$y = Hx + w \qquad (3)$$

where

y is a vector of the measurement residuals,

x is a four–dimensional vector consisting of the errors in the three components of user position and the user's clock bias error,

H is the result of linearization of Eq. 2, and

w is a vector of the remaining terms in Eq. 2.

Methods requiring solution to Eq. 3 can be mechanized when there is no a priori knowledge of user position or clock bias. These methods require, however, that the user position be constant for four measurements. Therefore, the user must be stationary or must have a simultaneous tracking receiver. (This paper does not consider the possibility of representing position by equations with four parameters and time and then estimating the four parameters.) If the user has some knowledge of his current state (position and clock bias), then he can use sequential filter techniques to update the current estimate of his state based on a single measurement. Thus, with sequential filter techniques, the user is no longer restricted to a simultaneously tracking receiver.

TIME INHERENT IN GPS PRN CODE

At this point, it would be helpful to describe the GPS navigation signal structure. The GPS navigation signals are pseudo–random–noise (PRN) sequences. The receiver correlates the incoming signal with a user generated PRN sequence which is identical to that transmitted by the observed satellite. The ideal auto–correlation function of a PRN–code is illustrated in Fig. 1. It is the job of the user's receiver to shift the locally generated code so that the output of the correlator is at the peak of the auto–correlation function.

Because of the character of the auto–correlation function, the satellite signal can be considered as a continuously available time tick. Knowledge of the state of the locally generated code (which is assumed to be correlated with the incoming signal) coupled with the knowledge of the code epoch (contained in the satellite data) will yield the time of signal transmission for use in Eq 1. Because the PRN signal is continuously available, this time of signal transmission is available on command of the user's computer.

Although the width of a code chip is 97.75

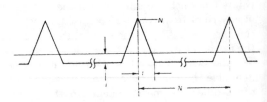

Fig. 1 – Ideal Auto-Correlation Function for an N-Bit PRN Sequence.

nanoseconds for the GPS precison (P) code, a receiver can take advantage of the PRN autocorrelation function so that it can track the incoming code with an RMS error on the order of 0.01 of the chip width with a signal-to-noise ratio on the order of 30 db [2: Par 4.1.2]. This translates to a 0.3 meter RMS error for a pseudo–range measurement. If the clear/acquisition (C/A) code is used, the RMS tracking error is 3 meters because the chip width is 977.5 nsec.

THE SEQUENTIAL FILTER

The use of sequential filter techniques, of which the Kalman filter is the most famous, has many advantages. It has been shown that, if the model of the dynamic system and the model of the measurement are linear and if the sequential filter is provided with the correct statistics of the dynamic system and the measurement, then the estimate generated by the sequential filter is the optimal estimate. To fully explore this statement, stochastic criteria and restricted definitions of "optimal" would have to be considered. The reader interested in such analysis is directed to the works of Jazwinski [3] and Meditch [4] as well as to the pioneering papers by Kalman [5] and Kalman and Bucy [6]. For purposes of this discussion, Brock and Schmidt have shown that if the sequential filter is provided with the best known information, then the filter estimate is the "best" estimate [7]. In addition, it has been shown that

1. A sequential filter is not difficult to implement. If the measurements are uncorrelated they can be processed as scalars, further simplifying the filter coding. In fact, the implementation of a sequential filter may be easier than the implementation of a matrix inversion required for the solution to Eq 3.

2. A sequential filter easily combines different measurement sources.

3. Non-stationary noise can be accommodated easily. Thus, a satellite at low elevation angle may be assigned a larger error statistic, and barometric altimeters can have error statistics which are functions of altitude.

THE EXTENDED SEQUENTIAL ALGORITHM

The extended sequential algorithm is designed to predict the state of a system between measurement times using the best available information, even if this includes non–linear equations. Covariance matrices, however, are propagated using the linearized system model. At the measurement time, the filter gains are computed and are multiplied by the observation residual to calculate the best estimate of the error in the propagated state. This error estimate is added to the propagated nominal state to rectify the nominal trajectory. If the filter is operating correctly, the rectified state will be closer to the actual trajectory than the nominal state so that any linearization required for the filter equations will be more accurate. After a measurement update of the covariance matrix, the filter again propagates the state to the time of the next measurement.

The system whose state is to be estimated can be described by the differential equation

$$\dot{X} = F(X, t) + Bu \qquad (4)$$

where
u is a random variable with statistics

$$E[u] = 0, \quad E[u(t)u^T(\tau)] = Q\delta(t - \tau) \qquad (5)$$

where
Q is the spectral level process noise covariance matrix.

For use in linearized techniques, the partial derivative of the system differential equation is required.

$$A = \frac{\partial F}{\partial x}(X, t) \qquad (6)$$

A discrete observation is given by

$$Y_k = G(X_k, t_k) + e_k \qquad (7)$$

where
e is a random variable with statistics

$$E[e_k] = 0, \quad E[e_j e_k^T] = R\delta_{jk} \qquad (8)$$

where
R is the measurement noise covariance matrix.

For linearized techniques the measurement partial is required.

$$H = \frac{\partial G}{\partial X}(X, t) \qquad (9)$$

The estimation process is summarized as follows.

1. Integrate to t_k the nominal state $\bar{X}$ and the covariance matrix $\bar{P}$.

$$\dot{\bar{X}} = F(\bar{X}, t), \quad \bar{X}(t_{k-1}) = \hat{X}_{k-1} \qquad (10)$$

$$\dot{\bar{P}} = A\bar{P} + \bar{P}A^T + BQB^T, \quad \bar{P}(t_{k-1}) = P_{k-1} \qquad (11)$$

where

$$\bar{P}_k = E[(\bar{X}_k - X_k)(\bar{X}_k - X_k)^T] \qquad (12)$$

$$P_k = E[(\hat{X}_k - X_k)(\hat{X}_k - X_k)^T] \qquad (13)$$

2. Compute the gain.

$$K_k = \bar{P}_k H_k (H_k \bar{P}_k H_k^T + R_k)^{-1} \qquad (14)$$

3. Determine the observation residual.

$$y_k = Y_k - G(\bar{X}_k, t_k) \qquad (15)$$

4. Estimate the perturbation state.

$$\hat{x}_k = K_k y_k \qquad (16)$$

5. Update the covariance matrix.

$$P_k = (I - K_k H_k)\bar{P}_k \qquad (17)$$

6. Rectify the nominal trajectory.

$$\hat{X}_k = \bar{X}_k + \hat{x}_k \qquad (18)$$

7. Replace k with $k-1$ and go to step 1.

AIRCRAFT MODELS FOR THE FILTER

The general behavior of an aircraft for more than a few seconds cannot be described accurately. In this analysis, two dynamic system models were considered for the time propagation of the aircraft state. The acceleration dead-reckoning (ADR) model was used with algorithms in which position, velocity, and acceleration were estimated. The ADR equations as implemented in the filter are

$$\bar{x}_k = \hat{x}_{k-1} + \hat{v}_{k-1}(t_k - t_{k-1}) + \hat{a}_{k-1}\frac{(t_k - t_{k-1})^2}{2}$$

$$\bar{v}_k = \hat{v}_{k-1} + \hat{a}_{k-1}(t_k - t_{k-1}) \qquad (19)$$

$$\bar{a}_k = \hat{a}_{k-1}$$

where

$\hat{x}_{k-1}$ is the *a posteriori* estimate of the position at t_{k-1},

$\hat{v}_{k-1}$ is the *a posteriori* estimate of the velocity at t_{k-1},

$\hat{a}_{k-1}$ is the *a posteriori* estimate of the acceleration at t_{k-1}, and

$\bar{x}_k$ is the *a priori* estimate of the position at t_k.

$\bar{v}_k$ is the *a priori* estimate of the velocity at t_k.

$\bar{a}_k$ is the *a priori* estimate of the acceleration at t_k.

The second model was the velocity dead-reckoning (VDR) model which applied to algorithms in which only position and velocity were estimated. The VDR equations are

$$\bar{x}_k = \hat{x}_{k-1} + \hat{v}_{k-1}(t_k - t_{k-1})$$
$$\bar{v}_k = \hat{v}_{k-1} \tag{20}$$

THE USER'S STATE

The user's state can be separated into a nominal part and a perturbation part. The nominal part will consist of the *a priori* best estimate of the state. This implies that the *a priori* best estimate of the perturbation is zero. The measurement process will yield the *a posteriori* best estimate of the user state.

In order to propagate the covariance matrices, the linear differential equations for the propagation of the perturbation state must be developed. The differential equations which apply to dynamic motion will be written as follows

$$\dot{r} = v, \quad \dot{v} = a, \quad \dot{a} = u_a \tag{21}$$

where

r is the vector position,

v is the vector velocity,

a is the vector acceleration, and

u_a is a random variable with statistics

$$E[u_a] = 0, \quad E[u_a(t)u_a(\tau)] = q_a\delta(t - \tau) \tag{22}$$

where

q_a is the spectral level acceleration noise.
The nominal state described in Eqs. 19 is the mean solution to Eqs. 21. If the true state is defined as the sum of the mean state and a perturbation state, then the differential equations for the perturbation state are

$$\delta r = \delta v, \quad \delta v = \delta a, \quad \delta a = u_a \tag{23}$$

where

$$r = \bar{r} + \delta r, \quad v = \bar{v} + \delta v, \quad a = \bar{a} + \delta a \tag{24}$$

Equations 23 define the propagation of the covariance matrices.

In addition to the aircraft states (position velocity, and, if required, acceleration), the estimated state vector included three measurement biases: user block bias, user clock drift and barometric altimeter bias.

NAVIGATION ALGORITHMS

Three basic navigation algorithms were tested. The first will be referred to as the infinite correlation time ADR algorithm. For this algorithm, Eqs. 19 are used for time propagation of the user's state and the time propagation of the covariance matrices is based on Eqs. 23. The spectral level acceleration noise term was varied in a parameter analysis. This term was assumed identical for all three directions. Results for the first 600 seconds of flight are shown in Table 1. The second algorithm will be referred to as the twenty-second correlation time ADR algorithm. For this algorithm Eqs. 19 are used to propagate the aircraft state and Eqs. 25 are used to propagate the covariance matrices.

$$\delta r = \delta v, \quad \delta v = \delta a, \quad \delta a = -0.05\,\delta a + u_a \tag{25}$$

Again, the spectral level acceleration noise was varied. Results for the first 600 seconds of flight for the twenty-second correlation time ADR algorithm are shown in Table 2.

The third algorithm tested will be referred to as the velocity dead-reckoning (VDR) algorithm. In this algorithm, Eqs. 18 are used to propagate the aircraft state and Eqs. 26 define the propagation of the covariance matrices.

$$\delta r = \delta v, \quad \delta v = u_r \tag{26}$$

where

u_r is a random variable with statistics

$$E[u_r] = 0, \quad E[u_r(t)u_r(\tau)] = q_r\delta(t - \tau) \tag{27}$$

where

q_r is the spectral level velocity noise.
Results of the parameter analysis for the VDR algorithm are given in Table 3. The spectral level velocity noise was assumed to be identical for all three directions.

SIMULATED ENVIRONMENT

The simulation program is extensive. Rather

Table 1 — Twenty-Second Correlation Time ADR Filter Performance

Performance Item	Acceleration Noise Magnitude (m²/sec⁵)					
	.0225	.225	2.25	4.50	10.00	22.50
Root-Sum-Square Position Error (meters)	85.62	58.66	55.94	55.84	55.89	56.20
Root-Sum-Square Velocity Error (m/sec)	15.33	9.18	8.39	8.75	9.36	10.17
Maximum Position Error (meters)	248.24	149.36	141.80	141.34	139.23	139.78
Maximum Velocity Error (m/sec)	40.56	30.58	29.43	28.40	27.62	27.83
Ratio of RSS Position Error to RSS Standard Deviation of Position Error	1.84	1.04	.75	.67	.58	.49
Ratio of RSS Velocity Error to RSS Standard Deviation of Velocity Error	3.34	1.00	.44	.36	.29	.24
Position Error at t = 600 sec (meters)	26.35	50.01	80.46	88.12	94.10	97.48
Velocity Error at t = 600 sec (m/sec)	1.52	4.11	11.11	13.18	14.99	16.34

Table 2 — Infinite Correlation Time ADR Filter Performance

Performance Item	Acceleration Noise Magnitude (m²/sec⁵)					
	.018	.03	.18	1.80	18.10	180.00
Root-Sum-Square Position Error (meters)	63.70	60.40	56.95	55.80	56.50	60.15
Root-Sum-Square Velocity Error (m/sec)	10.95	9.91	8.28	8.67	10.79	14.92
Maximum Position Error (meters)	198.48	173.72	147.92	139.95	138.81	144.16
Maximum Velocity Error (m/sec)	32.30	28.96	31.37	28.73	28.08	43.57
Ratio of RSS Position Error to RSS Standard Deviation of Position Error	1.32	1.21	.98	.72	.48	.26
Ratio of RSS Velocity Error to RSS Standard Deviation of Velocity Error	2.00	1.59	.80	.42	.24	.14
Position Error at t = 600 sec (meters)	29.58	32.96	50.11	80.52	97.78	100.91
Velocity Error at t = 600 sec (m/sec)	1.68	1.93	4.25	11.51	16.81	24.16

Table 3 — Uncorrelated Acceleration (VDR) Filter Performance

Performance Item	Velocity Noise Magnitude (m²/sec⁵)					
	.9375	2.8125	11.25	28.125	100.00	281.25
Root-Sum-Square Position Error (meters)	203.78	131.14	85.51	71.30	62.30	59.58
Root-Sum-Square Velocity Error (m/sec)	27.88	21.64	16.19	13.87	12.02	11.40
Maximum Position Error (meters)	526.85	347.71	229.00	183.24	152.28	146.64
Maximum Velocity Error (m/sec)	61.48	48.12	36.94	33.49	30.65	29.11
Ratio of RSS Position Error to RSS Standard Deviation of Position Error	4.50	2.60	1.45	1.06	.72	.52
Ratio of RSS Velocity Error to RSS Standard Deviation of Velocity Error	7.08	3.54	1.50	.88	.44	.26
Position Error at t = 600 sec (meters)	50.22	52.83	64.00	73.26	85.66	92.63
Velocity Error at t = 600 sec (m-sec)	1.41	2.79	5.55	7.83	11.20	13.08

than describe all facets of the program, results of critical environmental segments will be presented. The baseline satellite constellation consists of nine satellites: three satellites evenly spaced in each of three orbit planes. Ascending nodes of the orbit planes are 120 degrees apart. Orbit inclinations are 63 degrees. The orbits are circular at an altitude of 20,000 km and have periods of 12 hours. With such a configuration, three satellites will be visible to most users 70 percent of the time [8]. Four satellites

will be visible only about 25 percent of the time. Since the purpose of the research was to evaluate navigation algorithms during GPS Phase II, the satellite epochs were chosen so that four satellites were visible during less than five percent of the simulated flight. Thus, a realistic but difficult Phase II situation was simulated. The user's satellite ephemeris was corrupted to cause errors in satellite position up to ten meters.

Atmospheric delays were simulated in two

parts: ionospheric and trophospheric. The results of the delay simulation were more severe than would normally be expected. The ionospheric vertical group delay was simulated as a random process. The realization of this random process is shown in Fig. 2. The user assumed that the vertical group delay was a constant 40 nsec. The vertical group delay was multiplied by an obliquity factor to account for the user-satellite geometry.

Tropospheric delay was simulated by modeling the sea level refractivity as a random process. Results are shown in Fig. 3. The user assumed that sea level refractivity was a constant 325. The sea level refractivity was propagated to the user's altitude using an exponential formula. The refractivity at altitude was then multiplied by a factor which accounts for user-satellite geometry. The result was a tropospheric delay which varied from one nanosecond to 47 nanoseconds depending on the user's altitude and the elevation angle to the satellite. Tropospheric and ionospheric delay scintillations were also considered. The RMS of these scintillations were functions of elevation and varied from one to three nanoseconds for ionospheric scintillation and from one to six nanoseconds for the troposphere.

The satellite clocks had biases as shown in Fig. 4. The user was provided with linear fits to these curves. The RSS error after removal of the linear trends was approximately five nanoseconds. This is about the error expected from rubidium clocks.

The bias and drift for the user's clock are shown on Fig. 5. This behavior is a possible realization of a high quality quartz crystal clock.

To simulate equipment noise, an additional Gaussian error, with RMS equal to one meter, was added to the indicated satellite time.

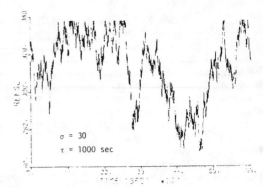

$\sigma = 30$
$\tau = 1000$ sec

Fig. 3 – Sea-Level Refractivity.

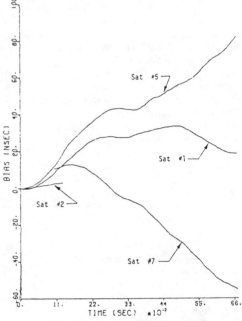

Fig. 4 – Satellite Clock Biases.

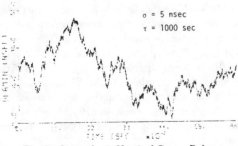

$\sigma = 5$ nsec
$\tau = 1000$ sec

Fig. 2 – Ionospheric Vertical Group Delay.

A PSEUDO-RANGE-RATE MEASUREMENT

The PRN code will modulate the L-band carriers using bi-phase-shift-keying (BPSK). This signal can be demodulated by a variety of receivers. Most receivers proposed for GPS include a carrier-tracking loop. The presence of a carrier-tracking loop easily leads to generation of a pseudo-range-rate measurement. This is a measurement of range-rate (Doppler) corrupted by the drift in the user's clock. The simulated generation of this measurement included the satellite clock drifts and an additional Gaussian error with 0.02 m/sec RMS as

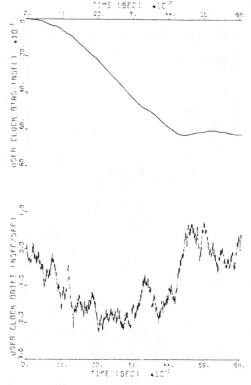

Fig. 5 – User Clock Bias and Drift.

well as the range–rate and the user's clock drift.

A BAROMETRIC ALTIMETER

With only three satellites visible, deterministic solutions require a fourth, independent measurement. This measurement can be a time measurement from a highly accurate, synchronized clock. This is, however, an expensive alternative. A cheaper solution is the addition of a barometric altimeter measurement. Barometric altimeters are available in all aircraft and, with the addition of an analog–to–digital converter, altitude information can be made available to the computer. The output of the altimeter defines a surface of position which intersects the two hyperboloids defined by two independent range–difference measurements from three satellites.

Because the altimeter is low cost but has high information content, it was incorporated into the tested algorithms. When the altimeter was removed, navigation errors increased considerably.

The altimeter was assumed to have a bias which could vary with altitude, distance, and time. The simulated altimeter bias is shown in Fig. 6. Gaussian noise with RMS 20 meters was added to the altimeter measurement.

MEASUREMENT FREQUENCY

Every 1.25 seconds, the user processes a pseudo-range and a pseudo–range–rate measurement from one satellite. After taking data from each visible satellite, an altimeter measurement is processed. Satellite measurements are randomly rejected five percent of the time and altimeter measurements are randomly rejected two percent of the time.

USER TRAJECTORY

The user was assumed to be a jet cargo aircraft on a New York to Chicago flight. Time of the flight is 111 minutes. Departure and arrival ground tracks are shown in Figs. 7 and 8. Horizontal speed and altitude profiles are shown in Figs. 9 and 10. A small amount of wind gust was included in the simulation. The satellite visibilities are summarized in Fig. 11.

FULL FLIGHT TESTS

Tables 1, 2, and 3 are the results of parametric analyses of the three navigation algorithms for the first 600 seconds of flight. Values of process noise were selected based on these analyses and other tests. Tables 4, 5, and 6 summarize the results of complete flight simulations for selected values of process noise for each algorithm. Figs. 12 depict the results for

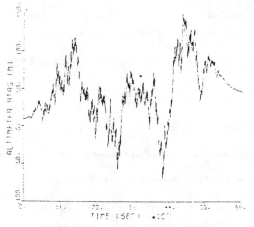

Fig. 6 – Correlated Altimeter Bias.

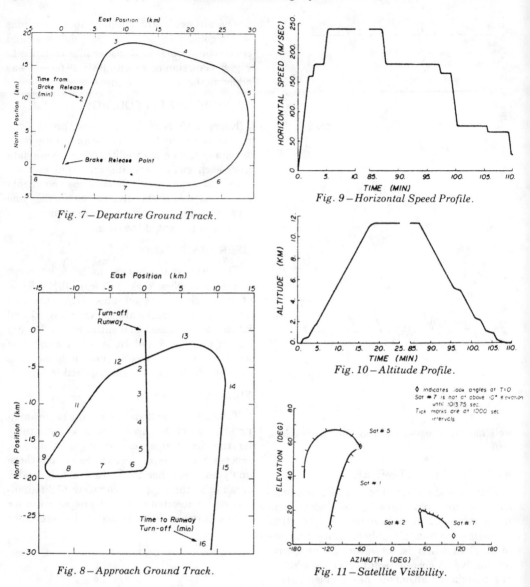

Fig. 7 — Departure Ground Track.

Fig. 8 — Approach Ground Track.

Fig. 9 — Horizontal Speed Profile.

Fig. 10 — Altitude Profile.

Fig. 11 — Satellite Visibility.

Table 4 — Full Flight Performance of Twenty-Second Correlation Time Filter (q_a = .225 m²/sec⁵)

Performance Item	Flight Phase Final Times (sec)					
	598.75	1013.75	1295.00	2760.00	5100.00	6687.50
Root-Sum-Square Position Error (meters)	58.66	139.66	18.98	236.35	101.07	52.62
Root-Sum-Square Velocity Error (m/sec)	9.18	2.64	.52	2.11	1.81	2.50
Maximum Position Error (meters)	149.36	227.49	128.45	872.41	312.17	110.60D
Maximum Velocity Error (m/sec)	30.58	6.27	1.85	10.92	13.27	18.62
Ratio of RSS Position Error to RSS Standard Deviation of Position Error	1.04	1.75	1.02	.86	1.13	1.65
Ratio of RSS Velocity Error to RSS Standard Deviation of Velocity Error	1.00	.36	.14	.30	.31	.66

Table 5 — Full Flight Performance of VDR Filter (q_v = 2.8125 m²/sec³)

Performance Item	Flight Phase Final Times (sec)					
	598.75	1013.75	1295.00	2760.00	5100.00	6687.50
Root-Sum-Square Position Error (meters)	131.14	147.46	18.66	238.81	97.48	57.75
Root-Sum-Square Velocity Error (m/sec)	21.64	3.02	.65	1.59	1.17	5.48
Maximum Position Error (meters)	347.71	253.01	127.52	819.03	368.41	131.75
Maximum Velocity Error (m/sec)	48.12	6.57	2.64	7.28	7.51	37.56
Ratio of RSS Position Error to RSS Standard Deviation of Position Error	2.60	1.79	.76	.81	1.05	1.74
Ratio of RSS Velocity Error to RSS Standard Deviation of Velocity Error	3.54	.48	.14	.25	.21	1.23

Table 6 — Full Flight Performance of ADR Filter (q_a = 0.18 m²/sec⁵, CT = ∞)

Performance Item	Flight Phase Final Times (sec)					
	598.75	1013.75	1295.00	2760.00	5100.00	6687.50
Root-Sum-Square Position Error (meters)	56.95	140.40	19.35	235.70	101.81	51.71
Root-Sum-Square Velocity Error (m/sec)	8.28	2.67	.52	2.44	2.31	2.43
Maximum Position Error (meters)	147.92	228.55	131.01	872.11	302.03	111.06
Maximum Velocity Error (m/sec)	31.37	7.02	1.95D	15.98	18.61	18.81
Ratio of RSS Position Error to RSS Standard Deviation of Position Error	.98	1.76	1.05	.86	1.13	1.62
Ratio of RSS Velocity Error to RSS Standard Deviation of Velocity Error	.80	.34	.14	.32	.36	.63

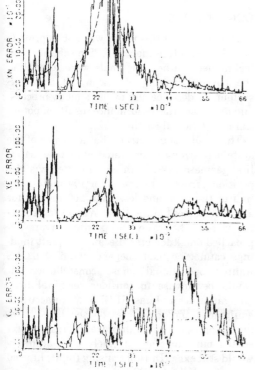

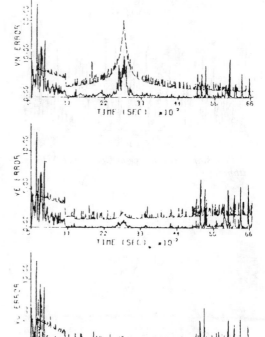

Fig. 12a — Position Performance of Correlated ADR Algorithm.

Fig. 12b — Velocity Performance of Correlated ADR Algorithm.

the twenty–second correlation time algorithm. Plots for the other algorithms are similar to Figs. 12.

In all cases, the North component error is significantly higher than the East component or altitude errors. Figs. 13 and 14 summarize the results of a geometric dilution of precision

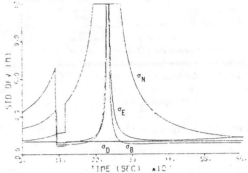

Fig. 14 – Geometric Dilution of Precision (North, East, Down, and Clock Bias State).

(GDOP) analysis which was performed using the satellite visibilities in the simulation. Fig. 13 assumes that only the three position components (North, East, and vertical) are estimated. Fig. 14 assumes that the clock bias is also estimated. In both figures, pseudo–range and altimeter measurements are considered. The similarity between the GDOP figures and the actual performance is remarkable.

CONCLUSIONS

The purpose of this paper was not to provide an exhaustive treatment of GPS mechanization techniques. Rather, the goals were to outline the passive ranging philosophy of the GPS system, to describe the measurement process, and to present the performance results of potential navigation algorithms.

The results demonstrate that accuracy of the system is strongly correlated with user–satellite geometry. With three satellites visible, position errors were less than 100 meters for half of the time and less than 200 meters for about 80 percent of the time. When the geometry is poor, however, the position errors approached one kilometer. Because aircraft landings cannot be made dependent on the GPS limited operational phase constellation, it would be unwise to consider terminal area navigation using Phase II GPS. More accurate equipment and/or updates on sea level barometric pressure would improve the results presented but times of extremely poor accuracy would still exist. During cruising flight, limited operational phase GPS accuracies are competitive with LORAN and OMEGA with the added

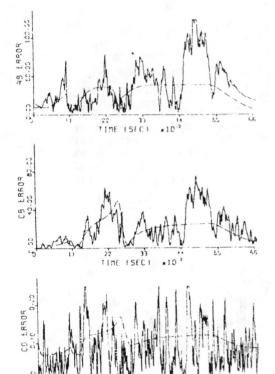

Fig. 12c – Bias Performance of Correlated ADR Algorithm.

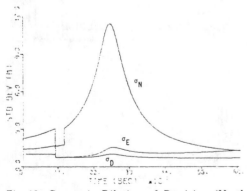

Fig. 13 – Geometric Dilution of Precision (North, East, and Down State).

benefit of global coverage from the constellation.

ACKNOWLEDGMENTS

The Author wishes to acknowledge the guidance of Dr. Byron D. Tapley, The University of Texas at Austin, and the support of the Global Positioning System Joint Program Office, in particular, Col Bradford W. Parkinson, Maj Mel Birnbaum, Capt Walter Murch, and Lt Scott Rounce.

REFERENCES

1. Anderson, E. W. *The Principles of Navigation.* American Elsevier Publishing Co., New York, 1966.
2. Cahn, C. R., et al. *Timation Modulation Study.* Magnavox Research Labs, Report R-4439, Torrance, CA, AD 902855, August 1972.
3. Jazwinski, Andrew H. *Stochastic Processes and Filtering Theory.* Academic Press, New York, 1970.
4. Meditch, J. S. *Stochastic Optimal Linear Estimation and Control.* McGraw-Hill Book Co., New York, 1969.
5. Kalman, R. E. "A New Approach to Linear Filtering and Prediction Problems," *Journal of Basic Engineering,* pp. 35–45, March 1960.
6. Kalman, R. E., and R. S. Bucy. "New Results in Linear Filtering and Prediction Theory," *Journal of Basic Engineering,* pp. 95–108, March 1961.
7. Brock, Larry D. and George T. Schmidt. "General Questions on Kalman Filtering in Navigation Systems," in Cornelius T. Leondes (ed.), *Theory and Applications of Kalman Filtering,* NATO AGARDograph 139, London, AD 704306, February 1970, pp. 205–230.
8. Bogen, A. H. *Geometric Performance of the Global Positioning System.* AF Report SAMSO-TR-74-169, Aerospace Corp. Report TR-0074(4461-02)-2, El Segundo, CA, June 1974.

A Navigation Algorithm for the Low-Cost GPS Receiver

P. S. NOE, K. A. MYERS, and T. K. WU

ABSTRACT

THE GLOBAL POSITIONING SYSTEM (GPS) is a satellite navigation system currently under development by the Department of Defense. A recent note described the numerical properties of a proposed navigation algorithm for the low-cost GPS receiver under static conditions. This note evaluates performance of this algorithm in a realistic dynamic simulation of a typical flight profile for an Air Force C5A transport aircraft. Numerical convergence and long-term dynamic stability of the algorithm are demonstrated in a noise-free environment; typically, a single iteration of the algorithm maintains position estimate errors below 0.2 ft at each position fix for the duration of the flight. Stochastic error models are implemented in the simulation to produce a realistic noisy environment; in this case, the algorithm provides navigation accuracies on the order of 400 ft. In addition, the performance of two GPS satellite selection routines is compared in the simulations.

INTRODUCTION

The Global Positioning System (GPS) is a satellite navigation system currently under development by the Department of Defense.[1] It will consist of 24 satellites in circular, 12-hour orbits at an altitude of 11,000 NM and inclined

Dr. Noe is with Department of Electrical Engineering, Texas A&M University, College Station, TX 77843. Major Myers and Dr. Wu are with AFAL/RWA-3, Wright-Patterson AFB, OH 45433. They presented this paper at the National Aerospace Meeting in Warminster, PA on 27 April 1976.

63° to the equator. The satellites will broadcast pseudo-random noise codes and ephemerides on two L-band signals to users worldwide. A user will be equipped with a small receiver (GPS user equipment) which measures pseudo-range and pseudo-range-rate from the user to the satellite. Typically, four satellite signals may be received simultaneously by the user equipment. In a recent note[2] a position-fix algorithm was proposed for the low-cost GPS receiver, and its numerical properties were tested under static conditions (fixed user and satellites). It was demonstrated that with initial user position estimate errors as large as 1000 NM, the algorithm converges to the user's true position in 3 or 4 iterations. The purpose of this paper is to demonstrate performance of the algorithm in a realistic dynamic configuration involving a moving user and moving satellites. In addition, the performance of two GPS satellite selection algorithms is compared. Results are presented for a computer simulation of an Air Force C5A aircraft flight from Travis AFB, California, to Hickam AFB, Hawaii.

DESCRIPTION OF THE SIMULATION

Two computer programs are utilized in the C5A aircraft simulation. The first, PROFGEN, is an aircraft profile generator developed at the Air Force Avionics Laboratory for use on the CDC 6600 Computer. For specified initial conditions and a set of inputs involving path and lateral acceleration, pitch angle, and heading changes, PROFGEN numerically integrates the equations of motion for the aircraft with a fifth-order, variable-step Kutta-Mercer algorithm. Key parameters and events in the C5A flight profile are displayed in Table I. Outputs from PROFGEN at specified time intervals in-

Table 1—C5A Flight Profile Data

Flight Time (Min)	Latitude (Deg)	Longitude (Deg W)	Altitude (Ft)	Speed (Ft/Sec)	Heading (Deg)	Mission Events
0	37.0	123.0	100	112	270	Take-Off from Travis AFB, CA
3	37.0	123.1	1300	278	270	Climb; Begin 28° Left Turn
5	36.9	123.3	4263	456	242	Continue Climb
12	36.7	123.9	12373	548	241	Decrease Rate of Climb
32	35.7	126.1	25720	678	240	Slow Climb During Cruise
130	29.6	137.1	30017	703	234	Continue Slow Climb
288	17.6	153.0	37281	745	228	Level Off; Perform 70° Right Turn
336	20.1	158.5	37665	745	296	Begin Descent
343	20.4	159.2	29862	555	296	Increase Rate of Descent
349	20.6	159.6	4040	301	295	Slow Descent; Turn Right 90°
350	20.7	160.0	2132	273	25	Level Off On Approach Leg
360	21.0	159.4	2111	230	26	Begin Final Approach
362	21.1	159.5	144	100	26	Touch Down at Hickam, AFB, HI

clude aircraft latitude, longitude, altitude, and velocity and acceleration components with respect to a geodetic reference ellipsoid in the WGS–72 coordinate system[3]. These outputs are stored on tape and used to drive the second program, NAVSIM, which contains the following routines: a true aircraft trajectory routine, which adds simulated perturbations to the PROFGEN trajectory data; the user navigation algorithm (Hotelling); a satellite selection routine (SATSEL); a satellite orbit generation routine (SATGEN), which propagates the positions of the 24 GPS satellites in circular, two–body orbits about the earth; and, a range measurement generation routine (RANGE), which provides simulated range measurements from the user to the GPS satellites.

TRUE AIRCRAFT TRAJECTORY ROUTINE

The position output data from PROFGEN (latitude ϕ_p, east longitude λ_p from Greenwich, and altitude h_p) are corrupted with a discrete, stochastic Gaussian noise sequence to simulate the effects of aircraft turbulence and random control disturbances as follows:

$$\lambda_t = \lambda_p + \sigma_h \sqrt{\Delta t}/(R_e \cos \phi_p)\bar{w}$$

$$\phi_t = \phi_p + \sigma_h \sqrt{\Delta t}/R_e \bar{w} \qquad (1)$$

$$h_t = h_p + \sigma_v \sqrt{\Delta t}\ \bar{w}$$

The subscript indicates a true aircraft position component and Δt is the time interval between GPS position fixes. The standard deviation for horizontal perturbations is $\sigma_h = 1$ ft and for vertical perturbations is $\sigma_v = 6$ ft[4] and the earth's

radius is symbolized by R_e. The $\bar{w}$ are random numbers obtained from a Gaussian distribution with zero mean and unity variance. The true geodetic quantities in (1) are then transformed into cartesian components (u_1, u_2, u_3) in an earth–fixed frame by a series of reference ellipsoid relationships. Basic geometry for the simulation is depicted in Fig. 1.

THE USER NAVIGATION ALGORITHM

The GPS navigation position fix problem can be stated as follows: Solve the nonlinear system for the user state vector $U \equiv [u_1 u_2 u_3 b]^T$,

$$\sum_{j=1}^{3} (x_{ij} - u_j)^2 = (r_i - b)^2 \quad i = 1 \rightarrow 4 \qquad (2)$$

where $u_j, j = 1, 2, 3$ are the three user position components and b is the user clock bias error. The user state can be determined by solving (2) directly, given the measured pseudo–ranges $R \equiv [r_1 r_2 r_3 r_4]^T$ and the three satellite position components $x_{ij}, j = 1, 2, 3$, but this approach is computationally unwieldy. Instead, the approach here is to linearize (2) about the current estimate of user position and solve successively for position corrections based on new measurement residuals processed in the receiver[2]. Rearranging (2) and solving for r_i gives

$$r_i = [(x_{i1} - u_1)^2 + (x_{i2} - u_2)^2 + (x_{i3} - u_3)^2]^{1/2} + b \qquad (3)$$

A Taylor series expansion of r_i is given by

$$r_i = \bar{r}_i + (\partial r_i/\partial U)|_{\bar{u}}\delta U + (\partial^2 r_i/\partial U^2)|_{\bar{u}}\delta^2 U + ..., \qquad (4)$$

where $\bar{U}$ is the user's estimate of U and $\bar{r}_i$ is

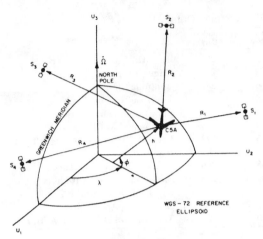

Fig. 1—Simulation Geometry.

computed from U in (3). Now (4) can be linearized by dropping all derivatives but the first, and the basic difference equation obtains

$$\delta r_i = [(\partial r_i/\partial u_1)\ (\partial r_i/\partial u_2)\ (\partial r_i/\partial u_3)\ (\partial r_i/\partial b)]|_{\bar{u}}\ \delta U \quad (5)$$

where $\delta r_i \equiv r_i - \bar{r}_i$ and $\delta U \equiv U - \bar{U}$. Now define

$$\delta r_i \equiv h_i \delta U \quad (6)$$

where h_i is the row vector in (5) given by

$$h_i = \left[\frac{u_1 - x_{i1}}{r_i - b}\ \frac{u_2 - x_{i2}}{r_i - b}\ \frac{u_3 - x_{i3}}{r_i - b}\ 1\right]\bigg|_{\bar{u}} \quad (7)$$

Thus, for the four-satellite case,

$$\delta R = \begin{bmatrix} h_1 \\ h_2 \\ h_3 \\ h_4 \end{bmatrix} \delta U \equiv H \delta U \quad (8)$$

where H is the 4×4 matrix of partials of R with respect to U, evaluated on $\bar{U}$, and $R \equiv [r_1 r_2 r_3 r_4]^T$. The desired position corrections are obtained by solving (8) as follows:

$$\delta U = H^{-1} \delta R \quad (9)$$

It is proposed that Hotelling's algorithm[9] be used to iteratively update H^{-1} in (8) as the major tool in solving for successive GPS position fixes. It is assumed that a standard matrix inverse algorithm would be employed to compute the initial H^{-1} after four satellites have been selected. Existence of the inverse is assured by a separate satellite selection algorithm which chooses those four GPS satellites that provide

good geometric dilution of precision (GDOP)[5]. Basically, Hotelling's algorithm proceeds as follows:

$$G_m = G_{m-1}(2I - HG_{m-1}), \quad m = 1, 2, \cdots \quad (10)$$

where G_0 is some initial estimate of H^{-1}. The G_1, G_2, G_3, $\cdots$, successively approach H^{-1} if it can be shown that

$$\| I - HG_0 \| = \| F_0 \| = k < 1 \quad (11)$$

The number of correct digits in the inverse increases geometrically as

$$\| G_m - H^{-1} \| \leq \| G_0 \| k^{2m}/(1 - k) \quad (12)$$

Here, the norm

$$\| X \| \equiv \max_i \sum_{j=1}^{n} |X_{ij}| \quad (13)$$

In summary, the suggested algorithm proceeds as follows.

1) Guess initial $\bar{U}$; select 4 satellites; compute $G = H^{-1}$.
2) Obtain r_i and x_{ij} from receiver data for $i = 1 \to 4$.
3) Compute $\bar{r}_i$ from (3) with $\bar{U}$ for $i = 1 \to 4$.
4) Compute $\delta R = R - \bar{R}$
5) Compute H from (7).
6) Update G via one iteration of (10) since required accuracy is assured with a single iteration here as shown in Ref. 2.
7) Compute $\delta U = G\delta R$.
8) Update position estimate $\bar{U} = \bar{U} + \delta U$.
9) Repeat steps 3) through 8) if $\delta U > \epsilon$, a specified tolerance; otherwise return to step 2).

This algorithm provides a very simple solution to the GPS navigation problem. Note that the previous position estimate $\bar{U}_k$ at time t_k is used to compute H and G_0 in steps 5) and 6); subsequently, corrections in step 7) give the desired current position estimate $\bar{U}_{k+1}$ at time t_{k+1}. This eliminates the need for a dead reckoning position update between successive range measurement times.

Satellite Selection Routine

Based on the user's position estimate $\bar{U}$, a search is made in the user's navigation computer to determine those GPS satellites in view. Only those satellites above a masking elevation angle of $E_{min} = 5°$ are selected, since satellite signal power rapidly attenuates due to atmospheric delays and noise at the lower elevations. Typically, from 5 to 9 satellites are always in view above 5° for the C5A trajectory considered. Two modes of satellite selection were employed in SATSEL to select four satellites for navigation: (1) a suboptimal criterion based on geometric dilution of precision (GDOP) and (2) an optimal GDOP criterion.[5] The suboptimal algorithm first selects those three satellites which have maximum range vector components in the vertical, east, and north directions. A fourth satellite is selected from the remaining satellites in view which produces minimum GDOP. The advantage of the suboptimal approach is computational efficiency since only n-3 computations of GDOP are required where n is the number of satellites in view. On the other hand, the optimal procedure requires $\binom{n}{4}$ computations of GDOP to select those four satellites which provide the absolute minimum GDOP. The required frequency of satellite selection is a function of time and user velocity to insure that the satellites remain in view and the GDOP remains good. In this simulation it was determined that a new satellite selection is required every 15 minutes. At satellite selection the G matrix (the inverse of H) must be calculated in Step 1) of the algorithm by a matrix inversion routine; however, during satellite measurement updates the Hotelling algorithm updates G as in Step 6) of the algorithm.

Satellite Orbit and Range Generation Routines

The satellite orbit generation routine, SATGEN, propagates the positions x_{ij} of the selected GPS satellites in two-body orbits in the earth-fixed cartesian frame. True pseudo–ranges r_i are generated in the RANGE routine by corrupting the true relative range from the user (u_1, u_2, u_3) to the i-th selected satellite S_i as follows:

$$r_i = \left[\sum_{j=1}^{3} (x_{ij} - u_j)^2 \right]^{1/2}$$
$$+ b_k + \sigma_R \bar{w} - \sigma_S \bar{w} + \sigma_I \bar{w} + \sigma_T \bar{w} \quad (14)$$

where the $\bar{w}$ are independent Gaussian random variables with zero mean and unity variance. The satellite positions x_{ij} from SATGEN are perturbed by random numbers with a Gaussian distribution to simulate random GPS satellite

ephemeris errors as follows: $x_{ij} = x_{ij} + \sigma_E \bar{w}$, where $\sigma_E = 5$ ft. The user crystal clock phase error b_k is recursively generated by

$$b_k = b_{k-1} + \dot{b}\Delta t + \sigma_b\sqrt{\Delta t}\,\bar{w} \quad (15)$$

where $b_0 = 5$ ft, and k advances by one at each GPS measurement time (at intervals of Δt). A constant frequency drift of $\dot{b} = 1$ ft/sec is employed with a clock phase noise standard deviation of $\sigma_b = 20$ ft/sec$^{1/2}$,[6] receiver range measurement noise has a standard deviation of $\sigma_R = 100$ ft, and the uncompensated satellite clock phase error standard deviation is $\sigma_S = 20$ ft. Uncompensated ionospheric and tropospheric delay errors are computed, respectively, with the following standard deviations[7]

$$\sigma_I = 8.3 \; \text{Csc} \; (E_S^2 + 18°^2) \quad \text{ft}$$
$$\sigma_T = 0.9 \; \text{Csc} \; E_S \quad \text{ft} \quad (16)$$

where E_S is the elevation angle measured from the user's local horizon to the satellite in degrees. These noise parameters are typical of those expected in an actual GPS receiver design; their verification however requires additional research and experimental data. The pseudorange measurement r_i from (14) for each satellite is employed in the Hotelling algorithm above, along with the corrupted satellite ephemeris data x_{ij} and the estimated position and clock bias in $\bar{U}$ to derive position fix corrections δU.

Simulation Results

The C5A flight profile is simulated both with and without noise in the above routines. Position fixes are obtained at an interval of $\Delta t = 5$ sec and the GPS satellites are re-selected every 15 minutes with the suboptimal satellite selection algorithm. A total of 4320 fixes are taken during the 6–hour flight.

For the noise-free case, $\bar{w}$ is set to zero in all of the above noise models. Typically, for a convergence criterion of $\epsilon = 10^{-5}$ ft (in Step 9), the Hotelling algorithm requires three iterations to converge and results in RSS position errors of 10^{-6} ft or less after each fix. The RSS position error is defined as follows:

$$\text{RSS Error} \equiv [(u_1 - \bar{u}_1)^2 + (u_2 - \bar{u}_2)^2$$
$$+ (u_3 - \bar{u}_3)^2 + (b - \bar{b})^2]^{1/2} \quad (17)$$

When the convergence criterion is relaxed to

provide a single iteration for each position fix, the RSS position errors are maintained below a very satisfactory level of 0.2 ft over the entire flight profile, as shown in Fig. 2a. This test verifies suitability of the Hotelling algorithm in this navigation problem; i.e., numerical errors, the absence of a dead-reckoning update, and the effects of satellite geometry are insignificant compared with other expected GPS system error sources. Noise free results for the optimal GDOP satellite selection criterion, shown in Fig. 2b, indicate that the optimal criterion offers negligible improvement over the more simplified suboptimal selection algorithm.

When the noise models are implemented in the simulation, the RSS position errors are maintained below 1700 ft with an average value of about 400 ft. These results are displayed in Fig. 3a for a single iteration of the Hotelling algorithm at each fix with the suboptimal satellite selection algorithm. Additional iterations produce no detectable differences on the plots. Results for the optimal satellite selection algorithm with a single iteration are displayed in Fig. 3b. Again, the optimal criterion seems to offer no substantial benefit over the suboptimal cri-

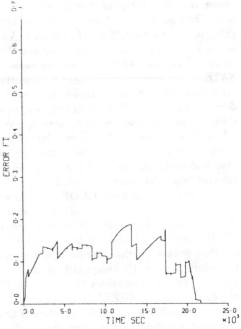

Fig. 2(b)—Optimal Satellite Selection Criterion.

terion, although all errors are under 1600 ft.*

Although the basic Hotelling algorithm offers a simple approach to position fixing, it does not provide navigation data in between GPS range measurement times, unless some form of dead-reckoning update is included. This would constitute a very simple addition to the Hotelling algorithm. However, if receiver ranging measurements are generated at less than 1-second intervals, dead-reckoning velocity errors would be comparable to other system errors; e.g., a velocity of 600 ft/sec would produce 600-ft errors after individual fixes, which are comparable to 400-ft average system errors on the plots.

It is clear that the navigation problem can be solved by explicit computation of the inverse of H at each position fix. However, the Hotelling algorithm provides a 34% central processor time advantage over direct inversion.

Conclusions

It has been demonstrated in a realistic dy-

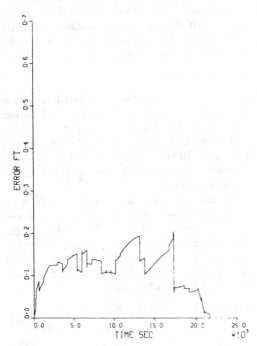

Fig. 2(a)—Suboptimal Satellite Selection Criterion.

---

* Recent results have been obtained to show how the RMS position error varies as a function of σ_R. These results are shown in Fig. 4 for $0 \leq \sigma_R \leq 100$ ft.

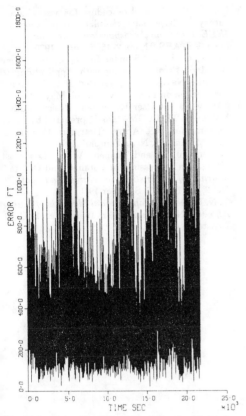

Fig. 3(a)—Suboptimal Satellite Selection Criterion.

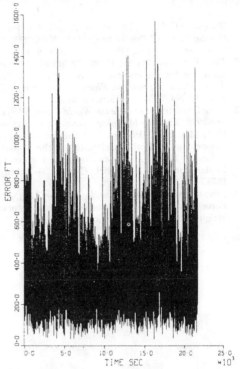

Fig. 3(b)—Optimal Satellite Selection Criterion.

namic simulation that the proposed Hotelling navigation algorithm is a fast, accurate, stable, and convergent routine that offers sufficient position determination accuracy to a variety of potential low–cost GPS users. Therefore, it should be considered for implementation on a microprocessor as part of a low–cost GPS receiver system. Such a system has been defined already for Loran–C and Omega navigation processing.[8] Further study is warranted on the optimal versus suboptimal satellite selection algorithm, although results in this particular problem indicate that the suboptimal criterion requires substantially less computation and provides essentially the same performance as the optimal criterion.

Acknowledgments

The authors acknowledge the contributions of Messrs. Stanton Musick, Jay Burns, and Don Melman in the development of PROFGEN and the C5A flight profile and Lt Ronald Butler in the development of SATGEN. All are members of the Analysis and Evaluation Branch, Reconnaissance and Weapon Delivery Division at the Air Force Avionics Laboratory.

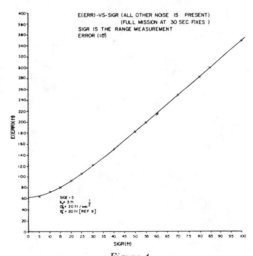

Figure 4.

REFERENCES

1. Shoemaker, H., "The NAVSTAR/Global Positioning System," *Proceedings of the NAECON 75 Conference*, Dayton, Ohio, 10–12 June 1975.
2. Noe, P. S. and Myers, K. A., "A position-fixing algorithm for the low-cost GPS receiver," *IEEE Trans. on Aerospace and Electronic Systems*, Vol. AES-12, No. 2, March 1976, pp. 245–298.
3. *"The Department of Defense World Geodetic System 1972,"* Defense Mapping Agency, Washington, D.C., May 1974. (Presented at the International Symposium on Problems Related to the Redefinition of North American Geodetic Networks, Fredericton, New Brunswick, Canada 20–25 May 1974.)
4. Private communications with Dr. Jon Lee, Air Force Flight Dynamics Laboratory, Wright–Patterson AFB, Ohio, 1975.
5. Lee, H. B., "A novel procedure for assessing accuracy of hyperbolic multilateration systems," *IEEE Trans. on Aerospace and Electronic Systems*, Vol. AES-11, pp. 2–15, January 1975.
6. Mealy, G. L. and Vander Stoep, D. R., "Time Standard Error Modeling with Applications to Satellite Navigation," presented at 29th Annual Symposium on Frequency Control, May 1975.
7. "Army Navsat User Equipment Design Study," Volume 1, TR ECOM-0275-F, prepared by TRW Systems for U.S. Army Electronics Command, Fort Monmouth, N. J., February 1974.
8. Delorme, J. F., and Tuppen, A. R., "Low Cost Navigation Processing for Loran–C and Omega," *Journal of the Institute of Navigation*, Vol. 22, No. 2, pp. 112–127, Summer 1975.
9. V. N. Fadeeva, *Computational Methods of Linear Algebra*, New York: Dover, 1959 (Transl.: C. D. Benster).

Satellite-Aided ATC System Concepts Employing the NAVSTAR Global Positioning System

B. D. ELROD and A. WEINBERG

ABSTRACT

THE DOD NAVSTAR GLOBAL POSITIONING System (GPS), expected to be implemented by the mid-1980's, is designed to provide a highly accurate, three dimensional, worldwide navigation capability. The FAA has been investigating its use with other resources for potential ATC applications in which surveillance and data communications, in addition to navigation, are provided. Utilization of the GPS, either unmodified or modified, to support future ATC requirements, is of considerable interest because of the potential economic advantages associated with the joint use of satellites.

This paper describes several concepts that have been investigated, for possible CONUS ATC applications, together with some of their significant features. These include user, space and ground segment configurations, spectrum requirements, and surveillance capacity. For the latter, two specific aircraft accessing schemes are considered—polling and time division multiple access (TDMA). The results indicate a high technical potential for providing the surveillance, navigation and data communications functions, but economic tradeoffs

his paper is based upon satellite system studies performed at MITRE/METREK for the FAA's Office of Systems Engineering Management, under Contract o. DOT FA70WA—2448. The information presented oes not necessarily reflect the official views or policy f the FAA.

Dr. Elrod and Dr. Weinberg are with Stanford Telecommunications, Inc., McLean, VA. They presented this paper at the 33rd Annual Meeting of the Institute in Costa Mesa, CA, on June 24, 1977.

must still be examined in terms of user equipment complexity and overall system costs.

The FAA has been pursuing substantial utilization of new technology as a means of meeting projected future demands for ATC services and offsetting the continuing escalation in operation and maintenance (O&M) costs. The Upgraded Third Generation (UG3rd) ATC system currently under active development is the near term approach comprising all ground-based elements for CONUS.[1] The projected needs of aviation in CONUS are expected to be met by the UG3rd at least into the 1990's. A satellite-aided ATC system is a future alternative that could provide a number of potential benefits which include: expanded coverage, improved communications, and lower O&M costs via ground facility replacement.

The potential application of satellites in a future ATC system for the U.S. has been investigated in numerous studies over the past several years.* However, efforts to seriously promote satellites for ATC have been constrained by economic limitations, i.e., high initial costs to government for R&D and the space segment, as well as higher user equipment costs compared to alternative ground-based systems. Currently, there is renewed interest because the GPS is under development and operational deployment of 24 satellites is planned for the mid-1980's to provide worldwide coverage for navigation. Advances in digital technology and a potentially large civil user base offer the possibility of cost competitive avionics with greater capabilities and improved performance.

* See [2] for a comprehensive overview.

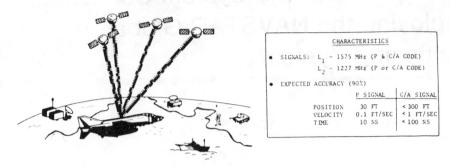

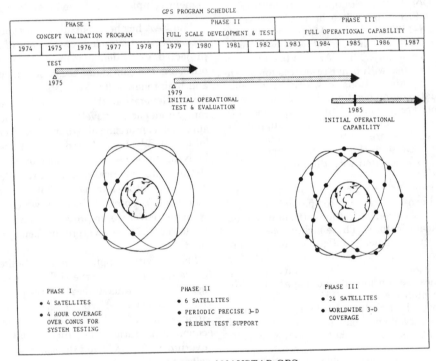

Fig. 1—Overview of NAVSTAR GPS.

Recent investigations of the possible joint role of the GPS and other resources in a future satellite–aided CONUS ATC system have resulted in a number of system concepts,[3,4] several of which are presented here. The following sections are organized to provide: a brief overview of NAVSTAR GPS; key factors considered in concept development; description of the system concepts and associated user, space and ground segments; discussion of performance characteristics; and lastly, some important issues which need to be addressed.

OVERVIEW OF GPS

The baseline NAVSTAR GPS is to provide signals in space for accurate determination of position, velocity and system time by appropriately equipped users. Implementation of the system is currently scheduled in three phases as indicated in Fig. 1. It will include three elements: space, ground and user segments.

In the operational phase the *space segment* is planned for 24 satellites in 10,900 nm, circular orbits with an orbital period of 12 hours. Eight evenly space satellites are to be arranged in each of three orbital planes, inclined 63° and spaced 120° apart.* Each GPS satellite will transmit a precision (P) signal and a coarse/acquisition (C/A) signal on two L Band carriers, L_1 and L_2. The P signal, to be available only to authorized users is designed for highly accurate positioning performance (10m, 2σ) and resistance to jamming, spoofing and multipath. The C/A signal, to be available to both military and civil users, is designed for less accurate positioning performance (<100m, 2σ) and as an aid to acquiring the P signal. Both signals are to be continuously transmitted in phase quadrature on L_1, while only one is to be transmitted on L_2 at any time. In the present design L_2 is reserved for the P signal.

The ground segment performs satellite tracking and control functions and determines the navigation data (e.g., ephemerides, clock biases and signal propagation error data) to be superimposed on the coded satellite navigation signals. This will require several monitor stations (MS) for appropriate coverage; a Master Control Station (MCS) and an Upload Station (US) located at Fortuna, Wisconsin. High quality measurement data from each MS is processed at the MCS and used to develop the navigation data which is uploaded at S or X band once per day to each satellite via the US.

The user segment consists of receiver/processor equipment for air, marine and land mobile users of various classes depending upon user dynamics and military requirements for navigation accuracy and jamming immunity. User equipment for many civil applications would probably be functionally similar to the military set which sequentially acquires and tracks the C/A signal from 4 satellites in the navigation process. Baseline GPS receiver functions are indicated in the section on Avionics Configurations.

KEY FACTORS IN CONCEPT DEVELOPMENT

Communications and position determination are the principal areas in which satellites are potentially attractive for supporting ATC functions. Position determination is a major element

in the surveillance of controlled airspace by a central facility as well as in aircraft navigation. The communications area includes both voice and data for two-way air/ground and ground/ground communications.

In this paper our attention is restricted to system concepts utilizing the GPS which could support the surveillance, navigation and air/ground data communication functions for a CONUS ATC system in the 1990's and beyond. Such concepts would be possible alternatives for either total or partial replacement of the ground-based systems (existing or planned) which are listed in Table 1. Some of the key factors considered in the concept development are discussed below.

Role of the NAVSTAR GPS—The baseline GPS is designed to provide signals for navigation with no capability for communications. Expanding its use to also support this function would be undesirable, since the GPS satellites would move continuously relative to a user and pose significant handoff and control problems. The data communication function for CONUS ATC can be provided better with satellites in geostationary orbits (as are all domestic and most military communication satellites). In the proposed concepts the GPS would only support the position determination function by providing the ranging links and the geometrical deployment needed for acceptable navigation and surveillance accuracy. This is desirable, since achieving acceptable accuracy is not as feasible with a purely geostationary satellite constellation.

Potential 1995 Performance Requirements *

Table 2 lists some potential requirements for system performance items which were previously assembled[3] as a guide in developing possible configurations for a future satellite-aided ATC system.* The figure of 50,000 for peak instantaneous airborne count (IAC) is the capacity which the ATC system may have to provide, if current services are to continue and FAA projections materialize for continued substantial growth in general aviation. The bit error rate (BER) of 10^{-6} for data communications is to assure low message error probabilities for time

---

Geometric properties of this GPS constellation are considered later in the section on Performance Characteristics.

---

* Further discussion of the rationale for these and other potential requirements is given in.[3]

Table 1—Ground-Based ATC Subsystems Supporting Surveillance, Navigation & Data Communications

System	ATC Function	No. of Facilities
Airport surveillance radar (ASR)	Surveillance	200*
Air route surveillance radar (ARSR)	Surveillance	120*
ATC radar beacon system (ATCRBS)	Surveillance	130*
Discrete address beacon system (DABS)	Surveillance/data comm.	>100**
VHF omni-range system (VOR)	Navigation	915*
Distance measuring equipment (DME)	Navigation/landing	740***

* Existing or approved.[5, 6]
** Planned.[5]
*** Included at FAA operated VORTAC and VOR/DME sites.

Table 2—Potential 1995 Performance Requirements for CONUS

Item	Surveillance	Navigation*	Data Comm. (A/G)
Capacity	50, IAC	Unlimited	50,000 IAC
Update interval	4–6 sec	0.5 sec	4–6 sec
Time to first fix	—	<60 sec	—
Accuracy (95%)			
—Terminal (HOR/VERT)	100 ft/200 ft	1000 ft/200 ft	10^{-6} BER
—En route (HOR/VERT)	400 ft/200 ft	3000 ft/200 ft	10^{-6} BER

* Includes non-precision approach capability.

critical ATC messages (e.g., 1 in 10,000 for a 100 bit collision avoidance advisory).

Degree of Independence Between Surveillance and Navigation

The function of surveillance in ATC systems is to provide the means for safe and reliable management of controlled airspace. Consequently, the FAA has traditionally strived to maintain a degree of independence between surveillance and navigation so each can backup the other in case of *failure* or *discrepancy*. Thus, the notions of independent and dependent have arisen as a means of classifying different approaches for surveillance. The use of primary radar provides purely *independent surveillance*, since it is completely separate from all aircraft systems, including navigation and communications. Secondary radar (ATCRBS), although it relies on an aircraft's transponder and altimeter, also provides a degree of independence, since it is separate from the navigation system. *Dependent surveillance* is a technique wherein navigation position derived by an aircraft is transferred via a communication link to an ATC facility. If used exclusively, the system would be completely dependent on the aircraft navigation system with no backup capability.

Since certain elements of commonality would most likely exist between navigation and surveillance in a satellite–aided ATC system, independence analogous to that of primary radar is not feasible. Therefore, criteria will ultimately have to be established as to what constitutes an acceptable degree of independence to provide the reliability and level of safety required. The approaches to providing surveillance in the concepts to be presented fall into two basic categories shown in Table 3. Each has different degrees of independence from navigation depending on user equipage and system facilities.

Separation of Military and Civil Signals in GPS—The baseline GPS was conceived to meet military requirements for navigation, so DOD may wish to retain full control over the C/A as well as P signal formats. Also it is not clear at this point whether the current C/A signal will or will not satisfy civil aviation needs in terms of performance, user acceptance and user equipment cost. To alleviate these potential concerns as well as institutional problems of coordination and constraint if signal alteration is ever required, it may be desirable to add a signal package for civil use to the GPS platform at some point. Thus, the concepts to be presented include some with the baseline GPS and others with modified GPS configurations.

Cost Constraints and Tradeoffs—User equipment costs are an important issue facing any future development of a satellite–aided ATC system. Potential economic benefits to the government from the use of satellites, which essentially result in transferring significiant costs to users are assumed not to be acceptable. Viable alternatives for a future system must not only meet FAA operational requirements and provide technical performance and economic benefits to the government, but also do so without an adverse effect on user costs. The system concepts considered next present various options which provide a basis for examining the economic tradeoffs relating to space segment complexity, user equipment requirements and total versus partial replacement of ground–based ATC systems.

SYSTEM CONCEPTS

Overview—Three principal elements comprising a satellite–aided ATC system are to be considered: the space, ground and user segments. The specific components contained in the first two depend on the extent of satellite involvement in the overall system. The latter element pertains to the user avionics. As a framework for describing the specific system concepts, it is convenient to first consider two generic system configurations.

The first, shown in Fig. 2a, is a hybrid space and ground–based system which employs satellites only for deriving positioning data for navigation and surveillance.* The data communications function is accomplished via a network of ground stations. Another alternative with this configuration is ground-based surveillance with only navigation accomplished via satellites. An example would be a network of DABS ground stations and the GPS satellite constellation. The ground stations provide the data link between the aircraft and the control centers (ARTCCs and TCCs).**

The second configuration, shown in Fig. 2b, is a fully space–based system in which all functions—navigation, surveillance, and data communications—depend on the space segment.

In this paper, "positioning data" means information (e.g., ranging measurement data) needed in the position location process, not actual position per se.

* Separate VHF air ground links are assumed to exist for voice communication with ground control facilities.

The supporting ground segment would contain a centrally located satellite control center (SCC) which collects and processes the surveillance data, and provides the primary data link between the aircraft and the control centers. An example is the ASTRO-DABS concept,[7] which includes a constellation of 3 geostationary and 6 geosynchronous satellites.

In the specific concept descriptions to follow emphasis is placed on the alternatives for surveillance and navigation. Since certain aspects are common to all concepts some preliminary description is appropriate. In the surveillance process, sufficient time must be allocated for both aircraft acquisition and tracking. The acquisition mode involves determining the identity and initial location of new aircraft entering the system. Once an adequate degree of information is obtained, the aircraft is placed into the tracking mode. In this mode aircraft regularly provide appropriate data to the ground via one of two direct access procedures: polling or time-division-multiple-access (TDMA). With *polling*, aircraft are discretely interrogated, once each surveillance update cycle, and respond accordingly. An interrogation contains the aircraft address, appropriate ATC messages and possibly requests for other information. With *TDMA*, an aircraft is provided, after acquisition, with an appropriate time slot in which to respond during each update cycle. Sufficiently accurate knowledge of system time is required on-board the aircraft, but this is possible as a by-product of GPS navigation. Interrogations are only necessary to provide ATC messages and modify TDMA assignments. Further consideration and comparison of polling and TDMA is presented in the section on Performance Characteristics.

System Concept I: Data Link + Baseline GPS—Navigation and surveillance are based on use of the C/A signals transmitted by GPS satellites. Two versions of the concept are summarized in Fig. 3. For surveillance,* positioning data derived on the aircraft from the relative times-of-arrival (TOA) of ranging signals from 4 satellites, is reported via a satellite data link or a direct air/ground data link. Independence between the two functions is obtained with separate GPS receivers for deriving the positioning data and verification of aircraft range by the

---

* Surveillance Type 1 (See Table 3).

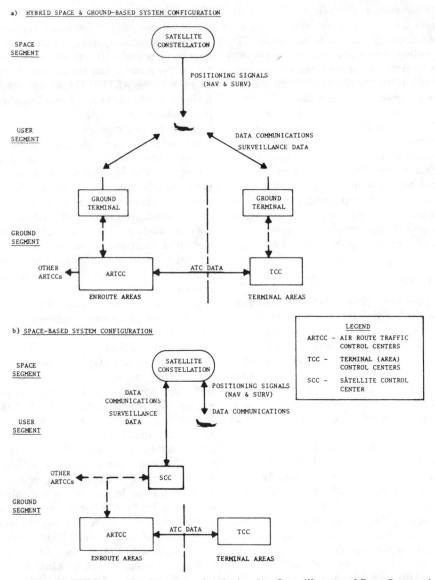

Fig. 2—Two Generic ATC System Configurations for Navigation, Surveillance and Data Communications.

ground. The latter is achieved by comparing the range derived from reported data with an independently derived range measurement based on the TOA of an aircraft surveillance reply. In Version B an additional degree of independence is obtained from the use of separate GPS transmissions, e.g., L_2 for surveillance and L_1 for navigation. This would require a modification to GPS to permit continuous transmission of the C/A signal on L_2.

Data communications are received by the aircraft on the forward link (L_3) and transmitted

on the return link (L_4). If relayed by satellite, a geostationary surveillance/data link (SD) satellite provides the link to the satellite control center (SCC) at C band. The data link might also be used to support navigation by providing aircraft, on a local area basis and at higher data rates,* GPS ephemerides, recommended satel-

---

* Time-to-first-fix and time-to-change satellites are affected by the time required to recover and process navigation data superimposed on the C/A signal of each GPS satellite.

lite quadruples, calibration corrections and other data. Calibration stations deployed around CONUS can provide correction data (e.g., signal propagation delays) to maintain both navigation and surveillance accuracy.

System Concept II: Data Link + GPS with Civil Signal Package

Navigation and surveillance procedures are similar to those in the previous concept, except for the signals used and the avionics required.

Two versions of this concept are summarized in Fig. 4. In both, surveillance is based on the use of a new signal added to the GPS platform for civil applications. Navigation is also based on this signal in one version, but the C/A signal on L_1 is employed in the other version to provide, if warranted, for an additional degree of independence by the use of separate signals.

The civil signal assumed here is a PRN burst type signal (high power/short duration) transmitted sequentially on L_3. This permits more

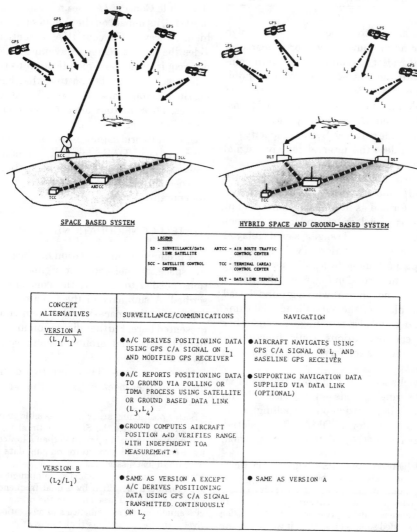

CONCEPT ALTERNATIVES	SURVEILLANCE/COMMUNICATIONS	NAVIGATION
VERSION A (L_1/L_1)	●A/C DERIVES POSITIONING DATA USING GPS C/A SIGNAL ON L_1 AND MODIFIED GPS RECEIVER[1] ●A/C REPORTS POSITIONING DATA TO GROUND VIA POLLING OR TDMA PROCESS USING SATELLITE OR GROUND BASED DATA LINK (L_3,L_4) ●GROUND COMPUTES AIRCRAFT POSITION AND VERIFIES RANGE WITH INDEPENDENT TOA MEASUREMENT *	●AIRCRAFT NAVIGATES USING GPS C/A SIGNAL ON L_1 AND BASELINE GPS RECEIVER ●SUPPORTING NAVIGATION DATA SUPPLIED VIA DATA LINK (OPTIONAL)
VERSION B (L_2/L_1)	●SAME AS VERSION A EXCEPT A/C DERIVES POSITIONING DATA USING GPS C/A SIGNAL TRANSMITTED CONTINUOUSLY ON L_2	● SAME AS VERSION A

* INDEPENDENT SURVEILLANCE, TYPE 1 (SEE TABLE 3-3)

Fig. 3—Concept I: Data Link + Baseline GPS (C/A Signal).

Table 3—Forms of Independent Surveillance

Type 1— Aircraft reports positioning data to ground; ground verifies A/C range

    a) Same signals for surv. & nav., but independent avionics (separate receivers), or

    b) Independent signals and avionics for surv. & nav. (separate receivers)

Type 2— Ground measures aircraft positioning data (via A/C ranging signal)

    a) Common system platform for surv. & nav. functions (e.g., GPS satellites), or

    b) Separate system platforms for surv. & nav. functions (e.g., DABS + GPS)

rapid signal acquisition, due to its pulsed, high peak power nature, and allows for a degree of avionics integration, because of spectrum commonality with the (sat $\rightarrow$ a/c) data communication channel. However, this also requires that the data link transmissions and civil signal transmissions, both on L_3, be appropriately interleaved to preclude garbling. System capacity can be affected unless the interval for civil signal transmissions is sufficiently short.*

System Concept III: Data Link + GPS with Civil Signal and Repeater Package—Navigation is performed as in previous concepts but surveillance is based on ground measurement and processing of aircraft ranging signals relayed by the satellite constellation. Two versions of this concept, pertaining to a fully space–based system, are summarized in Fig. 5. An alternative hybrid system (not shown) with a ground–based data link in place of the surveillance data link (SD) satellite could also be configured.[4] In either case, data communications would function as described earlier via the forward (L_3) and return (L_4) channels.

For surveillance,** the aircraft transmits an appropriate ranging code on L_4, either in response to an interrogation on L_3 (polling), or in an assigned time slot (TDMA). The relative times-of-arrival (TOA) of the ranging signal,

which is relayed by the SD and all visible GPS satellites, are measured by the SCC and processed to determine aircraft position.* As in Concept II, navigation is based on use of either the civil signal on L_3 or the GPS C/A signal on L_1.

*Comparison of System Concepts***—Table 4 provides a summary of the concept features and their impacts on the GPS and user segments for a fully space–based system. The possible impacts on the GPS and user segments are of major interest because they provide some indication as to the cost tradeoffs between government and user costs. As specific examples, Table 4 notes that while Concept IA does not affect the baseline GPS, its impact on the avionics is potentially high. However, Concept IIIA, potentially provides the largest degree of avionics integration but requires the most modification to the GPS satellites. Concept IIA, on the other hand, is a possible compromise between these two extremes. These matters are considered in further detail in the next session.

Several hybrid satellite–ground based system concepts—e.g., DABS for data communications and surveillance, and GPS for navigation—have also been investigated and corresponding results are contained in [4].

SYSTEM CONFIGURATIONS

A preliminary investigation has been made of the space, ground and user segment configurations needed to support the concepts just described. A summary of the functional configurations for the space-based system concepts is presented here. Further discussion including the hybrid space and ground system concepts is given in [4].

Space Segment—There are two distinct elements in the space segment: the surveillance

---

* Pairs of globally opposite GPS satellites sequentially transmitting precisely spaced burst signals (e.g., 500 watts/1 ms) would require <¼ sec for 12 pairs assuming a guardband of 18 ms between signals to assure non–interference worldwide; two pairs at a time using orthogonally coded signals for each pair would require <⅛ sec, etc.

** Surveillance Type 2 (see Table 3).

* Better positioning accuracy is possible than in Concepts I and II, since the SCC would make TOA measurements with higher precision than a low cost avionics user and could also utilize ranging data involving more than just 4 satellites.

** Throughout the preceding development each concept has been identified by a dual frequency assignment, e.g., L_3/L_1. These apply to the primary frequencies employed for surveillance and navigation, respectively. In the discussions that follow, this nomenclature will be often used to simplify referrals to specific concepts.

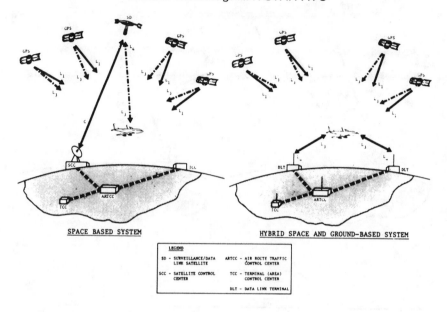

SPACE BASED SYSTEM   HYBRID SPACE AND GROUND-BASED SYSTEM

LEGEND

SD - SURVEILLANCE/DATA   ARTCC - AIR ROUTE TRAFFIC
     LINK SATELLITE   CONTROL CENTER

SCC - SATELLITE CONTROL   TCC - TERMINAL (AREA)
      CENTER   CONTROL CENTER

                                DLT - DATA LINK TERMINAL

CONCEPT ALTERNATIVES	SURVEILLANCE/COMMUNICATIONS	NAVIGATION
VERSION A (L_3/L_3)	●A/C DERIVES POSITIONING DATA USING CIVIL SIGNAL TRANSMITTED SEQUENTIALLY ON L_3 ●A/C REPORTS POSITIONING DATA TO GROUND VIA POLLING OR TDMA PROCESS USING SATELLITE OR GROUND BASED DATA LINK (L_3, L_4) ●GROUND COMPUTES AIRCRAFT POSITION AND VERIFIES RANGE WITH INDEPENDENT TOA MEASUREMENT*	●A/C DETERMINES POSITION USING CIVIL SIGNAL ON L_3 AND SEPARATE NAV RECEIVER ●SUPPORTING NAVIGATION DATA AVAILABLE VIA DATA LINK
VERSION B (L_3/L_1)	●SAME AS VERSION A	●A/C DETERMINES POSITION USING GPS C/A SIGNAL ON L_1 AND BASE-LINE GPS RECEIVER ●SUPPORTING NAVIGATION DATA AVAILABLE VIA DATA LINK (OPTIONAL)

* INDEPENDENT SURVEILLANCE, TYPE 1 (SEE TABLE 3-3)

Fig. 4—Concept II: Data Link + Modified GPS (Civil Signal).

data link (SD) satellites in geostationary orbit and the GPS satellites in 12 hour, 63° inclined orbits. The communication subsystem configuration shown in Fig. 6 indicates the multiple repeater functions provided by an SD satellite. The C → L and L → C repeater channels serve as the basic forward and return air/ground data links. The C → C repeater serves as telementry link between satellite and SCC. The C-band antenna provides CONUS coverage, and the L-band antenna provides a switchable spot

beam capability with a multiple feed, 20–30 ft parabolic reflector. Also, noted in Fig. 6 is the potential inclusion of an additional signal generator which would provide either the baseline GPS C/A signal or the civil navigation signal. This would require adding a separate CONUS coverage capability to the L-band antenna assembly.

There are four possible GPS satellite configurations considered and these can be described with the aid of Figs. 7 and 8. Figure 7 presents

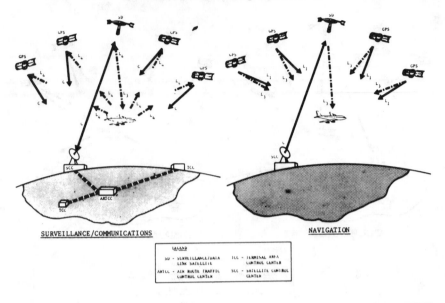

CONCEPT ALTERNATIVES	SURVEILLANCE/COMMUNICATIONS	NAVIGATION
VERSION A (L_4/L_3)	● A/C TRANSMITS CODED RANGING SIG- NAL (L_4) BASED ON POLLING OR TDMA PROCESS ● GROUND DETERMINES A/C POSITION FROM RANGING SIGNAL RELAYED BY GPS AND SD SATELLITES (C)* ● GROUND & A/C COMMUNICATE VIA SD SATELLITE DATA LINK (L_3, L_4)	● A/C DETERMINES POSITION USING CIVIL SIGNAL ON L_3 AND SEPARATE NAV RECEIVER ● SUPPORTING NAVIGATION DATA AVAILABLE VIA DATA LINK
VERSION B (L_4/L_1)	● SAME AS VERSION A	● A/C DETERMINES POSITION USING GPS C/A SIGNAL ON L_1 AND BASE- LINE GPS RECEIVER ● SUPPORTING NAVIGATION DATA AVAILABLE VIA DATA LINK

* INDEPENDENT SURVEILLANCE, TYPE 2 (SEE TABLE 3-3)

Fig. 5—Concept III: Satellite Data Link + Modified GPS (Repeater & Civil Signal).

the baseline, or unmodified, GPS satellite configuration. When only baseline GPS signals are employed, uploaded data (e.g., ephemeris, clock and ionospheric model corrections) are provided to the baseline PRN signal generator, the outputs of which are the encoded L_1 and L_2 signals. For Concept IA-(L_1/L_1) only the C/A signal on L_1 is utilized. If additional power is made available, and the modulator appropriately modified, so that the C/A signal could be transmitted continuously on L_2, then implementation of Concept IB-(L_2/L_1) is possible.

The remaining GPS satellite configurations may be described by referring to Fig. 8. Implementation of both Concept II options–(L_3/L_3)

and (L_3/L_1)— requires equipping each GPS satellite with the civil signal package, as shown. The civil signal generator, which operates in pulsed mode on L_3, is driven by the highly stable satellite clock. Required timing updates for signal transmission are provided over the satellite upload X-band link. Because an additional L-band transmitter is required to support the civil signal package, the satellite's power requirements must be increased* and a triplexer inco

* The additional power capability to support a burst type signal should be small because of its low *avera* power requirement (e.g., 1 watt for a 500W/1 ms bur transmission at 0.5 sec intervals).

Table 4—Comparison of Concepts (All Space Based System)

System features	Concept I		Concept II		Concept III	
	IA-(L_1/L_1)	IB-(L_2/L_1)	IIA-(L_3/L_3)	IIB-(L_3/L_1)	IIIA-(L_3/L_3)	IIIB-(L_4/L_1)
Surv and data comm	• Polling or TDMA • Sat → air ranging (GPS L_1) • Sat → air ranging (GPS L_1)	• Polling or TDMA • Sat → air ranging (GPS L_2) • Sat → air ranging (GPS L_1)	• Polling or TDMA • Sat → air ranging (GPS L_3) • Sat → air ranging (GPS L_3)	• Polling or TDMA • Sat → air ranging (GPS L_3) • Sat → air ranging (GPS L_1)	• Polling • Air → Sat → Gnd ranging (A/C L_4) • Sat → air ranging (GPS L_3)	• Polling • Air → sat → Gnd ranging (A/C L_4) • Sat → air ranging (GPS L_1)
Nav						
GPS satellite modifications	• None	• Continuously transmit C/A signal on L_1 and L_2 • Moderate increase in satellite power requirement	• Add civil signal package • Minimal increase in satellite power requirement	• Add civil signal package • Minimal increase in satellite power requirement	• Add L → C repeater assembly and civil signal package • Moderate increase in satellite power requirement (• Use alternate L-band antenna)*	• Add L → C repeater assembly • Moderate increase in satellite power requirement (• Use alternate L-band antenna)*
Avionics requirements	• Data/ranging transponder (L_3) • Modified GPS receiver (L_1) • Baseline GPS receiver (L_1)	• Data/ranging transponder (L_3) • Modified GPS receiver (L_2)—surv • Baseline GPS receiver (L_1)—nav	• Data/ranging transponder (L_3) • Civil signal receiver—surv (L_3) • Civil signal receiver—nav (L_3)	• Data/ranging transponder (L_3) • Civil signal receiver (L_3)—surv • Baseline GPS receiver (L_1)—nav	• Integrated data/ranging transponder & civil signal receiver	• Data ranging transponder (L_3) • Baseline GPS receiver (L_1)-nav
Advantages	• No impact on GPS	• Separate GPS signals for nav and surveillance	• Significant reduction of avionics • Faster generation of positioning data	• Separate GPS signals for nav and surveillance • Moderate reduction of avionics	• Separate signals for nav and surveillance • Significant reduction of avionics • Potentially better surveillance accuracy • Faster generation of positioning data	• Separate signals for nav and surveillance • Moderate reduction of avionics • Potentially better surveillance accuracy
Disadvantages	• Same signal used for nav and surveillance • Significant impact on avionics	• Moderate impact on satellite power requirements • Significant impact on avionics	• Increases complexity of GPS satellites • Same signal used for nav and surv	• Increases complexity of GPS satellites	• Significant impact on space and ground segments • Potentially higher A/C transmitter power*	• Significant impact on space and ground segments • Potentially higher A/C transmitter power*

* Tradeoff between GPS satellite and user avionics complexity requires further analysis.

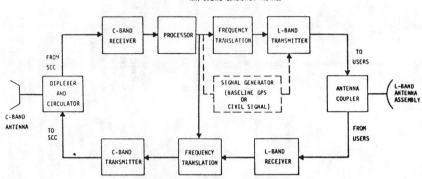

Fig. 6—SD Satellite—Communications Subsystem Configuration.

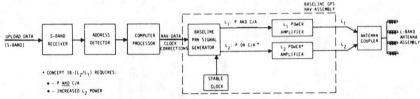

Fig. 7—Baseline GPS Satellite—Navigation Subsystem Configuration (For Concept II).

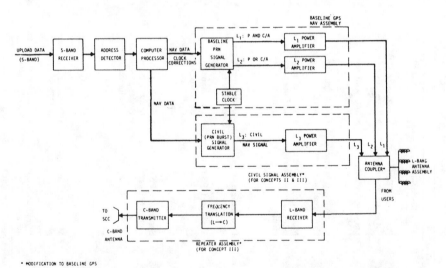

Fig. 8—GPS Satellite—Navigation and Add-on Subsystem Configurations (For Concepts II and III).

porated to properly combine the L_1, L_2, and L_3 signals.

Implementation of Concept III-(L_4/L_3) or (L_4/L_1)—requires that an L → C repeater assembly be added to the GPS satellites. For the latter the baseline GPS navigation assembly still provides the ranging signals, while implementation of the (L_4/L_3) concept requires the further addition of the civil signal package. For both cases however, additional satellite power, and additional satellite complexity is required to support the repeater functions.

Ground Segment

An overview of the ground configuration to support Concept III is shown in Fig. 9. The corresponding configurations for Concepts I and II require no antennas to receive GPS C-band transmissions. In all cases the SCC is the central component for all CONUS, and it, together with an identical backup, interfaces with the calibration stations, ARTCC's and the GPS Master Control Station. Major SCC functions are summarized in Fig. 9.

The communication link to the GPS Master Control Station provides the SCC with necessary GPS satellite information including ephemerides, clock biases, and propagation delay data. This information is used by the SCC to process incoming surveillance data and to provide aircraft with appropriate navigation data. If the civil signal is incorporated into the GPS satellites, this link can also be employed by the SCC to relay appropriate data, such as signal timing updates, to the Master Control Station for upload to the satellites.

The remaining ground segment elements are the calibration stations, ARTCC's and terminal control centers. The calibration stations are employed to acquire data for computation, by the SCC, of satellite ephemerides (SD and possibly GPS) and regional ionospheric propagation corrections. This data is relayed to both SCCs via an appropriate link. Finally, the ARTCC's will continue to provide en route services and interface with terminal control centers, so that re-

gional information may be suitably exchanged. Also note that each ARTCC could be equipped with a C-band antenna to monitor SD satellite transmissions and extract appropriate surveillance data of local interest.

User Segment

Possible avionics configurations for the satellite based system concepts are described with the aid of Figs. 10-12. In Concept IA-(L_1/L_1), the supporting avionics functional block diagram would appear as shown in Fig. 10. For Concept IB-(L_2/L_1) the only required modification would be the addition of a second RF amplifier, to receive the L_2 signal. This is necessitated by the large frequency separation (~300 MHz) between L_1 and L_2.

The avionics block diagram consists of three distinct elements: data/ranging transponder, surveillance receiver and navigation receiver. The former, which appears in all concepts, consists of a data detector, logic, modulator and L-band transmitter. The data detector incorporates the correlators, filters and timing devices necessary for detection of the received signals. Output data consists of aircraft address bits, ATC messages, navigation data (e.g., ephemeris and ionospheric corrections), and TDMA time slot information (if appropriate). The logic portion receives this data together with that pro-

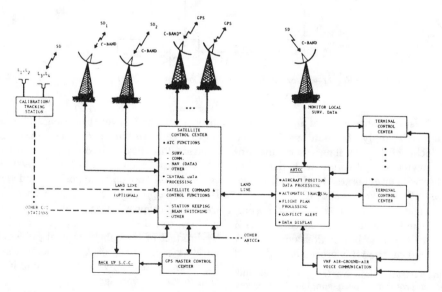

Fig. 9—Ground Configuration for Space Based System.

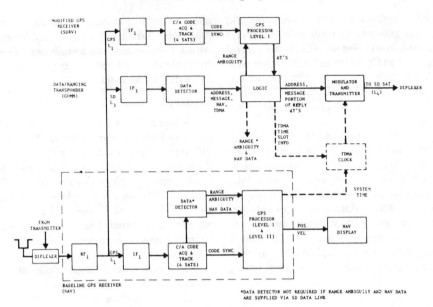

Fig. 10—*Avionics Functions for Concept IA-(L₁/L₁).*

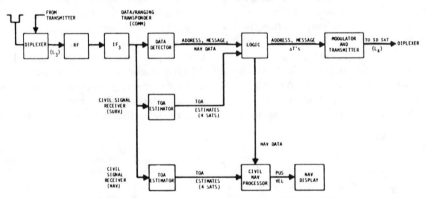

Fig. 11—*Avionics Functions for Concept IIA-(L₃/L₃).*

vided by the surveillance element and generates the appropriate reply. It could perform the TDMA clocking functions, if necessary, and provide the navigation processor with data that would otherwise be generated by the data detector in the GPS receiver, as shown.*

The navigation receiver essentially accomplishes all the functions of the baseline GPS Z set receiver, which only operates on the C/A signal. As shown, the GPS processor is divided

---

* Providing navigation data over the primary data link may enhance processing speed, simplify the receiver, and possibly reduce costs.

into Level I and Level II portions. The Level I portion converts the code synchronization data from satellites into pseudo-range measurements, which are then employed by the Level II processor to compute updated position and velocity. Receiver support functions, such as code and frequency prepositioning, could also be accomplished by the Level I processor. Since a by-product of the computational process is accurate system time, an ATC reporting scheme based on TDMA may use this timing information to great advantage.

The final component of interest is the surveil-

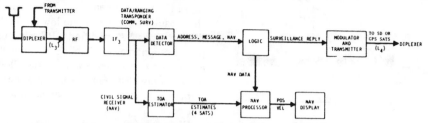

Fig. 12—Avionics Functions for Concept IIIA-(L₄/L₃).

lance receiver. As shown in Fig. 10 it consists of a modified GPS receiver which does not contain the baseline data detector and Level II processor. Since surveillance is accomplished by having the aircraft transmit only the ranging data (e.g., Δt's), the Level II processor is clearly not required. Other information needed aboard the aircraft for the ranging measurements is data for GPS satellite selection and range ambiguity resolution.* However, if this were provided to the aircraft via the data link then a separate data detector in the surveillance receiver would not be necessary.

The avionics configuration pertaining to Concept IIA-(L₃/L₃) is shown in Fig. 11. Here the civil signal is used to generate both surveillance and navigation positioning data. An important aspect of this configuration is that navigation data is available via the existing data link. This can lead to substantial reduction of the avionics computational and memory requirements. It should also be emphasized that due to the sequentially transmitted, burst–type nature of the civil signal, each satellite could transmit the same navigation ranging signal, as opposed to 24 different PRN codes in the case of the GPS C/A signal. Thus, use of the civil signal, also reduces the TOA estimation avionics hardware requirements. Furthermore, a degree of avionics integration is possible because both data communications and ranging signals used for navigation and surveillance are transmitted on L₃. For Concept IIB-(L₃/L₁) the civil signal is still employed for surveillance, but the L₁ signal would be used for navigation. The corresponding

avionics configurations would then appear as in Fig. 11, but with the "nav" portion replaced by the baseline GPS receiver shown in Fig. 10.

The remaining concept requires the incorporation of L → C repeaters on the GPS satellites. Figure 12 describes the configuration related to Concept IIIA-(L₄/L₃). Only data communication and navigation elements are required, since surveillance is achieved by ground processing of an aircraft's transmitted ranging code. As indicated, navigation is accomplished here via the civil signal. The remaining configuration, which is not shown, pertains to Concept IIIB-(L₄/L₁) and would have the civil signal navigation portion replaced by a baseline GPS receiver.

SYSTEM PERFORMANCE CHARACTERISTICS

In the previous sections system concepts were presented, together with a description of the supporting space, ground, and user segments. Several key factors affecting the technical potential of the various concepts are now considered. These are: spectrum requirements, channel qualities, geometric characteristics of the satellite constellation, and system surveillance capacity.

Spectrum Requirements—Different spectrum allocations would be needed to support the alternative concepts depending on the SCC/satellite and satellite/aircraft transmission links employed. A possible frequency plan is presented in Fig. 13, which indicates the general spectrum involved together with the specific assignments pertaining to each concept.

For the GPS → A/C link, the channels used are functions of the specific concept, as indicated. For the A/C → GPS and GPS → SCC links, however, dual L–band and C–band channels are employed. This latter requirement, which is applicable only to Concept III, is neces-

---

* Due to the 1 ms period of the C/A code, satellite-user range cannot be resolved to within an ambiguity of 200 miles. However, the baseline GPS receiver utilizes detection of data bit transitions (data bit duration = 20 ms) to obtain the necessary ambiguity resolution.

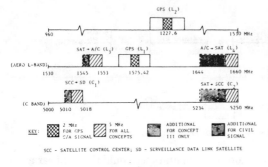

KEY: ▨ 2 MHz FOR GPS C/A SIGNAL ▨ 5 MHz FOR ALL CONCEPTS ▨ ADDITIONAL FOR CONCEPT III ONLY ▨ ADDITIONAL FOR CIVIL SIGNAL

SCC - SATELLITE CONTROL CENTER; SD - SURVEILLANCE DATA LINK SATELLITE

LINK	CONCEPT I		CONCEPT II		CONCEPT III	
	(L_1/L_1)	(L_2/L_1)	(L_1/L_1)	(L_3/L_1)	(L_4/L_3)	(L_4/L_1)
GND→SAT (SCC→SD)	C_1	C_1	C_1	C_1	C_1	C_1
SAT→GND (SD→SCC)	C_2	C_2	C_2	C_2	C_2^*	C_2^*
SAT→GND (GPS→SCC)	-	-	-	-	C_2^*	C_2^*
SAT→A/C (SD→A/C)	L_3	L_3	L_3	L_3	L_3	L_3
SAT→A/C (GPS→A/C)	L_1	$L_1 \cdot L_2$	L_3	$L_1 \cdot L_3$	L_3	L_1
A/C→SAT (A/C→SD)	L_4	L_4^*	L_4	L_4	L_4^*	L_4^*
A/C→SAT (A/C→GPS)	-	-	-	-	L_4^*	L_4^*

* TWO OR MORE CHANNELS REQUIRED.

Fig. 13—Spectrum Requirements for Space-Based System Concepts.

sitated by the fact that the GPS satellites would receive aircraft transmissions from all of CONUS via a single antenna beam. This, in turn, could result in garbled aircraft-to-satellite transmissions if only a single frequency were used by all aircraft. Use of dual channels adds the needed diversity to meet capacity requirements by providing the capability for simultaneous, ungarbled replies from two aircraft.*

A further consideration is the bandwidth of the channels required to support the various concepts. For data communications the primary concerns are data rate and detection performances. Since the L_3 and L_4 signals are relayed through the SD satellites—which have high gain antennas—a nominal 5 MHZ signal bandwidth should be sufficient to provide a reliable data communications capability. Additional bandwidth must be considered to provide acceptable ranging performance on all GPS links: GPS → A/C for the civil signal (L_3); A/C → GPS for L_4 and GPS → SCC for C_2, both in Concept III. The signal bandwidths should be increased (e.g.,

─────────

* Capacity results presented later indicate that a third A/C → Sat. channel may be necessary to support Concept III.

to 8 MHz) to compensate for the reduced SNR that results from use of the low gain GPS satellite antennas.* A modified GPS antenna, which provides a narrower CONUS coverage beam, in addition to earth coverage, could alleviate the wider bandwidth requirement, and the spectrum impact if a third A/C → Sat channel were required.

Channel Quality—A summary of the RF power budgets for the forward and return transmission links between satellite and aircraft is presented in Table 5. The links between the SCC and satellites are not considered, since they would be comparatively noiseless.

Table 5a indicates the data communications and ranging performance for Sat → A/C links and the corresponding satellite EIRP requirements. The TOA accuracy estimates reflect thermal noise and receiver quantization effects only. Receiver performance is also a function of the specific coding employed and the oscillator frequency characteristics. The results presented here are representative of those which may be expected, but further detailed analysis is necessary.

Table 5b indicates the data communications and ranging performance for the A/C → Sat links and the corresponding aircraft EIRP requirements. The SD satellites are employed for both data communications and ranging purposes, while GPS is considered for ranging only.** Different signal bandwidths are considered: 50 KHz pertains to a multi-channel narrowband return link for surveillance data; 5 and 8 MHz bandwidths pertain to single channel wideband return links.*** The large TOA uncertainty for the 50 KHz case is a potentially undesirable feature since it may limit the ground's range verification capability that may be necessary for reliable surveillance. Finally the A/C → GPS ranging performance in Concept III is an element for additional investigation, involving tradeoffs between GPS antenna gain, aircraft EIRP and spectrum requirements.

─────────

* Ranging error is inversely proportional to bandwidth and the square-root of signal-to-noise power ratio (SNR).

** The A/C-to-GPS link budget applies to Concept III only. Note the corresponding increased aircraft EIRP requirements.

*** See Section on Surveillance Capacity.

Table 5—Preliminary RF Link Budgets

A) Satellite-to-A/C*

	Data Link		Ranging (NAV/SURV)	
	SD (5 or 8 MHz)	SD (8 MHz)	GPS (8 MHz)	GPS (C/A) (2 MHz)
Sat. EIRP (dBW)	67.5**	54.5†	41.0***	27.2***
Received C/N_o (dB-Hz)	76.5	64.5	55.6	—
Margin (dB)	5.0	5.0	5.0	—
Net C/N_o (dB-Hz)	70.5	56.5	50.6	33.0
Bit error prob. (data)	$<10^{-6}$	—	—	—
TOA accuracy (1σ) (NS) (ranging)	—	18.5	25.0	28.0

B) A/C-to-Satellite

	Concepts I and II			Concept III	
	SD (50 kHz)	SD (5 MHz)	SD (8 MHz)	SD (8 MHz)	GPS (8 MHz)
A/C EIRP (dBW)	14.0**	27.0**	33.0**	33.0†	33.0***
Received C/N_o (dB-Hz)	64.5	77.5	83.5	71.5	63.6
Margin (dB)	6.0	6.0	6.0	6.0	6.0
Net C/N_o (dB-Hz)	58.5	71.5	77.5	65.5	57.6
Bit error prob (data)	$<10^{-6}$	$<10^{-6}$	$<10^{-6}$	—	—
TOA accuracy (1σ) (NS) (ranging)	400‡	9.0‡	< 5	8.0	22.0

Assumptions:
* 0 dB A/C antenna gain & 5 dB noise figure for RF preamp.
** 30 ft parabolic antenna.
*** 14 dB GPS antenna gain.
† CONUS coverage antenna.
‡ For A/C range verification.

Table 6—Geometrical Characteristics of 24 Satellite GPS Constellation over CONUS*

Characteristic / Minimum Acceptable Elevation Angle	Minimum Number of Visible Satellites	Maximum Duration of Minimum Visibility (minutes)	Lowest GDOP** During Minimum Visibility Interval		Typical GDOP Outside of Minimum Visibility Interval	
			Vertical	Horizontal	Vertical	Horizontal
5°	6	20	3.0	2.5	<4.0	<3.0
10°	4	4	1800	46	<4.0	<3.0
15°	4	30	230	44	<4.0	<3.0
20°	4	50	150	44	<4.0	<3.0

* Based on GPS Phase III constellation defined in [8].
** For users at 45° latitude in affected zone.

Geometrical Characteristics—Table 6 indicates some GPS visibility and GDOP characteristics in CONUS as a function of user-satellite elevation angle. If 5° elevation angles are acceptable, then at least six satellites, with satisfactory GDOP characteristics, would always be visible. The adequacy of such low elevation angles, however, particularly with respect to aircraft maneuvers, antenna properties, multipath considerations and signal acquisition at low altitudes must be investigated further. Multipath effects decrease for higher elevation angles, but the corresponding geometrical characteristics clearly indicate limited periods which are characterized by high GDOP situations in certain areas of CONUS.*

There are several possibilities for coping with the poor GDOP conditions. These include temporarily operating in a degraded mode with only 3 satellites in conjunction with: altimeter data (for both surveillance and navigation), or previously derived system time (for navigation only). Another, perhaps more attractive alternative, is to equip two or three geostationary SD satellites with GPS signal packages. This would always insure the presence of at least four satellites with satisfactory geometrical characteristics.

Surveillance Capacity—Among various performance characteristics which must be considered, one of the most important is the capability to provide adequate surveillance capacity. This pertains to the number of aircraft for which tracking data can be obtained over a specified update interval; it is a function of many factors which include:** signal diversity, aircraft-to-satellite message structure and reply format. *Diversity* may take one of several forms—time, frequency, spatial, and code. Since all diversity techniques may be comparably employed by the various implementations of a given concept, the following results make comparisons of surveillance capacity based on the availabilities of fixed spectrum for aircraft reply transmissions. As will be discussed later, this spectrum may be employed in different ways.

Message structure considerations may be divided into two parts. For Concepts I and II the aircraft responds with a sync word, ATC data and 3-D positioning data. For Concept III positioning data is derived by the ground, so the corresponding aircraft transmission consists only of a ranging sequence (comparable to the sync word) and ATC data.

With regard to *reply format*, two possibilities were considered—polling and time division multiple access (TDMA). Polling involves an or-

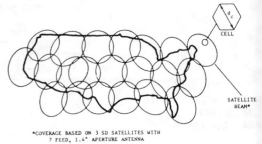

*COVERAGE BASED ON 3 SD SATELLITES WITH 7 FEED, 1.4° APERTURE ANTENNA

Fig. 14—SD Satellite Multi-Beam Coverage of CONUS (Space-Based System).

dered procedure of aircraft interrogations and replies. To implement TDMA, an aircraft would be provided with a time slot in which to report required data during each update cycle.

Satellite-based polling and TDMA, would both utilize the spatial division of CONUS provided by the SD satellite beams such as shown in Fig. 14. Further division into cells would be done for purposes of either implementing a range ordered roll call (polling) or arranging TDMA time slots. The polling procedure incorporates gaps between each interrogation to preclude garbling of replies to any satellite.[10] Additional gaps may also be inserted when transitioning from cell to cell. The TDMA scheme differs from polling in that all time slots are fixed, and the duration of each must necessarily account for the maximum propagation time across the cell and the longest possible message (to assure access for time critical ATC advisories).

In Concepts I and II, the SD satellites transmit and receive via a high gain, narrow beam antenna. Hence, a single A/C → Sat channel suffices for each SD satellite. In Concept III however, GPS satellites could receive simultaneous transmissions from aircraft anywhere in CONUS.* Thus, more than one repeater channel on GPS would be required to prevent garbling. The precise number is assumed here to equal the number of SD satellites.

The results of an initial analysis of surveillance capacity are presented in Fig. 15.** Achievable surveillance capacity is plotted as a

---

* If the Phase III constellation is defined as in [8], the affected regions lie in a strip across CONUS centered at 45°N which widens with increased elevation angle. Somewhat similar results occur for the constellation definition in [9], but in two strips centered at 26°N and 52°N [4]

** These aspects are considered only as they pertain to aircraft being tracked and already acquired into the system. Acquisition and possibly navigation also impact surveillance capacities, and their effects must be investigated further.[4]

---

* Each SD satellite could also be equipped with CONUS coverage antenna to provide an additional return link for aircraft interrogated by other SD satellites.

** Polling results are lower bounds while those for TDMA are upper bounds.

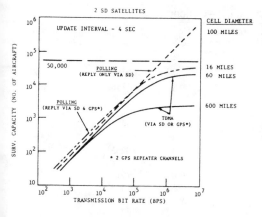

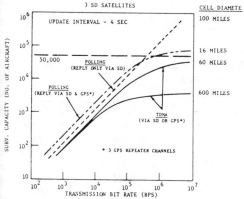

Fig. 15—Surveillance Capacity vs Transmission Bit Rate.

function of transmission bit rate assuming a surveillance update cycle of 4 seconds. Figure 15a pertains to a system containing two SD satellites, while 15b considers three SD satellites. The cell diameters were chosen to provide a representative indication of achievable capacities in each case.*

It can be observed from Fig. 15, that when positioning data reporting is employed, as in Concepts I and II, polling generally outperforms TDMA with the difference dramatically increasing for large data rates. This occurs since the major portion of a TDMA time slot must provide for message propagation across the cell, thus greatly reducing efficiency for large data rates. Fig. 15 also indicates that when aircraft reply

through all satellites (SD and GPS) in Concept III, polling still outperforms TDMA. However, the difference between them does not widen as data rate increases because the gaps between interrogations required to preclude garbling of replies at any satellite become more significant. With respect to achieving a surveillance capacity of 50,000 aircraft, it is observed that polling could meet such a requirement using a data rate on the order of 625 KBPS with 2 SD satellites in Concepts I and II or with 3 SD satellites in Concept III. It is also apparent that satellite-based TDMA could not provide this capacity with a comparable wideband channel and the same or even higher data rate. Simultaneous use of many narrowband TDMA channels could theoretically provide this capacity, but not within the same overall bandwidth as polling.

Table 7a gives a further comparison of alternatives for Concepts I and II assuming a common total bandwidth constraint of 5 MHz. Also included, for comparison, are some results derived for ground-based TDMA reporting, where CONUS is divided into a number of simultaneously operating networks.[4] It is apparent that ground-based narrowband TDMA could potentially meet or exceed a surveillance capacity of 50,000, since line of sight propagation properties may permit sufficient frequency reuse to achieve the necessarily large number of parallel operations. However, this approach would also require a large network of ground stations and possibly acceptance of only marginal accuracy for range verification.

Table 7b compares the alternatives considered in Concept III. Wideband operation is assumed, since ranging accuracy requirements preclude use of narrowband channels. TDMA performance is evidently inadequate even with three repeater channels on GPS satellites. While three channels appear to be required to achieve a capacity of 50,000 via polling, it should be noted that the polling results are lower bounds. Also, a more detailed examination of aircraft population densities throughout CONUS may indicate a means for improving the range ordered roll call's efficiency,* so that 2 SD satellites could then conceivably be sufficient.

The specific impact of cell sizes on the three reporting schemes are considered further in [4].

* Efficiency improves by reducing the number of inter-cell transition gaps.[10]

Table 7a—Surveillance Capacity—Concepts I & II

Access Technique	Parameter	No. of SD Satellites	No. of Reply Channels*	Cell Size (miles)	Cells per Net	No. of Parallel Operations	Bit Rate (BPS)	Capacity** (No. of A/C)
Polling								
	WB	2	1	100	—	2	0.625M	50,000
		3	1	100	—	3	0.625M	78,000
Satellite-based TDMA								
	WB	2	1	600	—	2	0.625M	2,400
		3	1	600	—	3	0.625M	3,600
	NB	2	50	60	—	100	6.25K	18,400
		3	50	60	—	150	6.25K	26,600
Ground based TDMA								
	WB	—	1	600	5	5	0.625M	6,000
	NB	—	50	600	5	250	6.25K	40,000
	NB	—	50	150	18	900	6.25K	162,000

Table 7b—Surveillance Capacity—Concept III

Access Technique	Parameter	No. of SD Satellites	No. of GPS Repeater Channels†	Cell Size (miles)	No. of Parallel Operations	Bit Rate (BPS)	Capacity** (No. of A/C)
Polling							
	WB	2	2	16	2	0.625M	23,500
		3	3	16	3	0.625M	50,000
Satellite-based TDMA							
	WB	2	2	600	2	0.625M	2,400
		3	3	600	3	0.625M	3,600

Notes:

* Operational spectrum—5 MHz; 1 WB channel or 50 NB channels (50 KHz each).

** Four second update rate; capacity figures are lower bounds for polling and upper bounds for TDMA.

† Operational spectrum—5 MHz per channel.

CONCLUSIONS AND OBSERVATIONS

This paper has presented a number of concepts for a satellite-aided CONUS ATC system employing the NAVSTAR GPS. A summary of some possible space, ground, and user segment configurations to support the concepts has also been included. Examination of several performance characteristics pertaining to the various system concepts indicated high technical potential for achieving the surveillance, navigation, and data communications functions subject to certain constraints on spectrum availability, channel qualities, and geometrical characteristics of the satellite constellation. A potential surveillance capacity requirement of 50,000 aircraft in 4–6 sec also appears to be achievable. Nevertheless, a number of key technical and economic issues must still be addressed. These include:

Non-Precision Approach Capability of GPS —In order for the GPS to be utilized as a future navigation system by civil aviation, it must provide an acceptable nonprecision approach capability. The most stringent capability, currently satisfied by the VOR/DME system, is a horizontal accuracy in terminal areas on the order of 2000 ft (95%). Although such accuracies appear theoretically achievable via GPS, experimental validation is necessary under opera ional conditions and employing low cost avionics.

GPS Satellite Visibility Aspects—On the basis of detailed geometrical studies of the planned GPS satellite constellation, unacceptably high GDOP situations can occur in CONUS when only 4 satellites are available. This will result for limited durations and in certain areas,* if usable satellite elevation angles of 10° or higher are required. Availability of less than four usable satellites for an extended period of time can also occur in case of a satellite failure. Another concern arises with respect to transitioning to a new satellite. Current transitioning schemes involve the tracking of 5 satellites for a limited period of time prior to changeover. Based on the above, however, this may not always be feasible. It thus appears that the availability of an encoding altimeter may be required to support GPS receiver functions during such reduced visibility conditions. Other alternatives would include equipping the SD satellites with the appropriate GPS signal packages or placing some GPS satellites in geostationary orbit. The technical and economic implications of such approaches need to be addressed.

Baseline GPS Signal Acquisition Time—Initial signal acquisition is based on acquiring the baseline GPS C/A code and the superimposed data (especially ephemeris) from each of four satellites. While C/A code acquisition per satellite may require an average time in the vicinity of 20 seconds, initial data acquisition per satellite requires an irreducible 30 seconds. Overall signal acquisition then exceeds 2 minutes and may require more than 4 minutes. The adequacy for civil ATC of acquisition requiring several minutes is unclear at this point. If acquisition takes place on the ground, then there is less concern. If however, acquisition must take place in flight due to multipath or airport noise, or as the result of some in–flight malfunction, an acquisition requirement of several minutes may very well be unacceptable.

---

* Regions where 3D positioning via GPS alone could be periodically poor are sensitive to the orbit ascending node locations and the choice of satellite phasing in the three orbits (i.e., relative displacement from ascending node at epoch). Other choices than those in [8] and [9] may be possible to minimize the effects noted here.

There are at least two possibilities for acquisition time reduction. First, code acquisition time can be reduced to a negligible amount via employment of code matched filters. Second, data acquisition time could be significantly reduced if a separate data link or additional receiver channel(s) are utilized. Forthcoming studies should not only evaluate the technical feasibilities of these approaches and the cost impact on the required avionics, but also the issue of acquisition time requirements.

Definition of Civil Signal Requirements—Transmission of a civil signal by each of the GPS satellites, to be used for navigation and possibly surveillance purposes, may be necessary to provide separate civil and military signals, and/or to minimize user avionics requirements. Specific issues which should be addressed include: signal format,* frequency spectrum availability and the means for providing supporting navigation data (incorporated on the signal or supplied by separate data link).

Degree of Independence Between Surveillance and Navigation—Each of the proposed system concepts provides a degree of independence between the surveillance and navigation functions. (See Table 3 and Figs. 3–5) Each has a corresponding impact on user avionics and system facilities. Criteria are needed for establishing which technique(s) would be acceptable in terms of meeting FAA operational requirements for reliability and safety. This will ultimately focus on which one(s) can provide the *necessary* degree of independence with the least impact on cost.

Economic Tradeoffs—Of major concern and importance are the economic factors involved in consideration of a potential satellite–aided ATC system. These include the tradeoffs between technical performance benefits, FAA operational requirements, and overall government and user costs. Also of importance are government costs to provide services to a limited user segment. For example, if TACAN ceases to be a military requirement in the future, it may become economically beneficial for the government to phase out the DME. incorporate the GPS navigation capability, and still maintain the VOR system. Total vs. partial replacement

---

* A candidate civil signal is presented in [4]

of ground systems by the GPS is then an additional fundamental consideration.

In accordance with the above, then, several questions need to be answered. These include: What combination of ground–based and satellite–based system elements provides an economically viable system? How costly would the transition be from a ground–based to a satellite–based system? Can satellite-based avionics be produced which would reasonably compete with existing ground–based equipment? Does a satellite–based system lead to overall reduced life–cycle costs?

Final Remarks—This paper has attempted to provide some insight into the potential roles that satellites might take in satisfying the navigation, surveillance and data communications functions of an operational ATC system. The emphasis here has been on the technical aspects of concepts in which satellites are necessary elements for fulfilling all three ATC functions.

Current studies include investigation of the partial replacement in the future of ATC ground system elements by satellites. For example, the GPS may be used for navigation purposes and to replace DME only or VOR/DME, with data communications and surveillance accomplished via a network of DABS ground stations. Some preliminary results on these possibilities, both technical and economic, have been obtained and are reported in [4].

ACKNOWLEDGEMENT

The authors are grateful to their former colleagues, Mr. R. Braff and Dr. L. P. Sinha for their suggestions and assistance in pursuing this work; and to various members of the Interagency Task Force on Satellite Systems for the stimulation provided in the development of several of the concepts presented.

REFERENCES

1. "An Overview and Assessment of Plans and Programs for the Development of the Upgraded Third Generation Air Traffic Control System," DOT/FAA Report, FAA-EM-75-5, March 1975.
2. McDonald, K. D., "The Satellite as an Aid to Air Traffic Control," in *A Survey of Modern Air Traffic Control*, AGARDOGRAPH No. 209, NATO AGARD, July 1975, pp. 659–697.
3. "Report of the Interagency Task Force on Satellite Systems," Vols. I and II, DOT/FAA Report (Final Draft), July 1977.
4. Elrod, B. D., Weinberg, A., and Sinha L. P., "Investigation of Some Satellite-Aided ATC System Concepts Employing the NAVSTAR Global Positioning System," The MITRE Corporation, MTR 7688, January 1978.
5. *The National Aviation System Plan*, 1976–1985, DOT/FAA, March 1975.
6. *ATS Fact Book*, DOT/FAA (Air Traffic Service), March 1977.
7. Schuchman, L., "ASTRO-DABS, An ATC Satellite Relayed Surveillance, Navigation, and Data Link Concept," Proceedings of AIAA 5th Communications Satellite Conference, Los Angeles, CA, Apr. 22–24, 1974.
8. Bogen, A. H., "Geometric Performance of the Global Positioning System," AEROSPACE Corp., SAMSO TR-74-169 (AD 783 210), June 1974.
9. Edwards, T. L., "Application of the GPS to the AEROSAT Test and Evaluation Program," AEROSPACE Corp., FAA-RD-76-142, May 1976.
10. Elrod, B. D., "Aircraft Interrogation Scheduling with ASTRO-DABS," *IEEE Trans. AES*, Vol. AES-10, September 1974.

GPS Application to Seismic Oil Exploration

C. JOHNSON and P. WARD

INTRODUCTION

This paper is to communicate the global positioning requirements of the geophysical oil exploration industry, shows that the NAVSTAR Global Positioning System (GPS) meets these requirements, and encourages the development of GPS as an international geodetic positioning resource whose peacetime use extends it far beyond its intended military use. The geophysical oil exploration industry has always needed high-precision global positioning. Most of today's oil exploration is by the seismic method. The end product of a seismic survey is a three-dimensional map of the subsurface geometry below the prospect area. The end objective is to precisely locate a subterranean formation that could support oil and to drill for oil in this location with a high expectancy of discovery. Oil is becoming increasingly difficult, hence more expensive, to find; it is either too deep for the resolution of prior surveys to discover and/or located in remote, sometimes hostile environments. Geodetic control is also becoming more of a problem for the seismic industry for similar reasons. GPS can solve the geodetic control problem, so perhaps the geophysical industry will become the first commercial user of GPS.

GEOPHYSICAL REQUIREMENTS

The geophysical seismic exploration requirements for geodetic survey control are equally as stringent for marine applications as for land. In practice, the marine surveys are less precise than

Dr. Johnson is Manager of Systems Engineering and Mr. Ward is Manager of Systems Software Engineering, Texas Instruments Equipment Group, GPS Phase II Program, Dallas, Texas 75222. They presented this paper at the ION Annual Aerospace Meeting, March 1979.

land because the best navigation and seismic sensor control available is less precise. The seismic method requires precise relative geometry (3-meter, 1-sigma error) between the seismic source and each seismic sensor array for each seismic event created by the source. The precise time (1-ms, 1-sigma error) of the seismic event is required along with a precise time interval clock (10-μs, 1-sigma error) to measure the time arrivals of the reflected seismic energy from the subsurface discontinuities of the earth. A seismic survey consists of numerous seismic events along a predesignated geometric pattern. Each event produces a multichannel recording of the reflected seismic energy. The recorded data are later subjected to extensive signal processing to remove noise. The level of signal enhancement achieved is in large part proportional to the geometric accuracy of the source/sensor relative positioning data.

If the survey is extended at a later date or if the postprocessed results indicate that the prospect should be drilled, it is important that the geometric data be related to a geodetic control that can be recovered accurately (10-meter, 1-sigma error).

MARINE SURVEY PROBLEMS

Traditional marine seismic survey problems and how they manifest themselves in marine seismic exploration fall into the following prioritized categories:

(1) *Coverage.* Precise navigation coverage possible by any navigation means in the prospect area is either weak or nonexistent. Water is too deep for the doppler sonar velocity measurement subsystem to support TRANSIT survey or the prospect is too close to poles for TRANSIT. Land is either too far away or oriented with respect to prospect area so as to geomet-

rically dilute survey precision from shore-based stations.

(2) *Logistics.* Overhead time and expense is caused by land crews and local government permits for residence and frequency authorizations when shore-based navigation aid stations must be set up and maintained by the user.

(3) *Relative Accuracy.* The short-term noise plus bias error performance for the control use periods of a few seconds through the survey use period of several days must be consistent and within the survey precision requirements of typically 10 meters (CEP). This is not only important to the fidelity of post survey processing, but also important during the survey execution so that the relative line spacing will meet the presurvey spacing requirements. Poor short term error performance can usually be attributed to defective or "over-sold" navigation equipment and/or natural perturbations due to signal path, weather, or time of day.

(4) *Reproducible Accuracy.* The long term bias error performance should be stable so that with the same navigation equipment, the same position may be located at a later date within 10 meters (CEP).

(5) *Absolute Accuracy.* The magnitude of the long term bias errors with respect to geodetic control should be small or correctable so that if the navigation equipment type is changed, the same position may be located within the combined uncertainty of the bias errors. This error should be within 10 meters (CEP).

LAND SURVEY PROBLEMS

Since land surveys are usually coordinated by conventional survey techniques, the most significant problem is remoteness of or lack of geodetic control. In hostile environments, such as the polar regions, this also presents a safety problem (e.g., it is not uncommon for a party member to get lost).

Land survey instrumentation is less complex than its marine counterpart; thus, there are fewer incidences of geodetic accuracy problems due to instrumentation on land. When problems occur, they are usually due to human error, either in the execution of the survey or the definition of the original geodetic control points. Loss of the geodetic control points on return surveys can sometimes cause a problem in re-establishing the absolute position accuracy of a prospect survey.

GPS CHARACTERISTICS OF IMPORTANCE TO GEOPHYSICAL EXPLORATION

Four-Dimensional Capability of GPS

Each space vehicle (SV) provides two independent observables to the user: pseudorange and range rate. The solution of four SVs observables produces not only a three-dimensional estimate of the user's position and velocity to 10 meters (CEP) and 0.01 meter/second (1 sigma for 1-second smoothing) respectively, but also absolute GPS time of the week to a few nanoseconds.

GPS time is aligned within a microsecond to Coordinated Universal Time (UTC) on 1-second boundaries. Presently, the GPS end-of-the-week time occurs at the precise second of Saturday midnight, UTC. However, UTC introduces discrete leap seconds into its time keeping each year, while GPS must remain monotone, but GPS will inform the user of the number of leap seconds of separation. Hence, the user can derive UTC to within 1 microsecond from his GPS solution.

Accuracy

The error sources of the GPS system are included in Table 1 along with the error estimates. A distinguishing characteristic of these errors is that some are essentially bias errors that change quite slowly with time. There are other errors that act like random errors on a short time basis (<1 second). The sources of the errors are either due to the Control Segment (CS), Space Segment (SS), or User Segment (US).

Position accuracy estimates can be obtained by multiplying the pseudorange by a horizontal dilution of precision (HDOP) factor, which for good SV geometry is 1.6 to 2.5. Therefore, for the survey and navigation mode, the resultant absolute accuracy will be:

	RMS Errors (meters)	HDOP	Accuracy (meters, CEP)
Navigation	5.3	1.6 to 2.5	8 to 13
Survey (bias only)	4.3	1.6 to 2.5	7 to 11

For relative navigation operation (where one GPS receiver is on a previously surveyed point and another receiver is on the location where data are required), the bias terms tend to cancel since they enter both sets in a similar way and are eliminated when the relative position computation is completed. Therefore, the following relative accuracies are estimated:

	RMS Errors (meters)	HDOP	Accuracy (meters, CEP)
Navigation	3.1	1.6 to 2.5	5 to 7
Survey (½ bias)	2.2	1.6 to 2.5	3 to 5

These accuracies are well within the requirements for geophysical exploration.

Operation Time Frame

The full set of 24 SVs to provide the truly global and continuous GPS capability will not be operational until the mid-1980s. There are currently four SVs operational and, by the third quarter of 1979, this total is expected to be six SVs. Figure 1 shows that with the present four SVs, there are several regions in addition to the Yuma, Arizona, GPS test site that have four SVs visible for about 2 hours and a very extensive area where these four SVs can sometimes be visible. Figure 2 shows that with the eventual six SVs, there will be a 3-hour coverage at a GDOP of five or less for four SVs in a large part of the world. Figure 3 shows a world contour of the time duration that two SVs will be visible for

Table 1—GPS system error budget

Error Sources	Statistics	Error Source Responsibility (meters)			System Budget (meters)
		SS	CS	US	
Clock and navigation subsystem stability	Bias	2.7	2.7	—	2.7
Predictability of SV perturbations	Bias	1.0	1.0	—	1.0
Other	White noise	0.5	0.5	—	0.5
Ephemeris and clock prediction	Bias	—	2.5	—	2.5
Other	White noise	—	0.5	—	0.5
Ionospheric delay compensation	Markov	—	—	2.3	2.3
Tropospheric delay compensation	Bias	—	—	2.0	2.0
Receiver noise and resolution	Markov	—	—	1.5	1.5
Multipath	White noise	—	—	1.2	1.2
Other	White noise	—	—	0.5	0.5
1-sigma system UERE					5.3

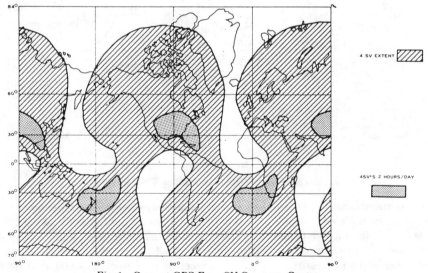

Fig. 1—*Current GPS Four-SV Coverage Contours.*

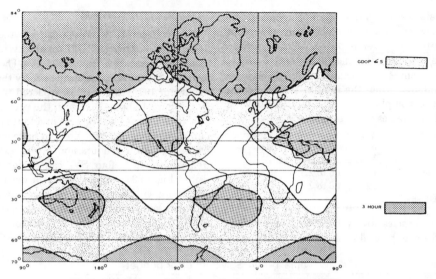

Fig. 2—Near-Term GPS Constellation (Six-SV) GDOP Contours.

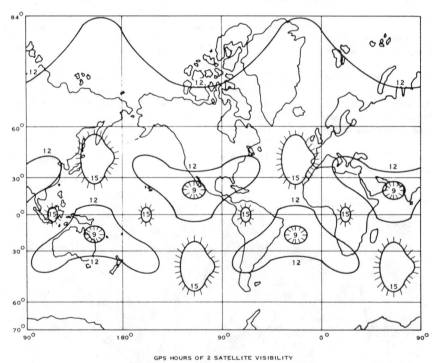

GPS HOURS OF 2 SATELLITE VISIBILITY

Fig. 3—Near-Term GPS Constellation Time Contours.

the six-SV constellation.

It has been demonstrated that a two-SV user solution is feasible for a low-dynamic user. This means that specialized early use of GPS could be feasible prior to the mid-1980s.

Economy-of-Use Time Frame

If GPS were fully operational right now, there would be a large area of geophysical applications that would be economically feasible even if the receiver cost were $150,000 to $300,000 each (which is about what they would cost in low production). This is because the receiver cost represents the entire time/navigation cost per user (except for perhaps recording equipment). GPS does not have to be augmented by a velocity measurement subsystem, a navigation computer or an external clock reference as is required on the TRANSIT system. These are intrinsic to the typical GPS receiver, although strictly speaking, the navigation computer does not have to be included in a GPS receiver. By the early 1980s, a GPS receiver suitable for geophysical exploration use could be adapted from the Phase II family of receivers and sold in the $20,000 to $40,000 price range, which is about the current price of TRANSIT receivers which have far less capability and independence of operation. This is probably how the GPS receiver will be introduced to the market: priced so high that only the sophisticated user whose navigation precision requirements justify the high instrumentation cost. However, the much larger market potential that the $5,000 receiver will develop will provide the design-to-cost and learning curve impetus to achieve that goal shortly after GPS becomes fully operational. That is, the commercial user community will provide the motivation and economy-of-scale to reduce the GPS receiver cost.

RECEIVER ARCHITECTURAL CONSIDERATIONS

Much of the GPS receiver expense is because of the number of receiver channels and microprocessors required to perform the searching, tracking, and navigation functions. High dynamic users require four or more receiver channels. The military class of GPS receivers require extra processor throughput and memory to support tactical features in the set that are not required by the commercial user, such as performance under high jamming conditions, fast time to first fix, inertial aiding interfaces, weapons delivery processing, direct acquisition of P-code without benefit of C/A-code acquisition, direct handover of P-code to another GPS receiver, magnetic variation corrections, markpoint, waypoint and moving waypoint computations, etc. The user dynamics are sufficiently low that a single-channel/single-microprocessor GPS receiver will meet the normal marine and

land geophysical exploration requirements. The single-channel receiver must time share its observations on four SVs at a typical rate of 1 or 2 seconds per SV, unless there is a requirement to take data from the SV. Data taking modes require the set to track the same SV for at least six seconds. Once the receiver has acquired SV data, it will not require updated almanac data for 2 days and it will not require ephemeris data for 2 or more hours. In practice, the receiver can be instructed not to enter the data taking mode for short periods when precision and/or dynamics are critical.

Since the GPS receiver navigates the phase center of the receiving antenna, in marine applications the GPS set should compensate for lever arm corrections to the mast-mounted GPS antenna. The set should be provided pitch and roll information from a set of low-cost pendulous inclinometers located as near the ship's center of bouyancy as possible. This, plus the lever arm constants, will remove the principle cause of velocity corruption in the GPS set during moderate to operational limit sea state conditions.

The issue of whether the receiver should be C/A-code only or both C/A- and P-code may be academic; however, for the geophysical exploration industry, clearly there is the need for P-code precision. Assuming that the commercial user is eventually given permission to access P-code, there would still be the possibility that accuracy would be denied at will to the GPS user who does not know which SV parameters have been altered during the denial of accuracy period. Hopefully, the user would at least be aware that accuracy is being denied. There would be no cost effectiveness motivation to develop a dual frequency L1 and L2 C/A-code-only receiver. The C/A-code-only receiver could not measure the ionospheric difference effect between the two frequencies accurately enough to improve the range computation significantly.

It may not even be justified for a commercial P-code receiver. Only experimental observation will determine the accuracy improvement from ionospheric correction using L1 and L2 pseudorange differences as compared to a stored model. Although it is known that the absolute ionospheric correction can amount to as much as 30 meters, it is less well recognized that the absolute ionospheric correction is not the determining factor on the ultimate precision of the user position. For example, if the ionospheric correction were the same for all four SVs being observed, then the dual frequency user who measured it and the single frequency user who ignored it would obtain identical position accuracy. It would appear only as an additional time bias to the single frequency user who ignored it, hence, his range computations would be the same as the dual frequency user and his GPS time estimate would be off by only 3 nanoseconds per meter in the additional bias. Thus, the performance improvement of dual frequency sets depends on the unbiased differential effect of the ionosphere of the pseudorange observations. This may or may not be significant. If a model would hold the differential error below 2 meters, it would not be significant to the geophysical exploration user and the single frequency (L1) C/A- and P-code receiver would be adequate and considerably less expensive.

INTERFACE STANDARDIZATION

It is perhaps premature to begin standardization on the GPS set interface. However, it might be prudent to summarize the set of data and control parameters that the GPS set would be expected to possess for the geophysical applications. The first issue would be what coordinate system should the set navigation system work in. The most practical decision would be to implement in Earth-Centered Earth-Fixed (ECEF) coordinates and provide for a North Slaved Local Level conversion to the user display. ECEF is the most natural coordinate system for GPS, it is simple because it is rectangular and it has no singularities at the poles. Recording of navigation data would use the ECEF state vector including bias and bias rate. In addition, the raw pseudorange, delta-range, SV ID, signal-to-noise ratio, tracking status, along with the GPS set time tag would complete the high rate data output. Perhaps on a page basis, at a considerably lower data rate than the previous data, the ephemeris data, and clock correction data would be transmitted out of the set. The set's basic processor clock rate (typically 20 ms) and a 1-second rate aligned to the clock rate should be available as a buffered output for user synchronization to his equipment. Also the set should output the UTC time every second.

There should also be available every second as part of the time data the most recent estimate of the set's time bias with respect to GPS time to an accuracy of 1 μs (LSB). This will enable any user to subtract the time bias from the set GPS time to obtain actual GPS time within 1 μs. There should be provision for operator inputs of simple initialization data such as time and position estimate, although these should not be essential for the set to bootstrap itself into operation, only helpful in speeding up the acquisition of SVs. Manual input and operator observable output is probably most effectively accomplished by a control display unit (CDU). There should also be a means for reading real time input aiding data such as the pitch and roll inclinometer data discussed earlier.

Starting at this point, certain design-to-cost tradeoffs must be made concerning what additional peripherals, if any, should be supported by the set. The more features added, the more customized the receiver will be and the less applicable to other users.

MARINE APPLICATIONS

Background

The typical marine seismic exploration requirement for navigation is to operate concurrently with the seismic exploration activity; i.e., to continuously locate both the marine seismic energy source and the marine seismic sensor array, called the streamer. Both these items are towed aft of the survey vessel while underway in the prospect area. The modern marine seismic source is usually a shallow submerged array of controlled acoustic energy impulse devices such as compressed-air-driven guns (air guns) or air/gas explosive chambers (gas guns). The source array is mechanically supported by heavy chain (or similar heavy mechanism) to decouple the towing stress from the hoses and firing lines that energize the array. The source is ballasted to hold a uniform depth and attitude for the survey speed anticipated and is towed as close to the survey vessel as safety and practicality allow. A typical "live" streamer section contains symmetrically spaced cylindrical hydrophones electrically connected as an in-line array. Each streamer section wire bundle is decoupled from the towing stress by inner stranded steel cables and insulated by an outer polyurethane jacket.

Each section is ballasted for neutral bouyancy with kerosene. The sections are designed modularly so that "live" sections and "spacer" sections are physically combined at distances which match an integer multiple of the anticipated shot point intervals, so that any trailing array will move forward and occupy a physical position previously occupied by a leading array during the previous shot point event. One can visualize the construction of a marine sampled data system wherein the seismic (digital) recording system is started, the seismic recorder is brought up to speed, and when recording begins, the source is activated (shot point). The event is recorded as a "timebreak" and shot point number and for a few seconds after time break, the seismic energy reflected from subsurface discontinuities is sensed by multiple arrays in the streamer, signal conditioned and recorded. Usually separate from this recording, another recording of the navigation data is taking place, but coordinated with the shot point number.

Although it is an accepted practice to "shoot on time," the introduction of navigation computers with the TRANSIT system has introduced the more desirable technique of "shooting on position." This is especially important in areas where the ocean current causes the survey ship to travel considerably faster or slower than the desired velocity. There are many other sophistications provided by the presence of a computer; e.g., course deviation indicators.

GPS Solution to Marine Seismic Survey Problems

When fully operational, GPS primarily solves the coverage and logistics problems while satisfying the relative accuracy and reproducible accuracy problems. This is possible because it will be truly global and continuous, and will perform in all weather to 10-meter CEP in P-code and to 30-meter CEP in C/A-code.

GPS solves future absolute accuracy problems equally as well, since the error performance is specified with respect to absolute WGS-72 datum. The Defense Mapping Agency's datum shift constants relate the WGS-72 datum of GPS to the numerous geodetic datum and reference ellipsoids used to establish geodetic control. By incorporating these datum shift constants into the GPS receiver, it is expected that the absolute

accuracy of GPS will be undisputed in the navigation world. Using these shift constants, the GPS receiver can convert in real time to any local geodetic datum selected by the user.

Although time coordination and the accuracy of absolute time does not present a serious problem in marine survey operation, the GPS receiver can output time synchronization with relative accuracy to a few nanoseconds and Coordinated Universal Time (UTC) to within a microsecond.

LAND APPLICATIONS

Background

The typical land seismic exploration requirement for surveying is nonconcurrent with the seismic exploration activity; i.e., the land survey is usually performed shortly ahead of the seismic exploration activity and visible markers are left behind denoting the locations for the land seismic source and the land seismic sensor array. The modern land seismic source is typically one or more heavy truck-mounted hydraulically controlled vibrators or a similar form of heavy mechanical impulse generator. Portable crews in remote areas still use dynamite. The geophone array, consists of physically small moving coil earth motion sensors mounted on a spike or other suitable earth coupling mechanism. Several geophones are electrically connected in parallel and physically distributed in an array pattern such as a star in order to sense lower seismic frequencies than the natural frequency response of any one geophone would permit. Many of these arrays (24, 48, 96, etc.) are physically placed at periodic intervals in the prospect area and electrically connected via a multiconductor cable to a recording truck. The truck-mounted land operation is designed to minimize the number of times the sensors are moved and to use the mobility of the source. Portable crews move the sensors to minimize the number of holes that must be drilled to hold the dynamite charges.

GPS Solution to Land Survey Problems

When fully operational, GPS can be used to achieve a very high precision benchmarking capability for the stationary land survey user, especially if the P-code capability is available to the commercial user. A manpack set solves the safety problem associated with advance party crew members who might get lost.

FUTURE APPLICATIONS

In future applications, the use of GPS is limited primarily by the receiver cost. Assuming the $5,000 receiver becomes a reality, many geophysical applications of GPS will help the industry's search for increasingly hard to find oil. Texas Instruments has pioneered the development of three-dimensional processing of exploration data. GPS can provide the survey precision and the exploration coordination required to produce the improved and consistent geometric fidelity needed by this processing tool. In marine survey work for example, considerable effort and instrumentation is currently being expended to more precisely locate the streamer, which can be up to a mile long behind the survey vessel. In general, the streamer does not trail straight behind the towing vessel; there is usually curvature and inclination. Some success has been achieved with magnetic heading sensors distributed along three or more streamer sections. A low-cost portable GPS receiver located in the tail buoy remotely stimulated periodically to power up, locate, time tag, and retransmit the tail buoy position data to the survey vessel could greatly improve the fidelity of the streamer angle sensor curve fit between two known points. If the streamer should be severed from the survey vessel, this feature would also provide an improvement over radar reflectors in locating the tail buoy so that the sections can be recovered. GPS also makes multiple boat survey operations practical since absolute time is intrinsic to all positioning and velocity data obtained with GPS. The master boat can be informed periodically with precision time, position, velocity, and extrapolated acceleration state of the GPS receiver in the slave boat(s). This state can be integrated for a considerable length of time to maintain continuous track of the slave boats before position degradation sets in and a new state vector is received. The master boat can issue shot point event, steering and velocity correction commands to the slave boat(s), time tagged to be executed at some future GPS time.

For land operations, GPS could provide the means for concurrent survey operation and the exploration operation in a manner similar to marine exploration. This would enable many more degrees of freedom during the land survey in terms of selecting alternate shot points or geophone locations to avoid unfavorable terrain or other obstacles.

Postmission processing of raw pseudorange delta-range and satellite data can enhance the precision of the survey, especially if the concept of translocation is used in GPS. In this method, a stationary "benchmark" GPS receiver is dedicated to tracking the same set of SVs being tracked during the prospect survey. The benchmark receiver is located as close to the prospect area as possible. In this manner, the SV ephemeris, clock correction, and atmospheric correction data can be further refined by reference to the benchmark GPS set. Most of the errors remaining are those introduced by the receivers themselves and this error is greatly minimized in the benchmark receiver after a relatively short period (1 hour or less) of GPS observations.

GPS PHASE I CONCEPT VALIDATION RESULTS

Texas Instruments has developed three dual-frequency GPS receiver sets for the Phase I concept validation. These sets cover the full spectrum of dynamic users. At the high end of the dynamic spectrum is the Missile-Borne Receiver Set (MBRS), a four-channel/four-processor system designed for the extremely high velocity, acceleration, and jerk that occur in a Minuteman missile. The MBRS is not intended for guidance, but for precise measurement instrumentation during test flights. An example of high-performance aircraft dynamic user GPS receiver is the High-Dynamic User Equipment (HDUE) set. The HDUE set is a five-channel/three-processor system designed to concurrently measure ionospheric data and acquire new SVs without disturbing the four continuous SV observations. At the lightweight end is the Man-pack/Vehicular User Equipment (MVUE) set. The MVUE is a one-channel/one-processor system designed for the dynamics encountered during military backpack or truck operation. All of these systems are operational to date and have undergone extensive field testing with excellent performance results. It is the MVUE set performance results which are most relevant to this paper. An example is shown in Figure 4.

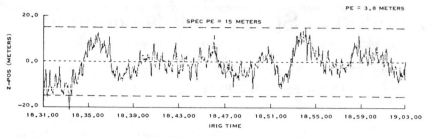

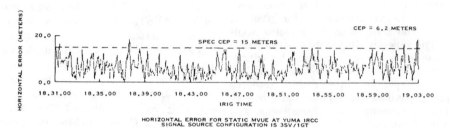

Fig. 4—Single-Channel/Single-Processor GPS Set Performance.

ACKNOWLEDGEMENTS

The authors would like to express their gratitude to Dr. Hal Bybee who developed the computer program that generated the four- and six-SV area and time coverage illustrations.

ADDENDUM

To quantify the impact of the GPS on oil exploration, consider the projections of oil industry experts for the period when the GPS is fully operational. By the year 1988 there will be approximately 9 billion barrels of new oil being discovered per year (total world effort).[1] GPS would of course, only be critical for a part of this discovery rate.

Dr. Jack Birks, Managing Director of British Petroleum,[2] said that about half of the future discoveries would come from offshore exploration. That would be 4.5 billion barrels per year in 1988. Current experience with normal 2D seismic exploration and the new 3D stratigraphic geophysical exploration (which requires better navigation) indicates that offshore, one quarter of the discoveries in 1988 will require the 3D techniques coupled with very accurate navigation. That would be 1.1 billion barrels of oil per year in 1988. Even with continued development of current state of the art navigation, only one half of this oil will be in areas and at depths where it could be found without the worldwide, 24 hour per day, 5 meter accuracy of GPS which will be available in 1986. It is therefore reasonable to expect that GPS will make possible the discovery of one sixteenth of 9 billion barrels of new oil per year or .6 billion barrels of new oil per year by 1988. At the present OPEC price of $16 per barrel, this oil made available by GPS would be worth $9 billion per year in 1979 dollars.

[1] Projection by Gulf Oil in the Nov. 20, 1978 issue of the Oil and Gas Journal.

[2] "Petroleum Technology 2000", Society of Petroleum Engineers, Dallas, Texas, February 1979.

The Global Positioning System and Its Application in Spacecraft Navigation

A. Van LEEUWEN, E. ROSEN and L. CARRIER

ABSTRACT

THE ADVENT OF THE GLOBAL Positioning System (GPS), developed by Rockwell International for the Department of Defense, opened a new era in navigation capabilities. GPS user equipment permits on-board, real-time computation of the vehicle state vector (position, velocity, and time) with unparalleled accuracy. The superior GPS system performance characteristics provide significant benefits in the areas of spacecraft navigation, satellite delivery, experiment positioning, resource mapping, payload deployment and retrieval, propellant economies, data processing, and mission planning.

This paper presents an overview of the GPS system as well as a discussion of the user system parameters governing the design of a low-earth-orbit spacecraft GPS navigation system. A specific application, the Space Shuttle orbiter GPS navigation system, is discussed in some detail, including the projected benefits accruing from the implementation of this system.

INTRODUCTION

Rockwell International's Space Systems Group has conducted a design and integration study of a GPS-based primary navigation system for the Shuttle orbiter that included the definition of all system hardware and software elements. In the course of this design study, a body

Andrew Van Leeuwen is Project Leader for the Shuttle Global Positioning System; Edward Rosen is a member of the Technical Staff; Louis M. Carrier is Manager of Electronic Systems on the Space Shuttle Program. They are with Rockwell International, Downey, California. This paper was presented at the ION Aerospace Meeting in March 1979.

of information was developed, generally applicable to the utilization of the GPS positioning system in low-earth-orbit space vehicles.

Other Rockwell Divisions involved in GPS system activities are the Satellite Systems Division, responsible for design and manufacture of the NAVSTAR GPS satellites; the Space and Secure Telecommunications Systems Division, systems engineering a GPS missile-borne receiver system (MBRS) for the Minuteman ICBM and developing a secure, spread-spectrum, X-band, ground-to-satellite uplink system and UHF/SHF and L-band NAVSTAR secondary payloads; Collins Division, developing several classes of GPS user equipment including a generalized developmental model (GDM) of GPS designed to evaluate antijamming techniques (Ref. 1).

THE GLOBAL POSITIONING SYSTEM

The Global Positioning System is a universal, all-weather, world-wide positioning system that provides position and velocity data along the three axes of a Cartesian earth-centered, earth-fixed (ECEF) coordinate system (Figure 1). Position can be estimated within 30 feet, velocity within 0.2 feet per second, and time within a fraction of a microsecond.

The system operates on the principle that the user determines his (pseudo) range and range rate to a number of GPS satellites (with precisely known ephemerides) by accurately measuring the transit time of the navigation signal between each satellite and himself and scaling it by the velocity of light. Since the user clock is not directly synchronized to the satellite clocks, this pseudo range measurement is in error by the amount of user clock offset (Figure 2). Acquisition of at least four satellites will permit the user to determine his position coordinates and obtain a user clock correction.

The system consists of three major segments and related systems (Figure 3) (Ref. 2) with the following principal functions.

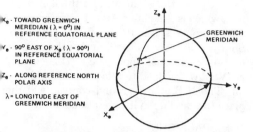

X_e - TOWARD GREENWICH MEREDIAN (λ = 0⁰) IN REFERENCE EQUATORIAL PLANE

Y_e - 90⁰ EAST OF X_e (λ = 90⁰) IN REFERENCE EQUATORIAL PLANE

Z_e - ALONG REFERENCE NORTH POLAR AXIS

λ = LONGITUDE EAST OF GREENWICH MERIDIAN

Fig. 1—Earth-centered, Earth-fixed coordinate system.

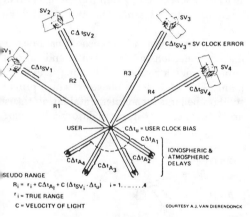

$C\Delta t_{SV_2}$

$C\Delta t_{SV_3}$ = SV CLOCK ERROR

$C\Delta t_{SV_1}$

$C\Delta t_{SV_4}$

USER $C\Delta t_u$ = USER CLOCK BIAS

$C\Delta t_{A_1}$

IONOSPHERIC & ATMOSPHERIC DELAYS

$C\Delta t_{A_4}$ $C\Delta t_{A_3}$ $C\Delta t_{A_2}$

PSEUDO RANGE

$R_i = r_i + C\Delta t_{A_i} + C(\Delta t_{SV_i} - \Delta t_u)$ i = 1 4

r_i = TRUE RANGE

C = VELOCITY OF LIGHT

COURTESY A.J. VAN DIERENDONCK

Fig. 2—The concept of pseudo-ranges.

The space segment comprises the NAVSTAR satellites, which function as "celestial" reference points. Upon completion of the system by 1986, a total of 24 active satellites (Figure 4) will circle the globe every 12 hours in 10,900 n.m. orbits and provide three-dimensional navigation coverage over most of the earth's surface and near-space region. Each satellite transmits its precise ephemeris, clock correction data, and an "almanac" of orbital parameter and clock correction estimates for all other system satellites. These data are contained in the navigation message (Figures 5 and A-2).

The user segment is the collection of all user sets and their support equipment. The user set receives and processes the satellite navigation signals, converting them to orthogonal position coordinates and velocity vectors and accurate user clock drift and offset bias terms. User equipment will range from relatively simple and light-

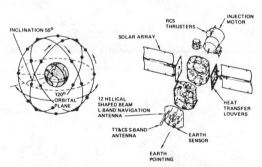

Fig. 4—24 satellite GPS constellation (Phase III).

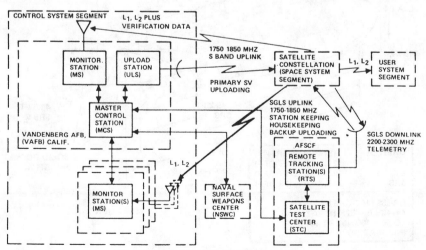

Fig. 3—NAVSTAR/GPS.

weight manpack-type receivers to sophisticated receiver/processors designed for accurate performance in high-dynamic environments such as encountered in fighter aircraft and missiles and adapted to meet the special requirements and rigors of manned or unmanned space flight applications.

The ground control segment consists of a central continental United States control center, an alternate control center, and a number of monitoring stations. The monitor stations, in conjunction with the Air Force Satellite Control Facility (AFSCF), provide system status moni-

toring and tracking support for the space segment. The control center daily uplinks emphemeris correction and other system data to all satellites for memory storage and subsequent relay to the user segment.

Related systems are the AFSCF, which supports the control segment, and the launch system, which is a modified Atlas F booster with an Agena upper stage. In the future, the Space Shuttle will serve as the launch vehicle, transporting an inertial upper stage (IUS) with its NAVSTAR payload to a low-earth parking orbit. The IUS, under ground control, will then place the satellite in its operational orbit.

THE SPACE SHUTTLE

The Space Shuttle (Figure 6) is a manned space transportation system consisting of an orbiter, an external tank, and two solid rocket boosters.

The Shuttle orbiter is a reusable, cargo-carrying combination of spacecraft and aircraft launched like a rocket and landing like an airplane. The solid rocket boosters, which provide solid propellants for supplemental lift-off thrust, are jettisoned two minutes into ascent, para-

(SPACE VEHICLE)
EPHEMERIS (X_s, Y_s, Z_s, t_s)
SV CLOCK BEHAVIOR (Δt_s)
HEALTH & STATUS (ALL SV'S)
SYNCHRONIZATION CODE
ALMANACS (ALL SVS)
SERVICE MESSAGES
50 BPS (1500 BITS/FRAME, 5 SUBFRAMES (300 BITS))

(USER)
ACQUIRES SIGNAL WITH UNKNOWN DOPPLIER (VELOCITY) AND CODE PHASE (RANGE) OFFSET, COMPUTES X, Y, Z & t_u AND DERIVATIVES

COURTESY A.J. VAN DIERENDONCK

Fig. 5—Navigation message summary.

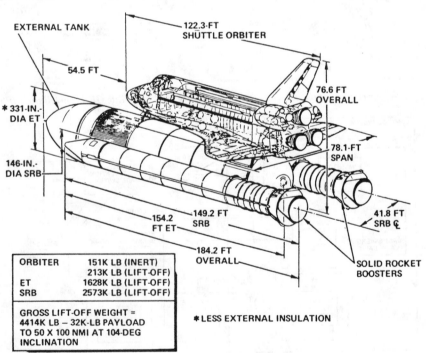

EXTERNAL TANK

122.3-FT SHUTTLE ORBITER

54.5 FT

76.6 FT OVERALL

*331-IN.-DIA ET

146-IN.-DIA SRB

78.1-FT SPAN

154.2 FT ET

149.2 FT SRB

41.8 FT SRB ₵

184.2 FT OVERALL

SOLID ROCKET BOOSTERS

ORBITER	151K LB (INERT)
	213K LB (LIFT-OFF)
ET	1628K LB (LIFT-OFF)
SRB	2573K LB (LIFT-OFF)

GROSS LIFT-OFF WEIGHT = 4414K LB – 32K-LB PAYLOAD TO 50 X 100 NMI AT 104-DEG INCLINATION

*LESS EXTERNAL INSULATION

Fig. 6—The space transportation system.

chuted into the ocean, and recovered for reuse. The external tank, the source of liquid fuel and oxidizer for the orbiter's three main engines, separates from the orbiter just before orbit insertion and disintegrates in the earth's atmosphere.

A Space Shuttle flight starts from either Kennedy Space Center, in Florida, or Vandenberg Air Force Base, in California (Figure 7). Launched vertically, the orbiter lifts off, enters a low-earth orbit, and then adjusts the orbit according to mission requirements. After the mission is completed, it slows to less than orbital velocity and begins its descent into the atmosphere. The orbiter lands like a conventional airplane at one of its launch sites where it undergoes maintenance and servicing, is loaded with new cargo, and is readied for another mission within two weeks.

The dictates of the various payloads and experiments transported and serviced by the orbiter, plus the paramount necessity for many successful one-shot approaches and runway landings in nominal as well as abort situations, serve to illustrate the need for an orbiter navigation system that will meet the most stringent requirements.

GPS SPACEBORNE APPLICATIONS

The various space vehicle applications can generally be classified according to mission trajectory requirements with attendant range signal dynamics and satellite visibility constraints as illustrated in Table 1.

An earlier study by the Lockheed Missiles and Space Company (Ref. 3) analyzed the performance of GPS for space satellite use for various altitude and trajectory regimes. The resulting

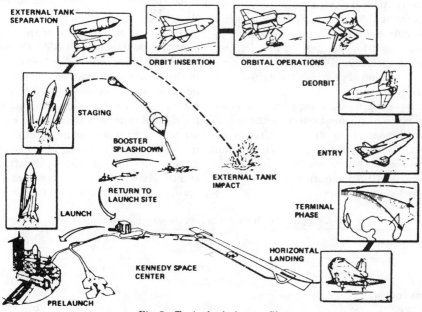

Fig. 7—Typical mission profile.

Table 1—GPS Applications

Vehicle	Trajectory	Dynamics	Satellite* visibility
Missile	Ballistic	High	Good
Orbital satellite	Orbital circular	Low	Good
Recoverable upper stages	Orbital elliptic	Medium	Poor to fair
Shuttle	Ascent Orbital Entry	Medium	Good

* For Phase III space vehicle deployment

range signal dynamics and dynamics uncertainties for three classes of users are shown in Table 2.

The study demonstrated that the use of on-board satellite GPS receivers for precise orbit determination was clearly feasible and it was concluded that:

- Low-altitude GPS users (500 n.m. maximum) can achieve performance accuracies equivalent to surface users. This is primarily due to the benign dynamics environment and greatly reduced uncertainties of orbital trajectories. Accuracies in the order of 45 to 60 feet are attainable in Phase III.
- Users in elliptical orbits, typically with a perigee of 400 n.m. and an apogee of 21,400 n.m., can attain accuracies of 30 to 50 feet at perigee and 200–300 feet at apogee.
- Users at altitudes near or higher than the GPS space vehicle (SV) operating orbit (10,900 n.m.) will either require higher-gain receiving antennas or the GPS SV antenna gain and/or transmitter power will have to be increased for the user to acquire and keep at least four SV's in view with geometric dilution of precision (GDOP) values below 30.
- For low-orbit users, a sequential receiver appears to be the most effective choice.

The conclusions on low-altitude orbital accuracies and sequential receiver implementation were corroborated by the results of Rockwell's Space Shuttle GPS navigation system design study reported in this paper.

The most significant benefits resulting from the implementation of GPS navigation systems for space applications are:

- Improved ephemeris and trajectory determination (i.e., increased mission accuracy and effectivity)
- Real-time ephemeris/trajectory determination (i.e., fast correction of trajectory deviations)
- Reduced reliance on ground tracking networks (i.e., increased mission autonomy)
- Reduced uncertainties in position determination resulting in reduced payload and experiment data processing with consequent overall program cost savings.

To obtain maximum program cost effectivity, a careful analysis of mission requirements and a detailed performance/system cost trade study must be carried out for each application.

SHUTTLE ORBITER BASELINE NAVIGATION SYSTEM (NON-GPS)

During the ascent phase of the mission, the inertial measurement unit (IMU) is the primary sensor providing attitude and acceleration data to the on-board Kalman navigation filter. This information is augmented by ground-based C-band radar tracking information uplinked over the S-band communication link to compute the orbiter state vector. During orbit coasting (i.e., minimal external [venting] forces applied to the orbiter), the IMU provides only attitude data, and the state vector is updated from the ground via Ku- or S-band based on two-way Doppler,

Table 2—Comparison of range signal dynamics and uncertainties*

Parameter	Units	Eccentric Medium-Altitude Satellite	Low-Altitude Satellite	ICBM
Range	n.m.	24,000–36,000	14,000	13,600–15,000
Range rate	fps	29,000–32,000	29,000	26,000
Range acceleration	fps^2			
Unpowered		40	40	40
Powered		—	—	$\simeq$200
Range jerk	fps^3			
Unpowered		0.06–0.09	0.04	0.1
Powered		—	—	$\simeq$16
Position uncertainty	n.m.	27	27	2.5–41
Velocity uncertainty	fps	200	200	105–250
Acceleration uncertainty	fps^2	0.25	0.25	0.76
Jerk uncertainty	fps^3	0.001	0.003	0.032

* Phase III deployment

one ranging, and radar tracking data (Figure 8). At various times during the mission, the IMU attitude error caused by gyro drift is corrected using startracker data. All navigation sensor information is supplied to a six-state suboptimal Kalman filter, which provides the orbiter navigation function with three position and three velocity states.

During the entry blackout period, no ground tracking measurement updates can be uplinked to the orbiter, which now propagates its state vector based on the last pre-blackout ground update and a pre-deorbit (one hour) startracker data-based IMU alignment. The state vector is augmented from 250,000 feet down with drag modeling data and pseudo altitude derived from the drag algorithm. Upon exit from blackout, contact is first established by the ground-based C-band tracking radar (Figure 9). A state vector update can be uplinked to the orbiter when S-band blackout terminates (Figure 10). Subse-

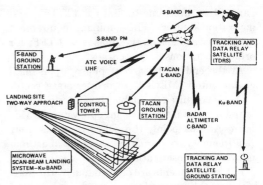

Fig. 10—*Atmospheric communication and tracking links.*

quently, the orbiter can receive the L-band TACAN station signals and begins area navigation combining TACAN range and bearing data with measurements obtained from barometric and radar altimeters (Ref. 4). The barometric altimeter provides data from 30,000 feet until the radar altimeter takes over at 2500 feet. Final approach and landing are accomplished with the microwave scan beam landing system (MSBLS), which is normally acquired at about 10,000 feet altitude and 10 n.m. downrange from touchdown.

SHUTTLE ORBITER GPS NAVIGATION SYSTEM

System Requirements

The GPS system will become the primary operational navigation system, replacing certain elements of the present baseline configuration, and will provide an autonomous navigation capability. It must operate during all mission phases, from prelaunch satellite acquisition and tracking through final approach navigation, until acquisition by the MSBLS. The system will be designed to limit the accuracy degradation caused by the occasional inability to acquire more than three satellites, particularly during entry trajectories flown during the Phase II constellation period. Volumetric, power, and cost considerations dictate the initial implementation of a dual redundant system with provisions for expansion to a three- or four-string system.

The design of the system is predicated on the requirements discussed in the following paragraphs. The two most significant performance

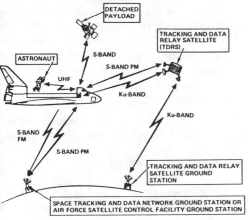

Fig. 8—*Orbital communication links.*

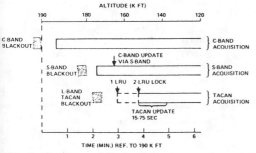

Fig. 9—*C–, S–, and L–band blackout and acquisition estimates.*

parameters are time-to-first-fix (TTFF) and navigation accuracy. The dominant requirement for the ascent and entry phases is TTFF; for orbital operations, it is accuracy.

At the end of the ascent phase, upon main engine cutoff (MECO), an orbiter state vector update is required to enable the execution of an optimum orbital maneuvering subsystem (OMS) burn. At this point, the TTFF and accuracy requirements are primarily driven by abort maneuvering considerations. The postblackout TTFF requirements are determined by the magnitude of the expected trajectory dispersions and descent time remaining until 130,000 feet altitude, where terminal maneuvering must begin to assure safe runway landing (Figure 11).

The on-orbit accuracy requirements are primarily dictated by payload and experiment positioning and velocity uncertainty limits imposed upon the orbiter.

A summary of key system requirements and constraints is presented in Table 3. It should be noted that the dynamic uncertainties, which constitute the basic acquisition scenarios, are based upon worst-case engine and IMU failure considerations. The orbiter line-of-sight dynamics are the result of extensive parametric computer analysis of relative space vehicle and orbiter on-orbit and descent trajectories including the effects of OMS burn and RCS thrusting dynamics. It will be noted that these values agree with the results from the LMSC study, which were presented in Table 2.

The system will receive both L_1 and L_2 frequencies and must be able to operate in the normal and direct acquisition modes. Data and command transfer to and from the orbiter avionics system are handled exclusively via a direct one-MBPS computer data bus interface. All GPS display and control functions, with the exception of primary power, will be handled by the existing on-board CRT and keyboard terminals (Figure 12) (Ref. 5). A separate and direct TLM interface is presently under consideration for handling large-volume system data during the flight test phase.

System Design Definition

Satellite Visibility. System performance depends primarily upon the number of satellites

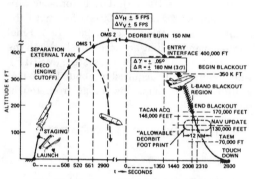

Fig. 11—Typical ascent and entry profile.

Table 3—GPS System operational requirements and orbiter dynamics

Parameter	Ascent	Orbit	Entry
TTFF (sec)	240	Not critical	150
Acquisition mode	Normal & direct	Normal & direct	C/A only/Normal
Accuracy (1σ)			
Position (ft)	≤ 500	<60	≤ 500
Velocity (fps)	≤ 1.0	<0.2	≤ 1.0
Time transfer (μsec)	—	<70	—
Range dynamics (3σ)			
Range (n.m.)	16,000	16,000	16,000
Range rate (fps)	30,000	30,000	30,000
Acceleration fps^2	75	75	75
Jerk (fps^3)	25	25	25
Dynamic uncertainties (3σ)			
Range (n.m.)	7.0	Depends on propa-	40
Range rate (fps)	150	gation time since	200
Acceleration (fps^2)	3.3	last state vector up-date	3.3
Jerk (fps^3)	<0.003 (est.)		<0.003 (est.)

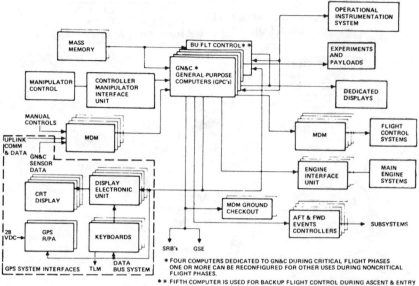

Fig. 12—Data processing and subsystems block diagram.

with a favorable GDOP configuration that can be received with adequate signal-to-noise ratio. Therefore, proper RF system design, including antennas, coaxial cabling, and preamplifiers, is of critical importance. In practice, the ideal, uniform gain, omnidirectional antenna pattern is constrained by inherent limitations in the antenna design, orbiter structural obstructions, and RF shielding of the lower GPS antenna by the external tank during ascent.

An extensive antenna coverage and satellite look angle analytical study identified all visible satellites with their look angles as a function of time for each proposed GPS antenna location on the orbiter (Ref. 6). This function was then parametrically related to orbiter trajectory and attitude, antenna pattern and location, and space vehicle constellation ephemerides. Based on the results of many runs covering the majority of ascent, orbit, and entry trajectories, it was found to be feasible to co-locate the GPS antennas with the existing upper and lower S-band hemi-antennas and to install a redundant upper GPS antenna in an existing TACAN antenna slot for the expanded system upon removal of the TACAN system (Figure 13). This approach eliminates the requirement to provide additional expensive skin penetrations for separate GPS antennas.

The adopted antenna configuration will pro-

vide approximately 85 percent spherical coverage with a 75 × 85 degree (−4 dB) elliptical upper and a 85 × 85 degree (−4 dB) lower conical beam shape. A summary of Phase III satellite visibility data is shown in Table 4. Performance of the analytical model was verified with the testing of full-scale microstrip and cavity antenna brassboards. The test results suggest that microstrip antennas may provide a maximum gain of +4 dBci and −4 dB look-angles in excess of +85 degrees. Co-location had no mutually adverse effects on the GPS and S-band antenna patterns, and RF isolation of better than 60 dB was obtained at S-band. The size and weight advantages of microstrip antennas are obvious, but further development is required to reduce the detuning effect of temperature on their inherently narrow-band characteristics. Also, long-term mechanical and electrical stability must be proven over the extended operating temperature range of −250° to +350°F.

Navigation Error. The proposed orbiter GPS antenna patterns and coordinates were used as inputs into a specially developed GPS navigation error/GDOP analysis computer program. This program selects and identifies four SV's with a favorable geometry (minimum GDOP) from the list of all visible satellites, adding and deleting satellites based upon the orbiter trajectory and attitude. It indicates whether a satellite is visible

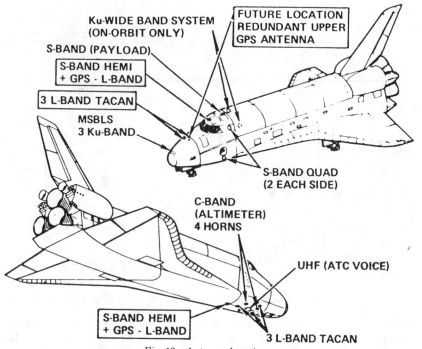

Fig. 13—Antenna locations.

Table 4—Satellite visibility data summary (phase III)

Mission phase	Visibility for 150 n.m./28.5-Degree Inclination Orbit (Various Orbiter Attitudes)
Prelaunch	60% of time 3 or more; never less than 2
Ascent	At least 2 until T_0 + 250 sec; 3 minimum after MECO
Orbit	80% of missions 4 or more; never less than 2
Entry & land	85% of missions 4 or more; never less than 3 (last 50 sec before touchdown)

through the upper or lower antenna and whether the signal is received in the primary (+4 to −1 dBci) or secondary (−1 to −4 dBci) gain zone.

From the calculated pseudo range and range rate measurements, it then computes, propagates, and updates an eight-state Kalman filter covariance matrix providing position, velocity, clock offset, and clock drift error components. The program can be "flown" with any orbiter trajectory or space vehicle constellation and takes into account system noise and SV ephemeris and clock errors. Antenna characteristics and coordinates are variables to permit close simulation of hardware characteristics. The program proved to be a useful analytical tool to establish the validity of the antenna system design parameters (Ref. 7). It confirmed that four satellites will be visible with a GDOP of 4 or less

for 85 percent of all missions (Table 5) and that in Phase III four satellites will always be visible when coming out of blackout.

A special area of concern is system accuracy during entry trajectories flown under a Phase II constellation when periodic intervals of poor SV visibility will occur (Figure 14). During the blackout period, which may last up to 15 minutes, no measurements can be taken and the GPS processor must then rely on the inherent accuracy of its internal clock for accurate propagation of the state vector. It is also during this period that maximum deceleration forces (approximately 3 g's peak) are experienced by the orbiter and the receiver local oscillator. A study revealed (Ref. 8) that with a typical high-stability crystal oscillator, position errors of several thousand feet can be accumulated during this

Table 5—Cumulative dilution of precision values for baseline antenna system

Mission phase	% Prob	GDOP	HDOP	VDOP	TDOP
		Estimated Cumulative DOP Values (Phase III)			
On-orbit	99	4.4	3.6	1.6	2.1
	70	3.2	2.6	1.2	1.4
Entry & descent	99	8.4	4.2	6.6	3.0
(Two entry trajectories)	70	2.9	2.1	1.5	1.0
	99	10.1	7.4	5.0	4.8
	70	2.8	2.2	1.5	0.9

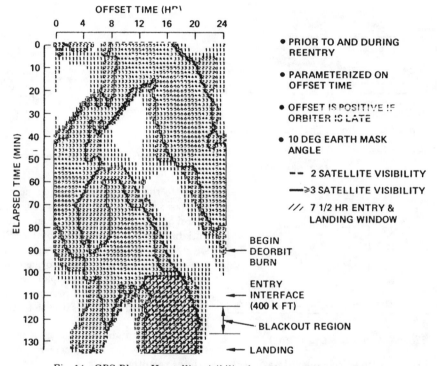

Fig. 14—GPS Phase II satellite visibility for 116 nm, 38 degree orbit.

period. These errors will persist if no user clock bias update can be performed (i.e., during any period when less than four satellites are visible). With an ultrastable clock to provide continuing accurate system time, performance accuracy will be improved dramatically during any period of low satellite visibility. An overview of various clock characteristics and resulting navigation errors is presented in Table 6. These findings led to a systems requirement for a rubidium or a g-compensated oscillator (Ref. 9).

Link Budgets. Another significant contributor to system performance is the RF signal-to-noise ratio at the receiver input port. Signal strength depends on satellite effective isotropic radiated power (EIRP) and is affected by space losses, antenna pointing and polarization losses, antenna gains, and user system losses with the system noise primarily determined by the preamplifier design.

Link analysis results, based on a minimum antenna gain of −4 dB to meet coverage requirements, indicate that link margins from 2 to 4 dB above the required C/N_o ratio of 31.6 dB-Hz can be expected (Ref. 10).

Sequential Detector. Concurrent with the link analyses and RF front end parameter definition, detector and tracking loop requirements must be established.

The detector acquisition process involves the

Table 6—Phase II one-sigma entry trajectory errors—end of 15-minute blackout—3g

Osc. type	Quartz	Compensated quartz	Rubidium	Number of satellites visible
g-Sensitivity	$1 \times 10^{-9}/g$	$3 \times 10^{-11}/g$	$1 \times 10^{-13}/g$	
Phase error (ft)	900	125	8	3
Freq. error (fps)	1.3	0.25	0.005	
Position error (ft)	1500	180	30	3
	60	40	25	4
Velocity error (fps)	2	1.3	1.0	3
	1.5	1.3	1.0	4

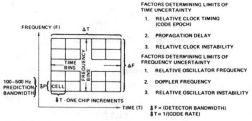

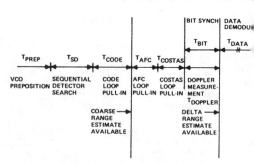

Fig. 15—Sequential detector ΔF/ΔT search domain.

Fig. 17—Acquisition sequence summary (one channel, one satellite).

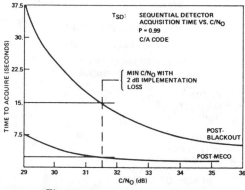

Fig. 16—Acquisition time f(C/N₀)

search through a time/frequency domain (Figure 15) with the dimensions of time uncertainty, ΔT, caused by range dispersion and unknown clock biases, and frequency uncertainty, ΔF, caused by velocity dispersion (i.e., unknown Doppler offset). A typical sequential search procedure has been described by Cahn (Ref. 11).

A number of computer simulation runs were performed to determine the 0.99 probability sequential detector acquisition times as a function of C/No for the Table 3 post-MECO and post-blackout scenarios. The results are presented in Figure 16 (Ref. 12).

The sequential detector acquisition time, T_{SD}, is the one of the significant variables in the total acquisition/demodulation time budget for a single channel (Figure 17). Total TTFF is propor-

tional to the number of satellites acquired and decreases with the number of receiver channels. Faster acquisition is possible when accurate time initialization is available, and total TTFF can be shortened if the latest satellite ephemerides are prestored in receiver/processor assembly (R/PA) memory by data bus upload so that the receiver does not have to perform a 30-second data acquisition for each satellite to obtain this information.

The studies indicate that, as a minimum, a two-channel sequential receiver will meet the orbiter requirements.

Assuming a two-channel sequential processor and allowing a minimum of three measurement passes to permit convergence of the navigation solution, the estimated TTFF values will adequately meet system requirements, as shown in Table 7.

Code and Carrier Tracking Loops. The required C/No for pseudo random noise (PRN) code tracking depends on the range (code) tracking accuracy requirements and type of tracking loop implemented. A reasonable tracking accuracy requirement is a one sigma-5 foot error, corresponding closely to the 1.5 meter GPS user equipment requirement (Ref. 2). The receiver can be implemented with either a delay lock or a tau-dither coherent or noncoherent tracking

Table 7—TTFF—0.99 Probability for two-channel sequential receiver

Scenario (Uncertainties—See Table 4)	TTFF (seconds)		
	$C/N_o = 29.6$ dB	33.0 dB[1]	Requirement
Post-MECO (C/A to P)			
±1 msec GPS time initialization			
Ephemerides loaded	≤180	≤140	240 max
Almanac loaded			
Postblackout (C/A only)[2]			
Predicted ephemerides loaded	≤135	≤100	150 max
Almanac loaded			

[1] Best max C/N_o, adding 4 dB link margin.
[2] Acceptable for initial orbiter state vector update.

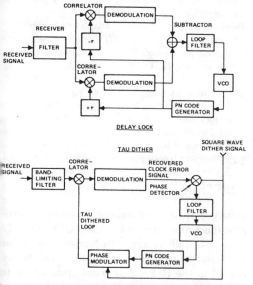

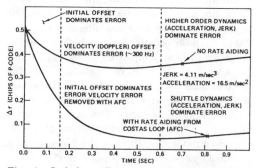

Fig. 19—Code loop offset vs. time during acquisition.

Fig. 18—Functional block diagrams for delay lock and tau-dither PN tracking loops.

loop, as shown in Figure 18. The tau-dither loop correlates the reference code to time sequentially received PRN chips, whereas the delay lock loop develops its error signal by simultaneously correlating the advanced and retarded reference codes with the same received PRN chip. This will result in eventual cancellation of the noise samples in the delay lock loop, giving it a 3 dB C/No advantage over the tau-dither loop.

The delay lock receiver does provide superior performance; but the final choice for the Shuttle system will be determined by trading off overall performance versus cost, power, and weight considerations. For a more detailed analysis, the reader is referred to Refs. 3 and 13.

The choice of a first-order code tracking loop

allows rapid code phase transient decay in the order of 0.6 second. The dynamics must be zero, however, to prevent the loop from gradually slipping out of lock. This presents a practical problem that can be overcome by using the divided frequency output of the carrier tracking loop as a reference frequency for the code loop. The effect of Shuttle dynamics on code loop behavior is shown in Figure 19, which demonstrates the benefits of removing the Doppler offset from the code loop reference, thereby reducing the static code error to 0.05 chip (i.e., five foot on P code) (Ref. 12). Acquisition time of the carrier frequency by the carrir tracking loop will be reduced with the aid of an AFC loop. Since the frequency uncertainty after code acquisition by the detector can be as high as 300 Hz and the carrier loop bandwidth is approximately 35 Hz, a long time can be spent acquiring the carrier. With the AFC loop, the frequency error can be reduced to 7 Hz within 0.3 second, bringing the offset rapidly within the carrier loop bandwidth. The requirements for the carrier tracking loop are primarily determined by the required Doppler measurement accuracy, the link signal dynamics, and the maximum allowable degradation in data detection by a noisy reference.

Previous analyses and experience with GPC receiver hardware suggests that a one sigma 15-degree rms phase error jitter is a reasonable requirement.

It has been shown (Ref. 13) that for carrier tracking, the minimum C/No. requirement is 29.6 dB. Since acceleration and jerk levels are moderate and generally of short duration, it appears very likely that a second-order carrier loop will adequately meet the requirements imposed by the Shuttle range signal dynamics.

Aiding. During acquisiton, the Shuttle velocity may be as high as 30,000 feet per second. The sequential detector sampling time may run from 100 to 400 milliseconds, during which period the range could have slipped by 30 to 120 P-code chips or 3 to 12 C/A code chips. Thus the receiver must be aided by adjusting the generated code phase at a rate proportional to the estimated Shuttle velocity. This state aiding can be obtained from the velocity output of the R/PA's own navigation filter or the ΔV state data supplied by the orbiter computer (GPC).

During initialization, the Shuttle position and velocity estimates are obtained from the GPC over the data bus to set the $\Delta T \times \Delta f$ search region boundaries and pre-position the code loop VCO. This assures the detector of a reasonable dwell time on a quasistationary signal.

System Software

To prevent software over- or underdesign, a specific partitioning between the GPS receiver and orbiter general-purpose computer (GPC) software was established. In essence, the R/PA performs all navigation functions autonomously under control of its own executive, while the GPC performs all data validity checks and redundancy management functions. The basic software partitioning is shown in Table 8.

The GPS receiver processor assembly (R/PA) software architecture is essentially the same as that shown in Figure A-6. The two underlying design premises are modularity to localize change impacts and graceful data degradation in the absence of new measurements.

The R/PA output register update rate as yet has not been determined, but it will be independent from and asynchronous with respect to the GPC acquisition cycle. This causes a variable

Table 8—GPS/GPC Software partitioning

GPS (R/PA)	GPC
Antenna management with crew override	I-Load support over launch data bus
Antenna path length differential compensation	System initialization
Satellite acquisition and data processing	Prelaunch track mode and system fiduciary test
Accept ground-based "pseudolite" data	Failure detection (bite)
Ionospheric delay compensation	GPS_1/GPS_2 state vector divergence test
Memory storage for 30 ephemerides	GPS/GPC state vector selection
Receiver moding and control	Redundancy management
Navigation processing, state vector estimation and propagation	Display and control
Internal health testing (bite)	Telemetry formatting
User clock calibration with launch pad coordinates and (single) satellite tracking	GPS/GPC time sync. support
GPS/GPC time sync. support	Delta velocity state aiding
	Orbiter attitude antenna management aiding
	Coordinate transformation

state vector time tag staleness preventing accurate synchronization of GPS and GPC time. To remove this uncertainty, an "age of data" value (with one microsecond resolution) may be included in the R/PA data block transmitted to the GPC. A data "refresh" bit will also be included to indicate when new data have been transferred to the output register, thus permitting the GPC to ignore old data processed in a previous cycle.

The time transfer accuracy between GPS and GPC or payload is primarily governed by the GPC data acquisition process and may be anywhere from 10 to 200 microseconds depending on the particular mechanization implemented. The GPS control system time will be known with respect to coordinated universal time (UTC–WWV) within 100 microseconds.

The GPC IOP will be programmed to interrogate both R/PA's once each second acquiring state vector and system health data at a one MBPS transfer rate. The GPC then checks the data refresh bit and, if true, proceeds to test the bite words for any hard failure indications. If ne failures are detected, both R/PA state vectors are propagated to a common epoch and tested for divergence. If both GPS state vectors fall within a predetermined error band, the GPS vector with the latest time tag is selected as input to the guidance, navigation, and control (GN&C) function. If the data fail the bite or divergence test, the baseline orbiter state vector will be selected to initialize the GN&C function (Figure 20). Appropriate interfaces with the caution and warning, display and control, and downlist telemetry software modules are provided (Figure 21). A preliminary software estimate sizes the minimum number of words required at 15K (16 bit) data words plus 25K words of code.

SYSTEM PERFORMANCE AND OPERATIONAL BENEFITS

The expected system performance figures are summarized in Table 9 and highlight the improved capability available with GPS with respect to the baseline system. The improvement in navigation accuracy is expected to provide significant benefits for Shuttle and payload performance and operation as discussed below:

- Abort performance margins will be reduced, and a larger number of contingency landing sites without TACAN or MSBLS installations can now be used.
- The autonomous on-board navigation ca-

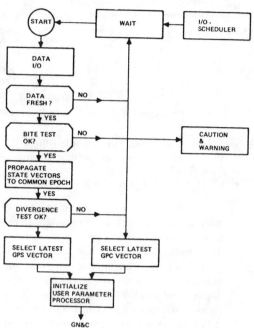

Fig. 20—GPS/GPC redundancy management flow diagram.

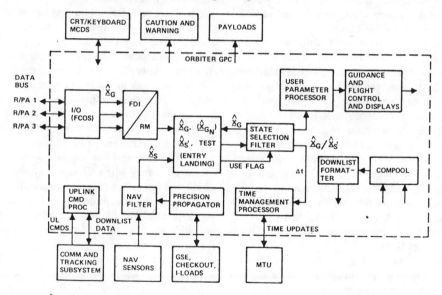

$\hat{\underline{X}}_G$ = GPS STATE ESTIMATE

$\hat{\underline{X}}_S$ = SHUTTLE BASELINE STATE ESTIMATE

Fig. 21—Orbiter G & C functional interface block diagram.

Table 9—GPS-to-Baseline performance comparison

Flight Phase	Parameter	GPS		Baseline	
Ascent	TTFF sec	200		—	—
(Post-MECO)	Position ft	100		1530	500[1]
	Velocity fps	0.6		7.0	10[1]
Orbit	Position ft	60		1000[1]	11,500[2]
	Velocity fps	0.2		1.0[1]	13[2]
	Time μsec	10–200		5×10^3	5×10^3
Descent	TTFF sec	130		—	—
(Post-blackout)	Position ft	60	100[3]	2.6×10^6	1200[4]
	Velocity fps	0.5	1.0[3]	30	7[4]

Based on best engineering estimates to date 1 sigma values, Phase III constellation

NOTES:
1. Ground updated after 1 minute of free flight
2. After 2-hour state vector propagation, deteriorated by attitude maneuvers
3. Phase II only
4. After 2 TACAN stations acquired

pability provides fast state vector updates after orbital maneuvers, dispensing with the need to obtain ground processed updates.

- The orbiter can now provide very accurate state vector initialization and time base synchronization to attached payloads prior to deployment and through the payload interrogator to deployed payloads. This, in turn, may lead to reduced payload hardware cost.
- Improved accuracy in payload deployment and positioning may result in reduced propellant consumption, benefitting payload on-orbit life expectancy.
- The high accuracy with which orbital and rendezvous maneuvers can now be executed is expected to result in improved OMS propellant management, thereby improving performance (delta velocity) margins.
- By more accurate knowledge of payload or experiment position (e.g., earth resource mapping) postflight data reduction time can be reduced with an attendant cost savings.
- Upon expansion of the GPS system to a triple or quadruple redundant system, it would become feasible to remove the onboard TACAN equipment, thus providing weight and power compensation for the addition of GPS.
- Finally, the system autonomy will reduce requirements for contingency planning and staffing and maintenance of ground tracking and telemetry network stations.

SYSTEM IMPLEMENTATION

The system will be implemented as a dual redundant system with two independent sets of hardware and future expansion capability to three or more strings (Figure 22). The upper and lower antennas are co-located with the S-band hemi-antennas. The preamplifiers are located on the forward payload by bulkhead to minimize RF cable losses between antenna and preampli fiers. The preamplifier outputs are connected to both R/PA's via power splitters. The R/PA's are located in an avionics bay (3B) on the lower flight deck (Figure 23).

The antenna's, RF cabling, and preamplifier are designed to withstand the extreme temperature and pressure variations of the space/earth environment. Since the preamplifier power dissipation is only 0.5 watt, thermal conditioning will be required to assure proper operation at −250°F. The receiver/processors are only exposed to the moderate shirtsleeve crew environment on the flight deck and are cold plate-cooled (Figure 24). To reduce peak loads on the orbiter ECLSS cooling and life support system during ascent and entry when all excess system heat is dissipated in limited capacity ammonia and water boilers, the maximum power consumption was kept at 50W peak per unit, which is consistent with existing state-of-the-art design level for two-channel sequential receivers. The total design weight for one set of hardware, including antenna, is 50 pounds; and the receiver dimensions must not exceed 12 × 19 × 7.6 inches.

The R/PA interface with the avionics computer data bus system is provided by a plug-in multiplex interface adaptor (MIA) card. The MIA is the standard interface module between

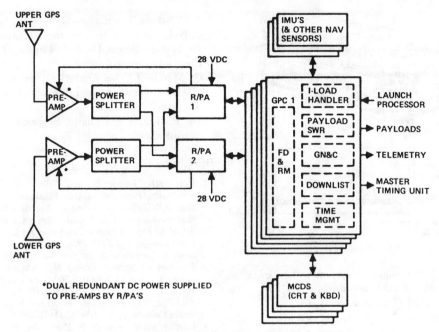

Fig. 22—*Dual redundant GPS system.*

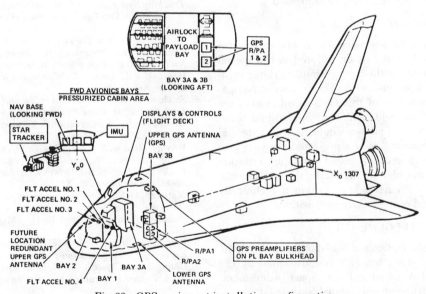

Fig. 23—*GPS equipment installation configuration.*

the orbiter data bus and all units connected to the bus. It is an integral part of the GPS receiver/processor and provides all receive and transmit control and data-handling functions between the R/PA and the GPC. It functions in a half-duplex mode, time sharing receive and transmit operations under control of the GPC

IOP by virtue of coded command words transmitted by the GPC over the data bus to the R/PA MIA.

The data bus signal is a one MBPS Manchester bi-phase L code, formatted in 28-bit words, sent in message blocks of various lengths, depending on the nature of the transaction.

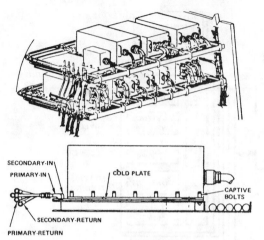

Fig. 24—Typical avionics installation.

The GPS navigation system will be installed in all orbiter vehicles, starting with the first system in the third quarter of 1982.

Afterobtaining operational experience, the questions of system expansion and baseline equipment deletion will be addressed.

CONCLUSIONS

The design approach for a low-earth-orbit GPS receiver/processor, tailored to the special requiements of the Space Shuttle orbiter vehicle, has been discussed. The improved navigation capabilities of this GPS-based system are expected to yield significant operational benefits. Initial cost analyses indicate that potential program savings over a projected ten-year program life span could exceed the implementation cost by an order of magnitude, thus making the Shuttle GPS navigation system a technically sound and cost-effective proposition.

ACKNOWLEDGEMENTS

The information published in this paper is the result of study contract commissioned by the National Aeronautical and Space Administration to define an operational Shuttle GPS navigation system.

The task was completed under auspices of John McLeod and Dr. B. H. Batson of NASA JSC and the direction of the author, supported by Dr. Jon W. Petway, Messrs. E. Rosen and R. E. Strelow and many others from the Rockwell Space Systems Group and the following subcontractors:

P.W. Nilsen, Axiomatix—RF System Analysis
C. Neily, Intermetrix—System Software
Dr. R.W.D. Booth, Dr. W.C. Lindsey, Lincom Corp.—Receiver Analysis
G. Matchett, The Analytical Science Corp (TASC)—General Operations and System Analysis
Dr. P. Noe, Texas Digital Systems—System Consultants

REFERENCES

1. Hemesath, Norbert B., and William M. Hutcheson. "GPS Overview and User Equipment Antijam Design," Collins Government Avionics Division Rockwell International, Cedar Rapids, Iowa. Published in *International Telemetering Conferenc Proceedings, Vol XIV, 1978.*
2. *System Specification for the NAVSTAR Globa Positioning System Phase II.* SAMSO, El Se gundo, California. SS-GPS-200 (1 Sep. 1977).
3. Beck, J. O., et al. *NAVSTAR GPS Satellite-to Satellite Tracking Study.* Lockheed Missiles and Space Company, Inc. LMSC-D491613 (Aug. 1975)
4. Carrier, L. M., and W. S. Pope. *An Overview c the Space Shuttle Orbiter Communication (Tracking System.* Space Systems Group, Rockwel International, Downey, California, SD 78-SR-002 (July 1978).
5. Carrier, L. M., and Richard A. Robitaille. *Spac Shuttle Orbiter Processing, Monitoring, and Te lemetry Systems.* Space Systems Group, Rockwel International, Downey, California, SD 78-SR-002 (November 1978).
6. Strelow, R. E. *Antenna Coverage and Satellit Look Angle Analysis Program.* Space Systems Group, Rockwell International, Downey, Califor nia, SOD 79-0074 (February 1979).
7. Petway, Dr. Jon. *Shuttle GPS GDOP/Navigatio Error Analysis Program.* Space Systems Group Rockwell International, Downey, California, SO 79-0074 (February 1979).
8. Matchett, G. *Shuttle/GPS Panel Support Studie Overview.* The Analytical Science Corporation Reading, Mass., SP-1001-10/11 (March–May 1978).
9. Przyjemski, Joseph M. *A Compensation Tech nique for Acceleration-Induced Frequenc Changes in Crystal Oscillators.* The Charle Stark Draper Laboratory, Inc., Cambridge, Mass (February 1978).
10. Nilsen, Peter W. *Shuttle Global Positioning Sys tem, System Design Study Final Report NAS9 15387C* (20 January 1979).
11. Cahn, C. R., *Spread Spectrum Applications an State-of-the-Art Equipment.* Magnavox Advanced Products Division, Torrance, California, Repor No. MX-TM-3124-74 (June 1973).
12. Booth, Dr. W., and Dr. R. C. Lindsey, *Shuttle GPS R/PA Evaluation Analysis and Performanc Tradeoff Study.* Lincom Corporation, Los Angeles

California, Report No. TR-0978-0278 (September 1978).

13. Nilsen, Peter W. *Investigation and Evaluation of Shuttle/GPS Navigation Systems.* Axiomatix, Los Angeles, California, Report No. R7710 (3 October 1977).

OTHER SOURCES

Rosen, E. E., and A. Van Leeuwen, *SSTS/ GPS Navigation System Design Definition Document.* Space Systems Group, Rockwell International, Downey, California, SD 78-SH-0042 (October 1978).

Huth, Dr. G. K. *"Spread Spectrum Techniques,"* Axiomatix, Los Angeles, California. Published 1978 WESCON: *Modern Communication Techniques and Applications, Part 1.*

Nakamoto, Dr. F. S. "Synchronization Topics," Rockwell International Corporation, Anaheim, California. Published 1978 WESCON: *Modern Communication Techniques and Applications, Part 1.*

Real Time Simulation of a Low Cost GPS Navigator for Nonprecision Approaches

C. SHIVELY

ABSTRACT

THIS PAPER describes a real time simulation designed to evaluate the flyability of a low-cost GPS navigator to be used by general aviation. The performance of such a GPS navigator may be degraded by satellite shielding during aircraft maneuvers associated with a nonprecision approach. Furthermore, the Department of Defense is proposing to reduce the navigation accuracy available to civil users of the GPS military satellite system. These concerns about the flyability of a low-cost GPS navigator have motivated the development of a real time simulation in which a human pilot flies a general aviation trainer along an approach course guided by a computer simulated GPS navigation algorithm. By including the pilot and aircraft response characteristics, this simulation provides a direct comparison of the operational performance of a proposed low-cost GPS navigator with the present VOR/DME system. Results of test pilots flying a simulated nonprecision approach procedure are given for VOR/DME and a low-cost GPS navigator with errors due to satellite shielding and a hypothetical intentional degradation of GPS signals. These results indicate that the operational performance characteristics of the low-cost GPS navigator are noticeably different from VOR navigation and may require different flying techniques as a result. Pilots may be confused by false wind indications due to intentional degradation of GPS signals. An unstable interaction between pilot and navigation may occur if more than one low-elevation satellite can be

shielded by turning the aircraft in different directions. The simulation described herein provides an experimental tool for investigating further the reaction of GA pilots to intentional degradation of GPS navigation accuracy and methods for reducing errors due to satellite shielding.

This paper is based upon future navigation system studies performed by MITRE for the Office of Systems Engineering Management, Federal Aviation Administration, under contract number DOT FA79WA-4184. The data presented herein do not necessarily reflect the official views or policies of the FAA.

INTRODUCTION

The NAVSTAR Global Positioning System (GPS) now under development by the Department of Defense (DOD) is being evaluated as a potential supplement to or replacement for VOR/DME, the current standard international short-range navigation system for civil aviation. Of the roughly 170,000 civil aircraft in use today, over 30%, or about 56,000, are single engine aircraft carrying single VOR navigation avionics averaging about $1,500.[1] Since the highest cost for implementation of GPS avionics falls on general aviation aircraft owners, considerable attention is being devoted to the development of a low-cost GPS receiver/navigator suitable for use by this large class of low-budget General Aviation (GA) aircraft owners. Of particular importance is the performance of such a minimum cost GPS navigation system in comparison to presently used VOR navigation.

In addition to en route navigation, the VOR/DME system provides guidance for terminal routes, holding patterns, and nonprecision approaches. Navigation accuracy requirements are

Mr. Shively presented this paper at the ION Annual Meeting, June 1979. He is with the METREK Division of the Mitre Corporation, 1820 Dolley Madison Blvd, McLean, VA 22102.

most stringent for nonprecision approaches, since azimuthal guidance is required down to decision heights as low as 400 feet, without benefit of vertical guidance signals from the ground. Concern has been expressed that a low-cost GPS navigator may produce position errors due to dynamic lag and satellite shielding during aircraft maneuvers associated with making a nonprecision approach. Furthermore, the DOD is proposing to intentionally degrade the GPS signals on which the low-cost navigator operates, in order to deny full GPS navigation accuracy to users other than the U.S. military.

Previous research in this area has included a fast time simulation of a low-cost GPS navigator providing guidance for a GA aircraft performing approach maneuvers.[2] Results of that simulation confirmed and quantified navigation errors during turns due to velocity tracker lag, satellite shielding, position update rate, and methods of sequentially processing the four GPS satellites. However, the aircraft was represented by a simple kinetic model flying an exact course, and no pilot response characteristics were simulated. The question remained as to what extent errors from a low-cost GPS navigator, operating on intentionally degraded signals, would hamper a GA pilot attempting to fly a nonprecision approach within tolerable limits of course deviation.

This paper describes a real time simulation in which a human pilot flies a General Aviation Trainer (GAT) along an approach course guided by a computer simulated GPS system and navigation algorithm. By including the pilot and aircraft response characteristics, and GPS system errors, this simulation provides a tool for predicting the operational impact of performance degradations associated with a low-cost GPS navigator. Results are presented for several instrument rated test pilots using this GPS navigator to fly a simulated VOR approach into Bader Field at Atlantic City, New Jersey. As a basis for comparison, simulation results are also given for pilots using a VOR navigation model to fly the same approach.

The next section of this paper describes the hardware and software systems used to conduct the GPS simulation experiments. Section 3 reviews the features and characteristics of the GPS and VOR navigation models, including error sources. Section 4 presents results of simulated nonprecision approaches used to evaluate the flyability of the low-cost navigator with satellite shielding, intentional GPS signal degradations, and variations of navigation computation rate. Section 5 summarizes observations and suggestions for further use of the simulation to investigate low-cost GPS navigator design.

DESCRIPTION OF SIMULATION SYSTEM

Hardware Functions

Figure 1 shows a block diagram of the real time simulation system. A General Aviation Trainer (GAT) is interfaced to a NOVA 800 minicomputer to which are connected two CRT terminals, one having graphics and hard copy capability. A floppy disk system (not shown) supports an operating system for program development on the NOVA, as well as allowing experimental data to be recorded for post-run processing. These hardware components are part of a more extensive ATC simulation laboratory[3] under continuing development at MITRE.

In the GPS real time simulation, the minicomputer reads variables of motion X, Y, Z, roll, pitch, and yaw from the GAT. From the GAT's motion, the computer generates the corresponding position estimates X, Y, and Z, including errors and lag, that would be computed by a low-cost GPS navigator. By means of a cockpit mounted switch, the pilot of the GAT selects the leg of the approach for which he wants guidance. Each leg is defined by a predetermined waypoint and course heading toward it. Based upon the GPS estimates of GAT position and the pilot selected waypoint, the NOVA computes values for course deviation (CDI), distance to go (DME), and the TO/FROM indicator. These GPS navigation outputs are displayed in the GAT cockpit on the same indicators normally used for VOR/DME navigation.

The computer graphics terminal displays a background map showing the location of VORs, desired course legs, waypoints, and missed approach point. As the GAT undergoes a simulated flight, the NOVA also plots the GAT trajectory and the GPS estimates of GAT position. Thus, this display permits a real time evaluation of how well the pilot is able to follow a desired course using the GPS navigator. The second

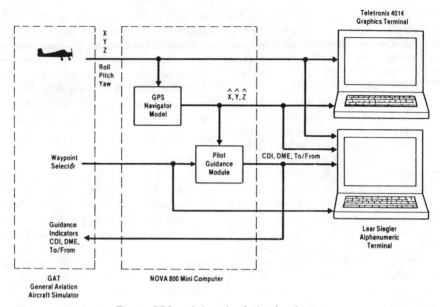

Fig. 1—GPS real time simulation hardware.

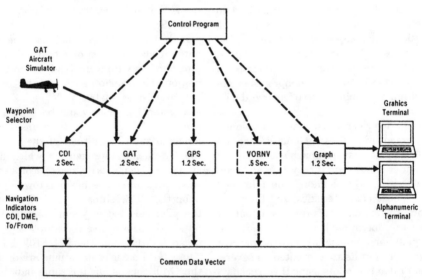

Fig. 2—GPS real time simulation software.

computer terminal displays various data sampled from the experiment every ten seconds. Actual and estimated values of GAT position, altitude, and ground speed are displayed. A. o shown are navigation crosstrack error, and whether any GPS satellites are being shielded due to aircraft banking. The pilot selected waypoint and resulting CDI, DME, and TO/FROM values being sent to the GAT are displayed to provide an understanding of the pilot's actions while flying the approach.

Software Organization

The organization of the simulation software is shown in Figure 2. The software is composed of a control program and four subtasks, which communicate among themselves through a data vector in common storage. The GAT subtask periodically samples derivatives of the GAT aircraft motion and integrates them to compute the aircraft actual position. From the actual position, the GPS subtask computes navigation estimates of GAT position, including the errors and lag of a low-cost navigator. The alternate VORNV subtask may be used in place of GPS to simulate VOR radial or VOR/DME area navigation in the same software environment. From the navigation estimates and pilot selected waypoint, the CDI subtask generates the guidance signals CDI, DME, and TO/FROM for cockpit display. Subtask GRAPH displays actual and estimated GAT positions and other data on the two CRT terminals as described in the preceeding section.

All subtasks and the control program are written in Fortran IV to execute in Data General's real time Fortran multitasking environment.[4] The control program causes each subtask to be executed at its own desired rate, the GPS navigation estimate being computed once every 1.2 seconds, for example. The GPS task runs concurrently with the GRAPH task, by stealing CPU time during pauses for terminal output from GRAPH. The slower GPS and GRAPH tasks are temporarily suspended every .2 seconds to allow execution of the shorter GAT and CDI tasks at a more rapid rate. This modular task oriented software structure lends itself well to the testing of different navigation algorithms and has been used successfully in other simulation efforts in MITRE's ATC Simulation Facility.[5]

NAVIGATION MODELS

Low-Cost GPS Navigator

The GPS navigator modeled in the real time simulation is identical to the low-cost GPS receiver/navigator modeled in the fast time simulation described in Reference 2. Here follows a brief review of the features and operation of that GPS navigator, including error sources. A more detailed discussion of this GPS navigation model and results of fast time simulations without a pilot may be found in Reference 2.

The GPS navigator simulated here is similar to the low-cost GPS military "Z-set" being developed by the Department of Defense. The features of the set being simulated are:

- Automatic Signal and Code Acquisition.

- C/A (Coarse Acquisition) signal only.
- No built-in ionospheric delay model.
- No direct velocity tracking using doppler measurements, velocity is derived by an $\alpha-\beta$ tracker.
- Sequential receiver, tracking a maximum of 4 satellites, one at a time. Dwell time on each satellite = 1.2 seconds (as in "Z-set").
- No integration with baro-altimeter.
- If satellites are shielded during a turning maneuver, no effort is made to acquire new satellites during the turn.
- Constellation selection algorithm which minimizes GDOP (Geometric Dilution of Precision).
- Simplified navigation algorithms followed by an $\alpha-\beta$ tracker, instead of a Kalman filter to interpolate between range measurements.

Figure 3 shows a block diagram of the simulated GPS receiver/navigator. Every ΔT the generation of a new pseudo-range by the sequential receiver is simulated by calculating the distance from the aircraft to each satellite in turn. Errors added to the pseudo-range include ionospheric delay,[6] multipath noise,[7] range measurement noise, clock bias and an error that may result from intentional degradation of GPS signals by the DOD.

Every ΔT, the navigator computes a new estimate of craft position, using the newly drived pseudo-range from one of the satellites and the most recent pseudo-ranges from the other three. To convert the pseudo-ranges from all four satellites into aircraft position, the navigation algorithm computes the difference between the measured pseudo-ranges and pseudo-ranges predicted from the previous estimate of aircraft position. These incremental pseudo-ranges are then transformed into an increment in craft position, which is passed through an $\alpha-\beta$ tracker to estimate craft velocity and compute a smoothed position estimate. In order to simulate the loss of data due to satellite shielding, the processing for each satellite includes computing the apparent satellite elevation angle as seen by an antenna mounted atop the aircraft. If due to satellite or aircraft motion, that elevation angle becomes less than 10 degrees, the satellite is declared to be shielded. When a satellite is deemed to be shielded, the incremental pseudo-range for that satellite is held constant at the

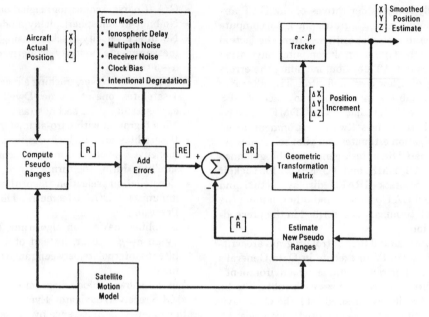

Fig. 3—GPS low-cost navigator.

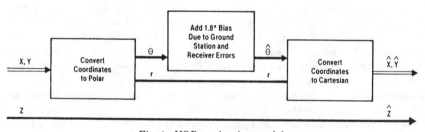

Fig. 4—VOR navigation model.

most recent unshielded value until the satellite is visible again.

VOR Navigation Model

Figure 4 shows a block diagram of the simple VOR navigation model used in the real time simulation for comparison with the low-cost GPS navigator. The total VOR navigation error is assumed to consist of independent angular biases of the signal-in-space and the airborne receiver. It has been suggested[8] that the error of the signal-in-space can be approximated by a random constant from a normal distribution with zero mean and standard deviation σ_T where $2\sigma_T = 2.0°$. Likewise, the bias of a given receiver may be selected from a normal distribution with zero mean and standard deviation σ_R where $2\sigma_R = 3.0°$. The sum of the transmitter and receiver

biases is therefore normally distributed with zero mean and standard deviation σ_S, where

$$\sigma_s = (\sigma_T{}^2 + \sigma_R{}^2)^{1/2} = (1.0^2 + 2.25^2)^{1/2} = 1.8°$$

The above choice of errors is also adopted by the FAA (AC 9045A). However, the signal-in-space error is conservative for two reasons. First, recent data indicate a two-sigma value of 1.4°. Second, the VORs used for nonprecision approach are usually sited and calibrated to yield a higher accuracy.

Simulation Results

This section presents simulation results comparing VOR navigation and several variations of the low-cost GPS navigation model, including both degraded and nondegraded GPS signals, and different data update rates. The examples discussed here were selected from a group of test flights by four instrument rated pilots, having in-flight instrument experience ranging from 50 to 350 hours. Even though only a few pilots are represented by these results, their interactions with the GPS navigator are believed to be indicative of responses from many other GA pilots as well.

Approach Scenarios

The VOR approach to Bader Field at Atlantic City, New Jersey was selected for exercising the GPS navigation because of the turning maneuvers required to carry out the approach and subsequent missed approach procedure. Figure 5 gives a map of the approach showing the location of VORs, missed approach point (MAP), and desired course, including missed approach holding pattern. To make the approach from the Sea Isle VOR (SIE), the pilot flys at an altitude of about 2000 feet on the 047° radial to its intersection at Avalo (AVA) with the 162° radial from the Atlantic City VOR (ACY), turns to a heading of 242° and flys 10.8

nm to the Atlantic City VOR (ACY). The pilot executes a parallel entry into the holding pattern at ACY by heading outbound on the 314° radial and turning through 180° to capture the final approach course of 134°. After station passage inbound at ACY, the pilot begins a gradual descent, reaching a minimum altitude of 740 feet at the missed approach point (MAP) 7.7 nm from the ACY VOR. To carry out a missed approach, the pilot initiates a climb at a heading of 188° to intersect the 047° radial from SIE, proceeds to the AVA intersection, and holds there if so advised. The first two legs of the approach are flown at an indicated air speed (IAS) of 110 to 120 kts. and the final approach with descent at an IAS of 80 to 90 kts.

In the real time simulation of VOR navigation, the cockpit indicators are driven according to aircraft position estimates from the VOR navigation model in the NOVA minicomputer. With a single switch in the GAT cockpit, the pilot selects one of the desired course radials numbered simply 1–5, radial number 1 being the 047° from SIE as shown in the figure. The CDI indi-

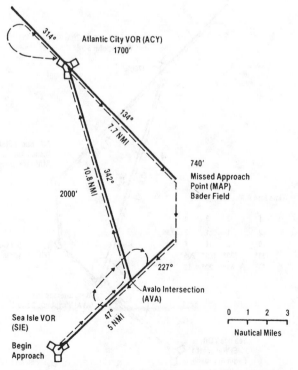

Fig. 5—Approach scenario for simulated VOR navigation.

cates the angular deviation of the craft estimated position from that VOR radial within ± 10° full scale. The DME reading is relative distance to the VOR associated with the selected radial, and the TO/FROM indicates station passage in the normal fashion for VOR navigation.

Figure 6 shows the approach map for simulating the use of GPS RNAV guidance to follow the same flight path as the VOR approach above. In the GPS RNAV scenario, numbered waypoints are located at the VORs, radial intersections, and missed approach point. With a single cockpit switch, the pilot selects one of the preassigned waypoints numbered 1 through 6 to which the GPS navigation estimates of aircraft position are compared to generate guidance information. The CDI indicates the linear crosstrack displacement (0.25 nm per dot and ± 1.25 nm full scale) of the craft estimated position from the desired course between the selected waypoint and the previous waypoint in sequence. The pilot thus flys toward each waypoint in turn, with the DME always reading distance remaining to reach the waypoint and

TO/FROM reading TO until the waypoint is crossed.

Figure 6 also shows a sample of the relative orientation of the four GPS satellites chosen for navigation during the approximately 20 minute time period covered by each simulated approach. Note that satellites 3 and 4 are located at elevation angles of 22° and 18° respectively above the horizon. This particular constellation configuration was chosen to investigate the navigation degradation due to satellite shielding during turns whenever the best available constellation includes two low-elevation satellites.

Comparison of VOR and GPS Navigation

Figure 7 shows the output plot from a typical simulated approach using VOR navigation. The plot includes both actual GAT trajectory and the VOR navigation model estimate of craft position. Since the VOR error is angular, the separation between the two traces becomes more evident with increasing distance of the aircraft from the VOR selected for navigation. In this particular approach scenario the MAP is almost

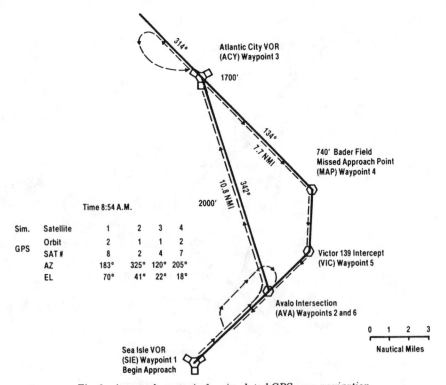

Fig. 6—Approach scenario for simulated GPS area navigation.

8 nm from the VOR used for guidance, and the VOR navigation error modeled here was about .25 nm at the MAP. Consequently, the craft was slightly off course at MAP even though according to the CDI reading, the pilot was tracking the desired course quite well. Simulation results would be different for other approach scenarios where the VOR is located closer to the MAP.

Figure 8 is a typical output plot from a simulated approach using the low-cost GPS navigator with iterative processing, and a dwell time or ΔT of 1.2 seconds, operating on GPS signals whose potential navigation accuracy has not been intentionally degraded. Note that the craft trajectory and GPS derived position estimate are practically coincident except for the triangle shaped deviations at points A, B, C, and D in the figure. The navigation errors at A and B are due to simulated shielding of the low elevation satellite #4 to the southwest, and those at C and D are from shielding of the other low elevation satellite #3 located to the southeast. The maximum horizontal position error due to shielding was about .5 nm and the GPS navigation algorithm recovered within about 30 seconds after each occurrence of shielding ceased. The pilot

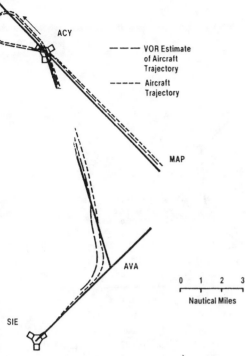

Fig. 7—Simulated approach using VOR navigation.

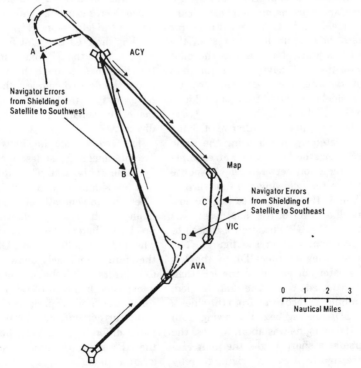

Fig. 8—Simulated approach using low-cost GPS navigator.

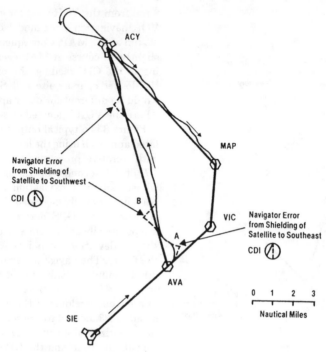

Fig. 9—Simulated approach showing course hunting with low-cost GPS navigator.

reported no difficulty in capturing the final approach course, and since he made no significant maneuvers thereafter, the GPS navigation error settled to less than .1 nm for the rest of the approach. In this particular example, the pilot was not aware that any navigation errors had occurred, but the interaction between pilot and GPS satellite shielding varied from one pilot to another as we see below.

Figure 9 shows results of another pilot flying the same simulated approach using the same low-cost GPS navigator. Here we see an example of feedback interaction between pilot response and navigation error following the first turn at waypoint AVA. As the pilot banked left, the low elevation satellite #3 to the southeast was shielded, causing the GPS position estimate to lag to the east (point A in the figure). The resulting large swing of the CDI to the left indicated a greater correction to the left than was actually required. When the craft leveled, the navigator quickly recovered from the shielding and the CDI reading began to swing from left to right. Believing he was about to cross the desired course at a sharp angle, the pilot executed a corrective bank to the right, thereby

shielding satellite #4 located at the southwest. Since the resulting navigation position error was now to the left, (point B in the figure) the CDI reading directed the pilot further off course to the east until the GPS navigator recovered from the shielding. Although the pilot in this instance found the desired course to be a bit evasive, he never strayed more than .7 nm off course and made the remainder of the approach without difficulty.

The feedback coupling between pilot and GPS satellite shielding just described was experienced by some of the test pilots during one of their first few simulated flights with GPS navigation. These pilots generally employed a flying technique which involved following the CDI more precisely when making turns than the test pilots who did not follow the CDI as closely, and therefore were largely unaware of GPS navigation errors. After being initially confused by unexpected behavior of GPS navigation during turns, the more experienced pilots seemed to avoid further difficulty by using a flying technique different from VOR navigation to allow the GPS navigator time to settle following an aircraft maneuver. Satellite shielding errors which can cause such pilot-navigation feedback, may possibly be reduced by improvements in low-cost GPS navigator design.

GPS Navigation from Hypothetically Degraded Signals

The real time simulation is also being used to assess the flyability of a low-cost GPS navigator if the DOD intentionally degrades GPS signals in order to deny full navigation accuracy to users other than the U.S. military. Figure 10 shows a typical simulated approach for one hypothetical model of such an intentional degradation of GPS signals. In this example, the intentional degradation produces an error from the low-cost navigator which is primarily along track for courses to the northeast or southwest, and across track for flight paths in the northwest or southeast directions. The error was also contrived to gradually pass through a null and change sign while the pilot was flying the final approach leg.

As can be seen from Figure 10, the test pilot in this case flew rather precisely according the CDI indications computed by the GPS navigator. Consequently, he had no way of knowing

that between waypoints AVA and ACY his diligence produced a course parallel to the desired track, but offset by about .3 nm GPS navigation error. When the navigation error began to drift and switch sign on the final approach leg, the pilot wondered whether a simulated crosswind had been activated. More simulated approaches will be flown by other test pilots to evaluate their reaction to an intentional degradation of low-cost GPS navigator performance.

Variation of GPS Navigation Update Rate

The previous simulation examples of GPS navigation were for a navigation position update period ΔT of 1.2 seconds, equal to the satellite dwell time of the GPS military Z-set. Since the navigator cost may possibly be reduced by a decrease in the computation speed required to evaluate the navigation algorithm, simulations were done with $\Delta T = 2.4$ seconds.

Figure 11 shows a typical real time simulation output plot for the low-cost GPS navigator with a ΔT of 2.4 seconds. As for the case of $\Delta T = 1.2$ seconds, the GPS navigation position errors are due mostly to satellite shielding during the turns

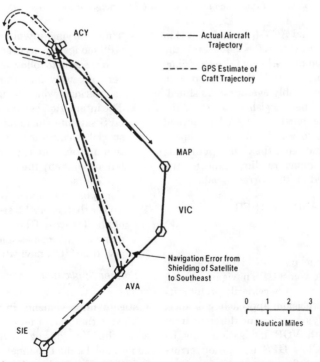

Fig. 10—Simulated approach with GPS navigator operating on hypothetically degraded signals.

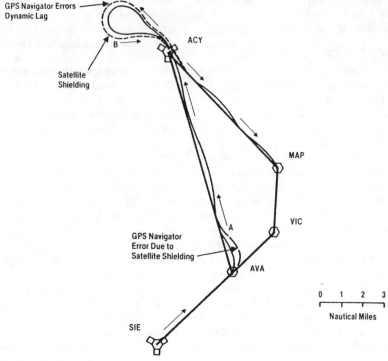

Fig. 11—Simulated approach with low-cost GPS navigator and 2.4 sec. dwell time.

at waypoints AVA and ACY (points A and B in Figure 11). However, with $\Delta T = 2.4$ seconds the navigator recovered more slowly from shielding, and during the turn at ACY the GPS position estimate lagged noticeably even prior to shielding of a satellite. The sluggish recovery of the GPS navigator after shielding at AVA prompted several test pilots to wonder if the simulation included a crosswind, since the CDI kept drifting even though the compass readings indicated the GAT was stabilized on the correct heading.

OBSERVATIONS AND FURTHER APPLICATIONS

Observations

- Relatively large position errors that may result from a low-cost GPS navigator during aircraft turns do not necessarily prohibit its use for nonprecision approach guidance. However, a flying technique different from that used with VOR navigation may be required to allow GPS navigation errors time to subside following an aircraft maneuver.

- Time varying intentional degradation of GPS navigation accuracy can deceive pilots who are able to follow navigation indicators very precisely into thinking they are encountering a wind change.

- The interaction between pilot response and GPS satellite shielding errors can in some special circumstances of satellite constellation and aircraft trajectory result in oscillations whereby the pilot hunts for an evasive course.

- For position update rates significantly slower than every 1.2 seconds, the response of the low-cost GPS navigator to aircraft maneuvers becomes noticeably more sluggish than VOR navigation.

Further Application

The real time simulation may be used to investigate improvements in the low-cost GPS navigator that would reduce errors due to satellite shielding during turns. The simulation could model a dual channel receiver that tracks a fifth satellite to be used for navigation when one of the original four is shielded. Other suggested solutions include the use of altimeter data or a more accurate clock to aid in aircraft position estimation when a satellite is shielded. The real time simulation may also be used to investigate the impact on low-cost navigator performance of intentional GPS signal degradations other than the one postulated here. Future experiments may devote special attention to the impact of GPS navigator errors on holding pattern guidance. The simulation described herein may serve as a basis for other simulation efforts which study in greater depth the human factors aspects of pilot workload and visual scene changes due to errors associated with guidance from a low-cost GPS navigator.

ACKNOWLEDGEMENT

The author would like to acknowledge Messrs. Rick Ellison, John Golden, and Bob Todd for their contributions to the development of the simulation hardware interfaces and real time software. Special thanks are also due to the four simulation test pilots, Dave Bailey, Al McFarland, Steve Satre, and Rick Telsh. The FAA Project Manager for this task was Mr. Jerry Bradley.

REFERENCES

1. Braff, R., and Joglekar, A. N., "Future Domestic Air Navigation System Analysis," *Navigation*, Vol. 25, No. 1, Spring 1978, pp. 71–79.

2. Joglekar, A. N. and Wong, G. A., "Evaluation of GPS Performance for Low-Cost General Aviation," The MITRE Corporation, Metrek Division, McLean, Va., M78-78, October 1978, paper presented at 1978 IEEE Position Location and Navigation Symposium at San Diego, California.

3. Pierson, H. L., and Telsh, R. W., "The MITRE METREK ATC Simulation Laboratory," The MITRE Corporation, Metrek Division, McLean, Va., M78-5, January 1978, paper presented at 1978 ATC Simulation Training and Technology Symposium at Orlando, Florida.

4. "NOVA Line Fortran IV User's Manual 093-000053-08," Data General Corporation, Southboro, Mass., February 1975.

5. Todd, R. E., "Developmental Active Beacon Collision Avoidance System—A Software Description," The MITRE Corporation, Metrek Division, McLean Va., MTR-7967, November 1978.

6. Elrod, B. D., "Correction for Ionospheric Propagation Delay...," MTR-6896, The MITRE Corporation, Metrek Division, McLean, Va., April 1975.

7. Khalil, M. A., "GPS Multipath Error Model," M78-36, The MITRE Corporation, Metrek Division, May 1978. Paper presented at 1978 ION National Aerospace Symposium at Atlantic City, NJ.

8. Hoffman, W. C., "Functional Error Analysis and Modeling for ATC System Concept Evaluation," Aerospace Systems, Inc., PB 213-148, Burlington, Mass., May 1972.

NAVSTAR Field Test Results

D. W. HENDERSON and J. A. STRADA

ABSTRACT

THE NAVSTAR GLOBAL POSITIONING SYSTEM (GPS) is currently in the Concept Validation phase of development. A variety of Navstar user equipment is being tested aboard test vehicles provided by the three military services. Testing has recently been conducted at the Yuma Proving Ground and, at sea, in local San Diego waters, using up to four Navstar satellites. This paper presents some of the more significant results of that testing.

Introduction

Since the early 1960s the Navy and Air Force have actively pursued the concept of navigation using radio signals transmitted by space vehicles whose positions in space are accurately known. The impetus for such a space based navigation system was the broad spectrum of military and civilian users to whom precise, global navigation is desirable, as well as the cost benefits which would result from reversing the trend toward proliferation of specialized navigation equipments. The Navy sponsored two such systems: TIMATION and TRANSIT which is presently operational. The Air Force concurrently embarked on the design of a highly accurate, three dimensional system called 621B.

On 17 April 1973 the Deputy Secretary of Defense issued a memorandum which designated the Air Force the executive service in an effort to develop a joint service navigation system which would build on the technological achievements of the predecessor Air Force and

Navy programs, and also incorporate the position/navigation requirements of the U.S. Army and Defense Mapping Agency. Thus the Navstar Global Positioning System (GPS) was born. Navstar GPS was briefed to the Defense Systems Acquisition Review Council (DSARC) on 13 December 1973 and was approved by the Deputy Secretary of Defense on 22 December of the same year.

The Navstar Joint Program Office (JPO) is located at the Space and Missile Systems Organization (SAMSO) in El Segundo California. In addition to the U.S. Air Force Program Manager, the JPO includes Deputy Program Managers representing the Army, Navy, Marine Corps, Coast Guard, Defense Mapping Agency, and the North Atlantic Treaty Organization (NATO). The JPO is staffed by military and civilian personnel from all of those organizations, including the NATO countries.

The JPO will go before the Defense Systems Acquisition Review Countil (DSARC II) in May of this year for authorization to proceed with Phase II, Full Scale Engineering Development. The planned schedule for Phase II Field Testing is shown in Figure 1.

System Description

Navstar GPS is a space based navigation system which is capable of providing highly accurate, three-dimensional position and time information to suitably equipped users anywhere on or near the earth. In its final configuration Navstar will deploy three planes of satellites in circular 17,000 kilometer orbits. Each plane will contain eight satellites for a total of twenty-four.

The Navstar satellites transmit a composite signal at two L-band frequencies—one for acquisition and coarse navigation and one for precise navigation. The signal contains satellite ephemeris information, atmospheric propagation correction data and satellite clock bias in-

COL. Henderson is the Program Manager and LCDR Strada is Test Director for NAVSTAR-GPS at the USAF Space and Missile Systems Organization, El Segundo, Calif. They presented this paper at the ION National Aerospace Symposium on 6 March 1979.

formation. The dual frequency transmissions permit determination of the signal delay resulting from passage through the ionosphere. Four ground based Monitor Stations located in Alaska, Guam, Hawaii and Vandenberg Air Force Base in California passively track the satellites as they come into view. The Master Control Station, also at Vandenberg, collects the ranging data from the Monitor Stations and generates the navigation message which it uploads to each satellite on a daily basis.

The Navstar User Set consists of a receiver and navigation processor which require signals from at least four satellites to solve for the user's three position coordinates and system time (see Figure 2). The position solution is computed in World Geodetic Survey—72 coordinates and can be converted to any convenient reference system or units. In high dynamic vehicles such as a fighter aircraft, the GPS User Set may be supplemented by an Inertial Measurement Unit (IMU) to maintain navigation accuracy during high acceleration maneuvers. Such a combination is referred to as an Aided User Set.

The entire Phase I system is depicted in Figure 3 and the characteristics of the operational system are listed in Figure 4.

Fig. 1—Phase II user equipment field tests

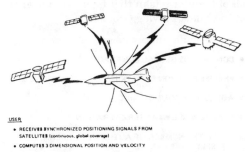

Fig. 2—Global Positioning System (GPS).

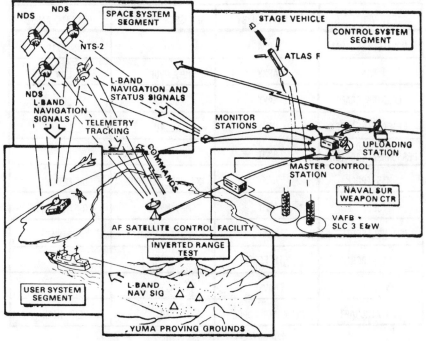

Fig. 3—GPS phase I system.

The Field Test Program

With the successful completion of DSARC I, Navstar entered the Concept Validation Phase of development, and large developmental-model user sets were mounted in specially instrumented pallets aboard a variety of vehicles provided by the military services and the Defense Mapping Agency (DMA). Those vehicles are listed in Figure 5. Testing of user sets manufactured by three contractors began at the U.S. Army Yuma Proving Ground in Arizona on 15 March 1977. The user sets and their peculiar characteristics are listed in Figure 6. At present all of the user sets in that figure are under test at the Yuma Proving Ground.

- **CONTINUOUS GLOBAL COVERAGE**
- **PRECISE POSITION & VELOCITY IN 3 DIMENSIONS & TIME**
- **WORLDWIDE COMMON GRID**
- **PASSIVE & ALL WEATHER OPERATION**
- **UNLIMITED NUMBER OF AUTHORIZED USERS/ SELECTIVE DENIAL**
- **HIGH JAM RESISTANCE**

Fig. 4—NAVSTAR characteristics.

Because Navstar testing commenced prior to the launch of any space vehicles (four are now on orbit), a ground system, called the Inverted Range (IR), was installed at YPG to simulate signals from four Navstar satellites. The system consists of four Ground Transmitters (GTs),

USER SET	FREQ	CODE ACQ	CODE NAV	NO. OF CHAN	IMU	CONTRACTOR
X	L1&L2	P C/A	P C/A	4	YES OR NO	GENERAL DYNAMICS/ MAGNAVOX
Y	L1&L2	P C/A	P C/A	1	YES OR NO	GENERAL DYNAMICS/ MAGNAVOX
Z	L1	C/A	C/A	1	NO	GENERAL DYNAMICS/ MAGNAVOX
GDM	L1&L2	P C/A	P C/A	5	YES	COLLINS
HDUE	L1&L2	P C/A	P C/A	5	NO	TEXAS INSTRUMENTS
MP	L1&L2	P C/A	P C/A	1	NO	GENERAL DYNAMICS/ MAGNAVOX
MVUE	L1&L2	P C/A	P C/A	1	NO	TEXAS INSTRUMENTS

Fig. 6—NAVSTAR user sets.

TEST VEHICLES	PROVIDED BY	GPS SETS ONBOARD	DYNAMIC RANGE
MOBILE TEST VAN	DMA	XU	STATIC
MAN	ARMY	MP, MVUE	LOW
LANDING CRAFT	NAVY	XU, YU	LOW
FRIGATE(FF1076)	NAVY	XU, YU	LOW
ARMORED PERSONNEL CARRIER	ARMY	MP, MVUE	LOW
M35 TRUCK	ARMY	XU, HDUE, MP, MVUE	LOW-MEDIUM
JEEP	ARMY	MP, MVUE	LOW-MEDIUM
UH1 HELICOPTER	ARMY	XU, YU, MP, HDUE, MVUE	MEDIUM
C141 AIRCRAFT	AIR FORCE	XU, XA, YU, YA, GDM, Z, HDUE	HIGH
P3 AIRCRAFT	NAVY	XU, XA, YU, YA, Z	HIGH
F4 AIRCRAFT	NAVY/AIR FORCE	XA	VERY HIGH

Fig. 5—NAVSTAR test vehicles.

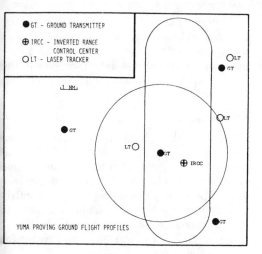

Fig. 7

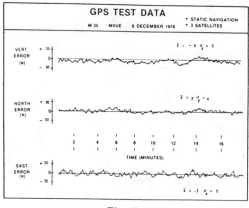

Fig. 10

NAVSTAR GPS TEST DATA
MANPACK TESTING
25 JAN 79

"ALL FOUR MANPACKS AGREED TO WITHIN 10 FEET."
— GPS TEST TEAM

10 FT   20 FT   30 FT

Fig. 11

MAJOR FIELD TEST OBJECTIVES	
NAVIGATION ACCURACY:	THREAT PERFORMANCE:
1. POSITION ACCURACY	13. JAMMING RESISTANCE
2. VELOCITY ACCURACY	14. DENIAL OF ACCURACY
3. EFFECTS OF DYNAMICS ON ACC.	ENVIRONMENTAL EFFECTS:
DEMONSTRATIONS OF MILITARY VALUE:	15. PROP & ROTOR MODULATION
4. PRECISION WEAPON DELIVERY	16. FOLIAGE ATTENUATION
5. LANDING APPROACH	17. MULTIPATH REJECTION
6. RENDEZVOUS	18. IONOSPHERIC & TROPOSPHERIC
7. PHOTOMAPPING	CORRECTION
8. NAP-OF-EARTH OPERATIONS	SYSTEM CHARACTERISTICS:
9. STATIC POSITIONING	19. SATELLITE CLOCK &
10. COMBINED OPERATIONS	EPHEMERIS ACCURACY
11. CROSS-COUNTRY	20. ACQUISITION & REACQ TIME
12. SHIPBOARD OPERATIONS	21. TIME TRANSFER
	22. SIGNAL LEVELS AND SIGNAL
	STRUCTURE

Fig. 8

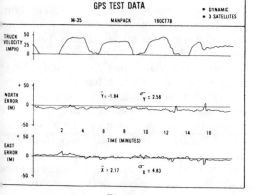

Fig. 9

each simulating a Navstar satellite, and the Inverted Range Control Center (IRCC) which monitors the GTs and maintains time synchronization among them. The IRCC can also control a mix of GTs and satellites during what is termed hybrid testing. In addition, three ground based laser trackers, which comprise the Precision Automated Tracking System (PATS), were installed to accurately determine the trajectory of the test vehicle for comparison with the GPS navigation solution. The lasers track optical reflectors mounted on the test vehicles to an accuracy of less than 1.0 meter and 0.1 meters per second. Figure 7 shows the relative locations of the GTs and lasers at YPG as well as two flight profiles which were used to collect some of the data presented in subsequent sections.

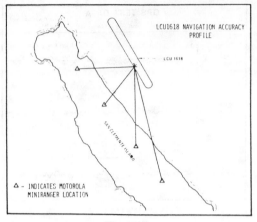

Fig. 12

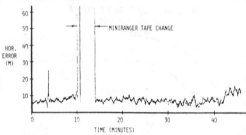

Fig. 13—LCU1618 navigation performance: 6 Dec 1978; X-set; 3 satellites.

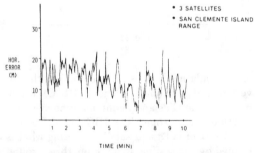

Fig. 14—GPS test data 11 Dec 1978: MX-1 channel set (Y); landing craft.

In preparation for DSARC II, test data is being collected to satisfy twenty-two Major Field Test Objectives (MFTO). These are listed in Figure 8. With the successful launches of Navstar 3 (6 October 1978) and Navstar 4 (10 December 1978), testing could be accomplished independent of the Inverted Range and its pseudosatellites. Three satellite testing, employing

an altitude-hold mode, and four satellite testing are now underway to collect sufficient data to satisfy each of the test objectives. This paper presents samples of that data from some of the more significant testing accomplished in recent months.

Navstar Accuracy

Figures 9 through 19 present navigation accuracy data for a variety of test vehicles and user sets, during three and four satellite testing conducted from October 1978 through January 1979. The errors depicted represent the difference between the Navstar solution and a reliable "truth" reference, i.e., the laser trackers for air and ground vehicles and a miniranger system for the Landing Craft.

The Magnavox Manpack (MP) was tested aboard the M35 truck at speeds up to 45 mph and the results are shown in Figure 9. More recently, the Texas Instruments Man/Vehicular User Equipment (MVUE), also a manpack set, was tested statically aboard the M35, yielding the data in Figure 10. Figure 11 shows comparative data from four manpack sets, two from each contractor, during operational testing conducted by the Army in January 1979. The four sets agreed to within 10 feet of each other.

In December of 1979 navigation accuracy testing was conducted aboard a Navy Landing Craft (LCU1618) on an instrumented test range off of San Clemente Island, California, during three satellite coverage. In this case the "truth" reference was a Motorola miniranger system installed at four surveyed positions on the island (see Figure 12). This system was tested against the laser trackers at YPG and found to have a ranging accuracy of about 1 meter. The four channel X-Set displayed P-code navigation accuracy of about 10 meters (Figure 13) in the horizontal plane. The single-channel Y-Set (Figure 14) was navigating on C/A code only, due to a software problem which has since been corrected. However, it achieved accuracies which are comparable to those of X-Set, as seen in Figure 15, which is a photo of the X-Set (left) and Y-Set (right) during LCU navigation tests. Note the remarkable agreement between the two solutions. Figure 16 summarizes the position and velocity accuracies achieved during the LCU testing.

Fig. 15

USER EQUIPMENT	DATE	AVER HORIZONTAL POSITION ERROR (METERS)	AVER HORIZONTAL VELOCITY ERROR (METERS/SECOND)
X-UNAIDED	6 DEC 78	7.7	0.28
	7 DEC 78	24.9	0.34
	8 DEC 78	9.1	0.30
	11 DEC 78	23.6	0.40
	12 DEC 78	8.6	0.25
	13 DEC 78	9.4	0.30
Y-UNAIDED	11 DEC 78	11.9	1.1
	12 DEC 78	19.6	0.63
	13 DEC 78	13.1	0.77

Fig. 16—LCU1618 accuracy summary: 3 satellites, X & Y sets.

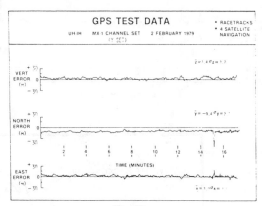

Fig. 18

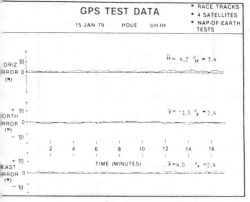

Fig. 17

Four-satellite airborne testing has only recently begun, but some data is available. Figure 17 shows navigation errors of the Texas Instruments, five-channel, High Dynamic User Equipment (HDUE) during nap-of-earth (low-altitude, terrain avoidance) testing aboard the UH1 helicopter. The single-channel Y-set also performed well aboard the UH1 helicopter (Figure 18), this time navigating on P-code. The first few minutes of recorded data from P-3 testing of the Magnavox, single-channel Z-Set are shown in Figure 19. This set is the only single frequency

(L1) set and was designed for C/A-only navigation. These initial results indicate surprising accuracy for this low-cost Navstar set.

Landing Approach

Most Navstar sets incorporate the capability to enter three-dimensional waypoints into the computer memory so that steering information (range, bearing, time to go) can be computed from one waypoint to the next. In the C141 and F4 aircraft this information is used to drive a Pilot Steering Display (PSD, Figure 20) which displays horizontal and vertical deviation from the intended flight path between subseque waypoints. If key landing approach points a entered as Navstar waypoints, the pilot is pr vided with a self-contained, landing-approac instrumentation system which is independent ground controllers or equipment. Tests of th concept were flown by the F4 aircraft and th actual approach paths of two of these a proaches are shown in Figure 21. Figure shows that all four of the test approaches flov on 26 September 1978 penetrated the imagina Instrument Landing System (ILS) window decision height. These approaches were flov using one satellite and three ground transmi ters.

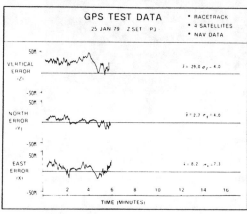

Fig. 19

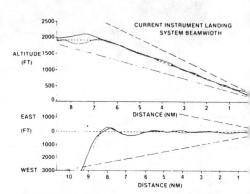

Fig. 21—GPS landing approach: F-4J, 26 Sept 19

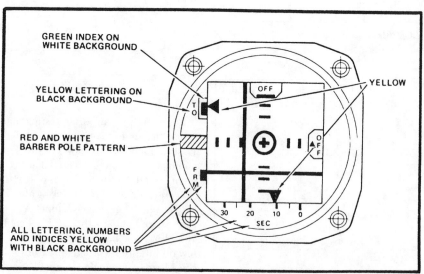

Fig. 20—Pilot steering display installed in C141, F4, and P3.

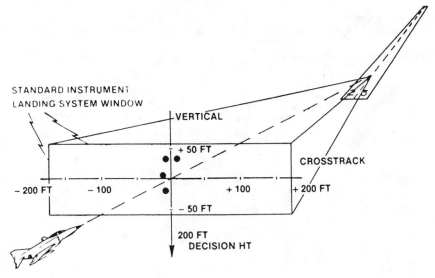

Fig. 22—*GPS landing approach: pilot steering errors.*

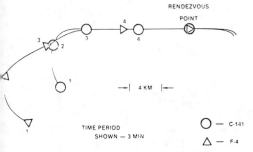

Fig. 23—GPS F-4/C-141 rendezvous flight profiles.

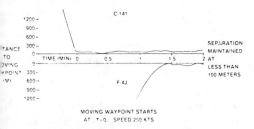

Fig. 24—GPS F-4/C-141 rendezvous: 18 Oct 1978.

endezvous

The Navstar moving waypoint feature can be mployed to effect an airborne rendezvous be- veen GPS-equipped aircraft. This feature per-

"I KNOW THIS IS ONLY AN EXPERIMENTAL SETUP, BUT THE WAY IT'S WORKING, I WOULD FEEL CONFIDENT IN GOING OUT THERE RIGHT NOW AND FLYING BLIND RENDEZVOUS TO 1000 METERS OR SO."

CAPT BILL NEELY
C-141 TEST PILOT, 4950 TW

Fig. 25

GPS SHIPBOARD OPERATIONS TEST OBJECTIVES

LCU1618:

O NAVIGATION ACCURACY
O COORDINATED ANTISUBMARINE EXERCISE
O MULTIPATH REJECTION

USS FANNING (FF1076):

O HARBOR NAVIGATION
O MAN OVERBOARD RECOVERY
O PRECISION ANCHORAGE
O MULTIPATH REJECTION
O SHIPBOARD RADIO FREQUENCY
    INTERFERENCE (RFI)
O EXTENDED AT-SEA NAVIGATION

Fig. 26

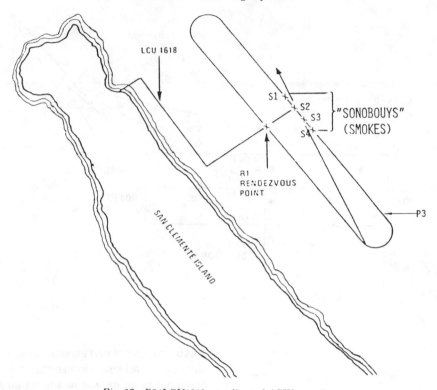

Fig. 27—P3/LCU1618 coordinated ASW exercise.

Fig. 28—Aircraft and GPS shipboard antenna during rendezvous.

RENDEZVOUS NUMBER	CLOSEST APPROACH TO RENDEZVOUS POINT (METERS)		TIME DIFFERENCE AT RENDEZVOUS (SEC)	RENDEZVOUS POINT	GEOME DILUT OF PRECI (GDO
	P-3B	LCU			
1	2	4	118	R1	2.
2	17	27	70	S2	3.
3	1	18	8	R1	7.
4	21	18	7	S2	14.

Fig. 29—Rendezvous test results: 3 satellites; 13 D 1978.

mits the pilot to enter a waypoint with a predetermined course and speed in three-space. In the rendezvous tests conducted in October 1978 at YPG using one satellite and three ground transmitters, a waypoint moving in a racetrack orbit

was entered by both the F4 and C141 aircra (Figure 23). Figure 24 shows the distance b tween each aircraft and the moving waypoi until the rendezvous is accomplished at appro imately 1.5 minutes. The test was designed demonstrate Navstar's potential value in an ai borne refueling scenario and Figure 25 provid excerpts from comments by the C141 test pil after flying the test mission.

hipboard Operations

In an effort to demonstrate Navstar utility in variety of Naval surface missions, a four-channel X-Set and single-channel Y-Set were installed in a Navstar instrumentation shelter hich was loaded in turn aboard a Navy Landing raft (LCU1618) and operational Frigate (USS anning, FF1076). The test objectives for each f these vessels are listed in Figure 26.

The navigation accuracy results aboard the CU are discussed above and the multipath

ARLY IN THE EXERCISE... IT QUICKLY BECAME APPARENT THAT THE S INFORMATION DISPLAYED TO THE PILOT WAS FAR SUPERIOR IN CURACY THAN THE VISUAL 'MARK ON TOP' FROM 200 FEET TITUDE. THE TACTICAL IMPACT OF A NAV SYSTEM OF THIS CURACY, TOTALLY INTEGRATED WITH THE CENTRAL COMPUTER, HAS EMENDOUS IMPLICATIONS.

STRONGLY FEEL THAT SIGNIFICANT ADVANCES CAN BE MADE IN E SEARCH, LOCALIZATION AND WEAPON DELIVERY PHASES OF THE W PROBLEM. THE ACCURACY FURNISHED BY GPS PROVIDES ARLY UNLIMITED POTENTIAL RELATIVE TO THE ASW MISSION. ALSO FEEL THAT INNOVATIVE, TACTICAL THINKERS CAN UTILIZE IS TYPE OF POSITIONAL DATA TO SIGNIFICANTLY ENHANCE THE W ANTI-SURFACE SHIP HARPOON MISSION OF THE P-3C UPDATE AIRCRAFT."

CDR LEIGH A. McCLENDON III
NATC P-3 TEST PILOT

Fig. 30

tests for several variable-height antennae are described in reference 1.

Coordinated AntiSubmarine Warfare (ASW) operations were simulated by the P3 aircraft and the LCU in December 1978. Referring to Figure 27, the LCU and P3 used Navstar to rendezvous at a common point (R1) and common time. The P3 pilot followed his Pilot Steering Display (Figure 20) and the LCU craftmaster steered by voice commands radioed to him from the Navstar shelter onboard. Figure 28 is a photograph of one of those rendezvous taken from the LCU. Note the miniranger antenna which is mounted on top of the Navstar shelter, just a few feet from the Navstar antenna. After this initial rendezvous, the P3 turned to drop four smoke bombs, simulating sonobouys, marking each drop with a GPS waypoint. He then designated one of these "sonobouys" as "hot" (simulated submarine contact) and passed its Navstar coordinates to the LCU by radio. A second rendezvous was then accomplished at the "hot sonobouy" (S2). This pattern was repeated several times and each of the P3/LCU rendezvous was conducted on Navstar information alone, without visual reference between the two test vehicles. Figure 29 summarizes the results of two

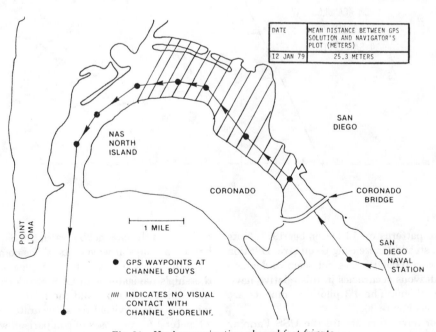

DATE	MEAN DISTANCE BETWEEN GPS SOLUTION AND NAVIGATOR'S PLOT (METERS)
12 JAN 79	25.3 METERS

Fig. 31—Harbor navigation aboard fast frigate.

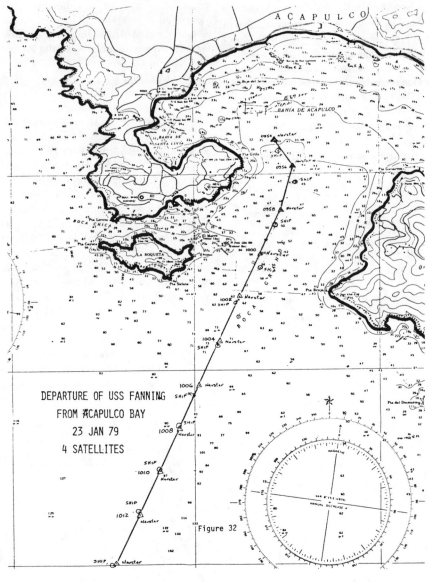

DEPARTURE OF USS FANNING
FROM ACAPULCO BAY
23 JAN 79
4 SATELLITES

Figure 32

Fig. 32

complete patterns on 13 December 1978. Note that the steadily increasing Geometric Dilution of Precision (GDOP) does not seem to degrade the rendezvous accuracies in this relative navigation problem. The P3 pilot's comments are included as Figure 30.

Harbor navigation aboard the USS Fanning (FF 1076) was accomplished by entering the positions of the channel buoys, in the San Diego harbor, as Navstar waypoints. Voice commands from the Navstar shelter to the bridge provided the ship's navigator with GPS steers from one waypoint to the next, and the navigator maintained a plot of visual fixes (accurate to about 20 meters) for purposes of comparison with the navstar solution. Figure 31 shows the Navstar

Fig. 33

DATE	NUMBER OF OBSERVATIONS	GPS-USNO* (NANOSECONDS)	
		MEAN	STANDARD DEVIATION
2 FEB 1979	8	-46	14
3 FEB 1979	10	-29	6
5 FEB 1979	7	-21	5
6 FEB 1979	11	+36	22
7 FEB 1979	9	-4	7
ALL ABOVE	45	-15	13

*USNO CLOCK FLOWN BETWEEN WASH D.C., YPG AND VANDENBERG AIR FORCE BASE.

Fig. 34—Time transfer test results: Feb 1979; MTV/ X-set; 4 satellites.

waypoints utilized and the mean difference between the GPS solution and the Navigator's plot for the testing conducted on 12 January 1979 when part of the transit was accomplished under low visibility conditions due to heavy fog.

During the latter part of January 1979 USS Panning embarked on a ten-day, round-trip cruise between San Diego and Acapulco, Mexico, taking the Navstar shelter and test team with her. Although no reference trajectory for the ship's precise track was available, it was

demonstrated that Navstar could provide continuous, real-time, navigation information during extended steaming. In addition, the cruise marked the first time that four-satellite navigation was accomplished in a part of the world other than the South West United States. Figure 32 is a portion of the ship's navigation chart, showing its track out of Bahia De Acapulco, marked with Navstar (triangles) and visual (circles) fixes.

Foliage Attenuation

In December 1978 the U.S. Army conducted qualitative foliage attenuation testing in light-to-medium foliage at Eglin Air Force Base. The ability of the Magnavox Manpack to obtain a static fix at a surveyed position was assessed as a function of satellite elevation. It was generally found that the Manpack had no difficulties with satellites at or above twenty degrees of elevation. Figure 33 shows the foliage environment of the tests and twenty degrees of elevation is indicated in the photo by the man's hand on the surveying pole. Note that a "rule of thumb" that seemed to emerge from the testing is that Navstar signals can be received through foliage at elevation angles for which some sky is visible.

Time Transfer

In conjunction with the U.S. Naval Observatory (USNO) in Washington, D.C., the Defense Mapping Agency (DMA) is currently conducting tests to demonstrate Navstar's ability to provide accurate time information to suitably equipped users. Using the DMA Mobile Test Van (MTV), which is equipped with a four-channel X-Set, Navstar system time is determined at the Yuma Proving Ground (YPG) in Arizona. This time is compared with a USNO cesium standard which has been flown from Washington D.C. to Vandenberg Air Force Base, for comparison with Navstar time in the Navstar Master Control Station, and then on to Yuma. Figure 34 shows the results of these time transfer tests to date, and from these it can be seen that Navstar's current capability is about 50 nanoseconds. This testing demonstrates the feasibility of Global time transfer using GPS, and better accuracies could reasonably be expected from equipment designed specifically for that purpose.

Conclusion

A great deal of Navstar testing has not been included in this paper, either because the results are classified or because it was the intent of the authors to restrict the scope to recent, significant accomplishments for which data is readily presentable. The testing accomplished to date has met or exceeded almost every expectation or goal of the program. In the main, this impressive test record is attributable to a determined and professional effort by the government organizations, military and civilian, and the contractors involved in the Navstar Concept Validation effort. The results presented represent, in distilled form, the contractor and government personnel—too numerous to mention—who believe in the vast potential of Navstar GPS and who are working to make it a reality to military and civilian user alike.

Reference

1. "Navstar Shipboard Multipath Test Results", Richard M. Akita and Ronald W. Major, ION Annual Aerospace Meeting, March 1979.

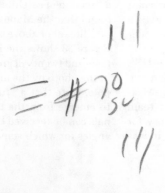